The Adolescent Community Reinforcement Approach:

A Clinical Guide for Treating Substance Use Disorders

Susan H. Godley
Jane Ellen Smith
Robert J. Meyers
Mark D. Godley

Chestnut Health Systems
Normal, IL 61761
http://www.chestnut.org

ISBN: 0-9980580-0-9 (ISBN-13: 978-0-9980580-0-9)

This guide, *The Adolescent Community Reinforcement Approach: A Clinical Guide for Treating Substance Use Disorders*, incorporates material from the *Adolescent Community Reinforcement Approach for Adolescent Cannabis Users*, volume 4 of a 5-volume series titled *Cannabis Youth Treatment Series*, a publication of the Substance Abuse and Mental Health Services Administration (SAMHSA), U.S. Department of Health and Human Services, HHS Publication No. SMA-08-3864, Rockville, MD, 2001 (first printing), reprinted 2008. Inclusion of SAMHSA material does not constitute or imply endorsement or recommendation by the U.S. Government, the U.S. Department of Health and Humans Services, or SAMHSA of any views, opinions, policies, products or services.

Some of the material contained in this manual was previously published in the chapter, Adolescent Community Reinforcement Approach (A-CRA) by Susan H. Godley, Jane Ellen Smith, Robert J. Meyers & Mark D. Godley, in the book, *Substance Abuse Treatment for Youth and Adults: Clinician's Guide to Evidence-Based Practice* (David W. Springer & Allen Rubin, Editors) Copyright © 2009 by John Wiley & Sons, Inc. It is reproduced in this publication with permission from John Wiley & Sons, Inc. and includes material on the following pages: 7-9, 24-27, 162-177. The permission to reproduce this material does not grant others permission to photocopy or otherwise reproduce this material except for accessible versions made by non-profit organizations serving the blind, visually impaired, and other persons with print disabilities (VIPs).

This work builds directly on an earlier book about alcohol treatment of adults, *Clinical Guide to Alcohol Treatment: The Community Reinforcement Approach* (Meyers & Smith, 1995), published by Guilford Press. Any similar content is reproduced herein with the permission of the copyright holders.

Library of Congress Control Number: 2016914988
Chestnut Health Systems, Normal, Illinois

All proceeds from the sale of this book support research and training at Chestnut Health Systems to improve treatment outcomes for adolescents with substance use disorders.

Table of Contents

Foreword

In the 1970s, along with the authors of this book, I became interested in the psychology of substance use disorders. The world of treatment was a somewhat authoritarian and gloomy place at the time. "Alcoholics" and "addicts" were assumed to be pathological liars with a personality burdened by immature defense mechanisms and an inability to perceive reality. Shaming, blaming, and "shut up and listen" were frequent fare within an atmosphere of "tear them down in order to build them up." I am heartened now that when I describe confrontational practices of that era, audience members sometimes comment incredulously, "No one ever really did that, did they?" We have come a long way.

Yet treatment is still so often focused on stamping out bad habits, educating and persuading people to give up their ingrained albeit harmful or risky practices forever. A "stop it!" approach often fails to appreciate that addictive behaviors are *rewarding*, otherwise no one would get snared in them. Some quite effective approaches for preventing and treating substance use disorders spend less time and focus on drugs than on the person's quality of life: developing positive social skills, enjoying prosocial activities, and strengthening family relationships.

The community reinforcement approach (CRA) is a prime example of such a positive approach. Rather than assuming uniformity, CRA takes care through functional analysis to understand how substance use fits into this particular person's life. Instead of a one-size-fits-all approach, CRA offers each individual the particular skills and self-management knowledge that a person needs for a better and happier life. The underlying theme is to help people develop a life without drugs that is so good they would never want to give it up. Every step in the right direction is encouraged. CRA is the only treatment method I know for which every single controlled trial to date has shown benefit, usually in competition with other bona fide treatments. That is quite unusual in the world of addiction treatment outcome research.

CRA was originally developed for severely alcohol-dependent adults, but it's not just for grown-ups anymore. There is a solid literature on the efficacy of CRA for adolescents, and it makes perfect sense. You're unlikely to attract and engage adolescents by telling them what they can't do. They are in a highly energized period of growing and learning, sampling the world's reinforcers and figuring out who they want to be. They are usually still part of a family, and their parents and significant others do influence the choices they make no matter how much they may protest otherwise. Like adults, adolescents with alcohol/drug problems have better outcomes when their family members are meaningfully engaged in treatment, and not just through an educational family night. CRA and Community Reinforcement Approach and Family Training (CRAFT) offer clear and well-tested methods for engaging the family in treatment in helpful ways.

So welcome to this comprehensive clinical guide for the Adolescent Community Reinforcement Approach (A-CRA). It describes all of the A-CRA procedures and incorporates lessons learned from having implemented this approach with more than 11,000 adolescents and young adults. It also summarizes research on A-CRA demonstrating its acceptability and effectiveness across ethnic groups, gender, and co-occurring mental health problems. Addiction treatment is such a rewarding field in which to work because the outcomes are so good, and A-CRA in particular provides a way to help people turn their lives around at an early stage.

William R. Miller, PhD
Emeritus Distinguished Professor of Psychology and Psychiatry
University of New Mexico
April 6, 2016

Preface

Genesis of the First A-CRA Manual

The first A-CRA manual was published in 2001 by the Center for Substance Abuse Treatment (CSAT) of the U.S. Substance Abuse and Mental Health Services Administration (SAMHSA). The manual was written to explain how to implement the Adolescent Community Reinforcement Approach (A-CRA) because it was one of the five interventions tested in the CSAT-funded Cannabis Youth Treatment (CYT) study. The CYT study was funded to test the effectiveness of five interventions designed to reduce or eliminate adolescent marijuana use and associated problems (see Diamond et al., 2002 for a description of the other four interventions, and Dennis et al., 2004 for the main findings from the CYT study).

The CYT study was important for several reasons. In 1996, marijuana use had reached a 12-year high among adolescents ages 12 to 18 years (Institute for Social Research, 1997). Among eighth graders, 23% reported lifetime use and 11% reported use in the past month. Among high school seniors, 45% reported lifetime use and 22% reported use in the past month. Among 12- to 17-year-olds, marijuana had been the primary substance identified at treatment entry and mentioned in emergency room admission and autopsy reports (Office of Applied Studies, 1995, 1997). At the time of the initial study, 79% of admissions for primary marijuana problems were treated in outpatient ambulatory settings; that is, about 69% in regular outpatient settings (1 to 9 hours per week) and 10% in intensive outpatient settings (9 to 15 hours per week). Moreover, there had been no randomized clinical trials to examine treatments for adolescents entering outpatient treatment with cannabis use disorders. Given the high percentage of adolescents entering outpatient treatment, there was a need to develop and evaluate short (e.g., 90-day), cost-effective treatments.

It is also important to note that while the CYT study was funded because of concerns about the prevalence of cannabis use, adolescents who also had problems with alcohol or other drugs were not excluded from the study. In early planning meetings of the CYT investigators, there was some discussion of limiting study participants to only those with marijuana use disorders. We discovered that this approach was not practical. After examining data on the use patterns of adolescents entering treatment, we learned that most of these adolescents had used alcohol, many had problems because of alcohol use, and many had experimented with other drugs. Among youth in treatment, alcohol was the second-most prevalent substance use disorder diagnosis, and combined with marijuana, the two substances constituted the vast majority of all substance disorder diagnoses among adolescents. However, adolescents who were considered appropriate for residential treatment were excluded from the study because we wanted to target those appropriate for outpatient treatment, and these criteria were operationalized to exclude adolescents who (a) reported use of alcohol 45 or more of the 90 days prior to intake, (b) reported use of other drugs 13 or more of the 90 days prior to intake, or (c) reported an acute medical or psychological problem that was likely to prohibit full participation in treatment (Dennis et al., 2004).

Since the CYT study, data collected in the U.S. continue to show that there are large numbers of adolescents and young adults with alcohol and drug problems entering treatment, and most of these are treated in outpatient programs. In 2012, there were 120,239 admissions for adolescents who were 12 to 17 years old. Of these, 69% were treated in regular outpatient programs, 14% were treated in intensive outpatient programs, 14% were treated in residential programs, and 3% entered detoxification programs. The primary drug of choice for the adolescents admitted to outpatient treatment continues to be marijuana (76.9%), followed by alcohol (14.2%), methamphetamines (1.8%), and opiates other than heroin (1.4%). The other drugs reported were each <1% of the admissions (see SAMHSA, 2012).

Additionally, the evidence for a variety of problems and health concerns related to the regular or heavy use of alcohol and drugs by adolescents has continued to grow. Compared with those who are not regular or heavy substance users, these adolescents demonstrate higher rates of HIV risk behaviors, poor school performance and dropout, and co-occurring mental health issues including conduct disorder, attention-deficit hyperactivity disorder, depression, anxiety, and traumatic stress (Bergen, Martin, Roeger, & Allison, 2005; Chan, Dennis, & Funk, 2008; Chan, Passetti, Garner, Lloyd, & Dennis, 2011; Diamond, Leckrone, Dennis, & Godley, 2006; Edlund et al., 2015; Gruber, Sagar, Dahlgren, Racine, & Lukas, 2012; Guo et al., 2002; Hopfer, Khuri, Crowley, & Hooks, 2002; Hopfer, Mikulich, & Crowley, 2000; Lynskey, Coffey, Degenhardt, Carlin, & Patton, 2003; Lynskey & Hall, 2000; M. H. Meier et al., 2012; Patton et al., 2002; Rey, Martin, & Krabman, 2004; Schweinsburg, Brown, & Tapert, 2008; Subramaniam, Stitzer, Woody, Fishman, & Kolodner, 2009; Wolitzky-Taylor, Bobova, Zinbarg, Mineka, & Craske, 2012).

We now have research that explains more of the effects of substance use on the young brain. The human brain is still developing throughout adolescence, and recent research has revealed that younger brains may be more vulnerable to the effects of alcohol, marijuana, and other substances and recover from them slower than adults (Cermak, 2015; Crews, He, & Hodge, 2007; Lyoo et al., 2015). Heavy-drinking adolescents have been found to have reduced volume and activity in different parts of the brain when compared with nondrinking adolescents or those with limited alcohol use (De Bellis et al., 2005; Medina, Schweinsburg, Cohen-Zion, Nagel, & Tapert, 2007; Medina et al., 2008; Nagel, Schweinsburg, Phan, & Tapert, 2005; Whelan et al., 2012). Heavy or regular alcohol or marijuana use has been associated with impaired cognitive functioning and brain development, including reduced working memory; impaired learning, attention, and performance on visuospatial tasks; and reduced higher-order executive functions, such as abstraction, sequencing, reasoning, judgment, task flexibility, and problem solving, planning and execution (Brown & Tapert, 2004; Brown, Tapert, Granholm, & Delis, 2000; Cermak, 2015; Hanson, Medina, Padula, Tapert, & Brown, 2011; Medina et al., 2007; Schweinsburg et al., 2008; Tapert & Brown, 2000; Tapert, Granholm, Leedy, & Brown, 2002; Volkow, Baler, Compton, & Weiss, 2014). Methamphetamine use has been linked to gray-matter alterations and executive dysfunction (Lyoo et al., 2015). There is some evidence to suggest brain abnormalities may be subtle at first and then become more extensive as substance use histories grow longer and if withdrawal symptoms appear (Medina et al., 2007; Sundram, 2006; Tapert et al., 2004; Winward, Hanson, Tapert, & Brown, 2014). However, further research is needed to determine the extent to which neurocognitive functions may recover over time with abstinence and to tease out the effects of substances and other independent influences on the brain (Gonzalez & Swanson, 2012).

A significant trend since the original A-CRA manual was published has been changes in laws related to marijuana use and a growing consensus that adolescent marijuana use should be decriminalized and treated more as a health problem than as a criminal problem (Ammerman, 2015). An ever-increasing number of U.S. states have decriminalized small amounts of marijuana possession or use or have legalized medical marijuana. There are concerns by some parents and treatment professionals that this trend will impact the frequency of marijuana use by adolescents through a combination of reduced perception of harm, increased availability, greater social acceptance, and marketing efforts (Hopfer, 2014; Levy, 2013; Resko, 2015). While some studies have been conducted internationally, there are not enough data to conclude whether these policies lead to increased use and problems for adolescents in the U.S. (Resko, 2015). For example, two studies using cross-sectional data found higher rates of marijuana use among adolescents in states that had legalized medical marijuana, but they were unable to determine whether the higher rates occurred before or after these policies were enacted (Cerdá, Wall, Keyes, Galea, & Hasin, 2012; Palamar, 2014; Wall et al., 2011). Friese and Grube (2013) found that voter approval of medical marijuana was positively related to adolescent lifetime and past-30-day marijuana use. The authors concluded that the relation between medical marijuana cards and youth use may be related to an overall normative environment that is more tolerant of marijuana use. Other research has generally not found an increase in recreational marijuana use by adolescents following state legalization of medical use (Choo et al., 2014; Lynne-Landsman, Livingston, & Wagenaar, 2013). In conclusion, the effects of legalization of marijuana for medical or recreational purposes on adolescent substance use and its implications for treatment are unclear and require further study and monitoring (Hopfer, 2014; Resko, 2015).

The number of adolescents presenting to treatment combined with the research revealing the negative health and behavioral consequences of problematic substance use continue to underscore the need for effective substance use treatment. The consequences of changing cannabis policies (in the U.S. and abroad) are unknown but will likely contribute to an increased need for effective treatments. The trend toward decriminalization of marijuana use is encouraging, and if it becomes reality, it will require treatment approaches that are less reliant on criminal justice sanctions and based more on positive approaches, like A-CRA. Finally, we can always hope that increased emphasis and funding is channeled to early intervention in schools, where the majority of adolescents spend most of their time, because A-CRA has proven adaptable to delivery in schools and effective.

Impetus for This A-CRA Manual

In the years since the first manual was published, A-CRA has been widely implemented with over 10,000 adolescents, 1,500 transitional age youth (ages 18 to 26), and in 44 U.S. states and territories. The original A-CRA manual has been translated into Dutch (by Novadic-Kentron, Netherlands), French (by Dave Smith Youth Treatment Centre, Canada), Spanish (by Fernández-Artamendi and Fernández-Hermida, Spain), and Portuguese (by Dias and Anderson, Brazil). Partly as a result of its wide dissemination and the amount of data collected across numerous organizations and treatment participants, additional analytic research has been published that can help inform future implementation of the model. We also have learned much anecdotally from the clinicians, supervisors, trainers, adolescents, and families who have used the model. In response to needs expressed by our trainees and funding emphases, we have added additional CRA procedures to the training package that is provided to A-CRA trainees because we wanted to provide a more comprehensive manual that adequately addressed current training of A-CRA therapists. Finally, along with the implementation of the model, the methods for assessing fidelity have been greatly improved with the introduction of the therapist coding manual (J. E. Smith, Lundy, & Gianini, 2007). The manual guides our trainers and is available to supervisors undergoing A-CRA supervisor certification. The coding manual has aided the development of A-CRA and is important for the certification process, and so this manual has been written to more closely match those guidelines.

Procedure Additions and Changes

In this manual, additional procedures are described and more components detailed for certain procedures. These are not "new" procedures or components but ones that have evolved to be part of the Community Reinforcement Approach and incorporated into the A-CRA training and certification process.

We no longer differentiate between "core" versus "optional" or "additional" procedures as we did in the earlier manual because we found that when we labeled the procedures this way, there was some confusion about the importance of each procedure. The procedures are equally useful, depending on the needs of the individual participating in treatment. There are still two levels of certification (discussed in Unit 3, Chapter 3[p. 241]), but only because there are so many procedures and we wanted to acknowledge significant progress by clinicians partway through the training process. Also, though we provide a suggested order of procedures for the first few sessions, we did so because this type of structure is helpful for therapists just beginning to learn a treatment like A-CRA. Once the therapist is comfortable with the procedures, the goal is for them to skillfully choose procedures during a session that will be most helpful to the client.

Settings and Populations

With A-CRA's widespread implementation, the developers and trainers also have worked with treatment organizations that implemented the treatment in new settings and with increasingly diverse target populations. Much of this work has been documented in peer-reviewed publications and in online courses that accompany A-CRA training. The new settings include residential treatment and schools. Also, many treatment programs that originally were funded to implement A-CRA in individual sessions wanted to provide A-CRA in groups as much as possible because of local funding constraints when their grants ended. Thus, guidance was provided about how to adapt several A-CRA procedures for group sessions. CRA procedures had been previously proven effective with groups of homeless alcohol-dependent adults (J. E. Smith, Meyers, & Delaney, 1998) and in the adolescent and young adult homeless study (Slesnick, Prestopnik, Meyers, & Glassman, 2007), so it was not difficult for Robert J. Meyers and Jane Ellen Smith, who had been involved in these studies, to provide guidance about how to adapt A-CRA for groups. Also, because the federally sponsored dissemination of A-CRA was occurring in many diverse U.S. communities, a cultural-responsiveness committee was formed to ensure that the intervention met the varied needs of all the communities served. This effort included data analyses to examine whether there were any differences in the implementation of A-CRA or treatment outcomes that varied by ethnic group or gender. We have included information in this manual on what has been learned about implementing A-CRA in these new settings and with different groups.

Acknowledgements

The development of A-CRA and this manual is due to the contributions of many people over a number of years. We would like to remember and acknowledge Drs. Nathan Azrin and George Hunt, whose seminal publication in 1973 established the Community Reinforcement Approach. We are grateful for the support of the Substance Abuse and Mental Health Services Administration's Center for Substance Abuse Treatment, the National Institute on Drug Abuse, and the National Institute on Alcohol Abuse and Alcoholism for the different roles these funding agencies played during the development, evaluation, and dissemination of A-CRA. Dr. Michael Dennis and Randy Muck played critical roles in the research that established the adolescent version of CRA and its widespread dissemination. We would like to thank Dr. Christy Scott and Russ Hagen of Chestnut Health Systems for supporting the time and resources needed to complete this manual. Rod Funk was helpful in securing the latest national data on substance use trends. Lora Passetti provided assistance with the literature review. We are also grateful to Drs. Bryan Garner, Sergio Fernández-Artamendi, Sarah Hunter, and many other scientists who have partnered with us to study A-CRA. We thank those who translated the first version of the manual into other languages: Drs. Hendrik Roozen and Peter Greeven with Novadic-Kentron in the Netherlands (Dutch translation); Dave Smith Youth Treatment Centre, with the financial assistance of the Champlain Local Health Integration Network in Canada (French translation); Maria Cristina S. Dias, with assistance from Lily Anderson and support from Jim Fraser with Chestnut Global Partners in Illinois and the staff of Hospital Samaritano and SAID in Brazil (Portuguese translation); and Sergio Fernández-Artamendi and José Ramón Fernández-Hermida with the Addictive Behavior Research Group at the University of Oviedo in Spain, supported by the Ministry of Education and Science in Spain (Spanish translation). We are also thankful for the work that Luis Flores and Dr. Kristen Hedges did while co-chairing the A-CRA Cultural Responsiveness Committee. Drs. Geetha Subramanian and Diana Chu have been very helpful by providing their psychiatric expertise as we developed the training for treating adolescents with co-occurring mental health disorders. We would like to thank Mychele Kenney and the staff of Chestnut Health Systems' adolescent treatment division for their support and implementation of A-CRA as well as their partnership in clinical trials. The review and comments of Courtney Hupp, Francie Hallahan, and Jennifer Smith Ramey on earlier drafts were invaluable during the writing of this manual; all three are clinicians and A-CRA experts who have worked with hundreds of clinicians during the A-CRA training and certification process. We also thank additional members of our A-CRA team who have worked closely with us through the years and made contributions to our work, as well as to our clinician and supervisor trainees: Dr. Brandi Barnes, Christin Libernini Bair, Karen Malek, and Laura Reichel. Brandi, Christin, and Karen also provided much assistance with the subject index. There are numerous other clinicians and supervisors who have helped with training, given us feedback, and gone through the process to become A-CRA fidelity raters; we thank you all for your dedication and what you have taught us in the process. Kelli Wright has contributed in so many ways: in the editing of this manual, in the organization of its publication, and by providing unwavering support to the training and writing work that we do. We thank our families for their support. Most importantly, we want to acknowledge and thank all the adolescents and their families that have participated in A-CRA and the clinicians who have worked so hard to partner with these families to help improve the quality of their lives.

UNIT 1: Background

This unit has three chapters with background information that will help in the implementation of A-CRA. The first chapter provides the history of A-CRA, its underlying theory, the goals of treatment, the expectations regarding therapist style, a description of the target population, and an orientation to the organization of the manual. The second chapter describes a number of practical details, including session flow and content, how clinicians learn about and use client reinforcers, the importance of role plays when teaching new skills, and several other clinical considerations. The third chapter defines and emphasizes the importance of good general clinical skills.

UNIT 1: CHAPTER 1: Introduction

Background

History of the Community Reinforcement Approach

The Community Reinforcement Approach (CRA) was first developed in the 1970s for alcohol-dependent patients in a state-operated hospital's inpatient program (Meyers & Godley, 2001). Next, it was tested in an outpatient setting. At the time, the approach was very different from the predominant treatment method, which was based almost solely on the twelve steps of Alcoholics Anonymous (AA). As CRA evolved through several studies, so did the "package" of procedures that make up CRA, often drawing upon other research from the early developers (George Hunt, Nathan Azrin, John Mallams, Robert Meyers, Robert Sisson, and Mark Godley), who were trained in behavioral psychology. The first complete clinical guide to implementing CRA was published by Robert J. Meyers and Jane Ellen Smith in 1995 (Meyers & Smith, 1995), and this book remains an important resource for therapists interested in the model. The target populations receiving CRA also broadened to include individuals who were homeless (J. E. Smith et al., 1998), and with the addition of vouchers to the treatment, to those who were cocaine and opioid dependent (Higgins & Abbott, 2001). The mix of procedures has varied somewhat from study to study; however, the current CRA checklist includes 19 procedures comprising 77 components (J. E. Smith, Gianini, Garner, Malek, & Godley, 2014).

Adaptation for Adolescents and History of A-CRA

The genesis for the adaption of CRA for adolescents was the Cannabis Youth Treatment (CYT) study. This 3-year study began in 1997 to evaluate different outpatient treatments for adolescents who had problems associated with this marijuana use. CSAT funded this study in response to annual survey data showing that in 1996, marijuana use among adolescents 12 to 18 years old had reached the highest levels in 12 years. Even though these data showed that marijuana use was very high among the nation's youth, there were no interventions that had been designed or evaluated specifically for use with adolescents. Other data indicated that most adolescents entering treatment because of marijuana use problems attended outpatient treatment programs. The CYT research team decided to evaluate five different outpatient interventions in an experiment across four different sites in the U.S. (see Diamond et al., 2002 for a description of the other four treatments). A total of 600 adolescents were randomly assigned to one of the outpatient interventions and were followed up at 3, 6, 9, and 12 months after they began their outpatient treatment. Additional funding allowed the follow-up period to be extended out to 30 months after adolescents began treatment.

One of the interventions chosen for the study was an adaptation for adolescents of the Community Reinforcement Approach (CRA), which was originally developed for treatment of adults with substance use disorders. An existing book had already outlined CRA procedures and forms for the treatment of adults with alcohol disorders (Meyers & Smith, 1995), and this book served as the basis for adapting the approach for adolescents. The first A-CRA manual described the developmentally appropriate adaptation of CRA for adolescents, and clinical staff working in the research study were trained and supervised according to the manual. Many of the procedures in the book and manual drew upon other research related to behavioral skill training and were adapted with little revision for adolescents, such as skill training in problem solving and communication skills. Adaptations included using examples in the manual and during training that emphasized how these skills might be used with adolescents; for example, in communicating with parents, school authority figures, or juvenile justice. Other procedures needed more adaptation. For example, CRA has had a long history of addressing marital relationships, and for the adolescent version, these procedures were revised to address relationship skills between adolescents and their parents. CRA used a goal planning procedure based on the participant's response to a clinical "happiness" or "satisfaction" scale. In A-CRA, the Happiness Scale was revised to reflect life areas relevant to adolescents.

The first A-CRA manual and the findings from the CYT study were published in 2001 and 2004, respectively. More details about the CYT study and its findings can be found in the research chapter (Unit 3, Chapter 4 [p. 243]). Beginning in 2006, there have been several large implementation efforts of A-CRA funded by CSAT in multiyear grants. These grants were awarded either directly to treatment provider organizations or to states, which in turn chose provider organizations to implement.

As of this writing, A-CRA has been implemented at over 250 treatment provider organizations across the US, and the number continues to grow. Over 90% were organizations that provided A-CRA in outpatient or intensive outpatient treatment, although several implemented A-CRA in school settings and a few adapted A-CRA for residential settings. The following data are based on over 12,500 adolescents and young adults who participated in the A-CRA intervention. The average age of the adolescents was 16.1 years, and 13% were transitional age youth (age 18–26). Most were male (75%). Thirty-four percent of the participants were White, 31% were Hispanic, 17% were African American, 3% were Native American, and 16% were from other race or ethnic groups. Twenty-six percent were from single-parent homes. The majority (86%) reported being in school in the preceding 90 days, and 21% reported working in the previous 90 days. Most (67%) reported current criminal justice involvement, and 58% reported some type of victimization. Overall, 62% reported symptoms indicative of one or more co-occurring mental health problems.

Starting in 2009, CSAT funded select treatment providers to implement A-CRA with a population that appeared to lack appropriate treatment services: transitional age youth (18 to 26 years). Often, the adult treatment system targeted older adults and the youth treatment system targeted adolescents. For therapists working with transitional age youth, all the original procedures used in the adult CRA treatment were incorporated back into the training in A-CRA and were required as part of the certification process. (See Unit 3, Chapter 1 [p. 231] for more on treating transitional age youth.)

To support these large implementation initiatives, an infrastructure that includes training and certification for clinicians and supervisors was developed to support quality implementation. Additionally, as new training needs arose (e.g., the large prevalence of adolescents with co-occurring problems, implementation of A-CRA in new settings such as residential treatment or schools), they were addressed within the training infrastructure. This information has been included in this manual.

Underlying Theory

Meyers and Smith (1995, p. 1) describe the theoretical underpinnings of CRA in this way:

> The Community Reinforcement Approach acknowledges the powerful role of environmental contingencies in encouraging or discouraging drug use, and thus attempts to rearrange these contingencies such that sober behavior is more rewarding than using behavior. CRA blends this operant model with a social systems approach. The overall philosophy is to use the community to reward nonusing behavior so that the client makes healthy lifestyle changes.

CRA procedures use operant techniques and skills-training activities to teach individuals new ways of handling life's problems without drugs or alcohol. Traditionally, CRA is provided in an individual, context-specific format that focuses on the interaction between clients and people in their environments. CRA clinicians teach clients when and where to use the techniques, given the reality of each individual's social environment. This tailored approach is facilitated by conducting a functional analysis of the client's behavior at the beginning of therapy. CRA clinicians then teach clients how to build on their reinforcers (something that increases the likelihood a behavior or response will reoccur), how to use existing community resources that will support positive change, and how to develop a positive support system.

CRA is rooted in early work by Azrin and his colleagues (Azrin, Sisson, Meyers, & Godley, 1982; Hunt & Azrin, 1973). Illustrative examples of studies evaluating CRA with special populations include:

- Concerned others seeking assistance to deal with a loved one's drinking (Meyers, Dominquez, & Smith, 1996; Meyers & Smith, 1997)
- Cocaine-addicted individuals (Higgins, Budney, Bickel, & Badger, 1994; Higgins et al., 1991; Higgins et al., 1993; Higgins et al., 1995; Shaner et al., 1997)
- Homeless alcohol-dependent individuals (J. E. Smith et al., 1998; Slesnick et al., 2007)
- Adolescents in an Assertive Continuing Care (ACC) approach following a period of residential treatment (M. D. Godley, Godley, Dennis, Funk, & Passetti, 2007; M. D. Godley, Godley et al., 2014)
- Smoking cessation (Roozen et al., 2006)
- Opioid dependence (Abbott, Weller, Delaney, & Moore, 1998; Roozen, Kerkhof, & Van Den Brink, 2003)
- Juvenile justice and substance use (Hunter, Godley, Hesson-McInnis, & Roozen, 2014)
- School-based A-CRA (Hunter, Godley, & Godley, 2014)
- Co-occurring mental health and substance problems (S. H. Godley, Smith, Passetti, & Subramaniam, 2014)

For a comprehensive bibliography of published studies using CRA, A-CRA, and CRAFT, see http://ebtx.chestnut.org/Resources.

A-CRA Goals

The goals of the individual A-CRA sessions with *adolescents* are to:

- **Promote a positive working relationship between the adolescent and the A-CRA therapist.** This is accomplished through unconditional positive regard and acceptance of the adolescent, working on initial treatment goals that are of greatest importance to the adolescent, avoiding confrontation, and praising even small increments of progress toward goals and healthy prosocial behavior.
- **Promote positive social activity.** A-CRA assumes that adolescents can be more successful at terminating substance use behavior if they learn how to increase their involvement in positive, reinforcing behaviors. A procedure called the Functional Analysis of Prosocial Behavior helps adolescents identify enjoyable prosocial activities that they currently engage in infrequently and helps them see the benefits of being involved in these activities more often. Systematic Encouragement is a procedure that can help the adolescent take small steps toward actually participating in a new activity. Clinicians then encourage adolescents to make commitments to spend more time in these activities, thereby gradually increasing their social repertoire over a number of sessions.
- **Promote positive peer relationships.** This goal parallels the goal on positive social activity. Adolescents with substance use problems often center activities with friends on substance use. With the goal on promoting positive peer relationships, A-CRA clinicians help adolescents identify attributes of healthy friendships and teach them how to find and make new friends, how to deal with negativity, and how to ask for support.

- **Promote improved relationships with family.** Adolescence can be a stressful time in the relationship between caregivers and their adolescents. This time is even more stressful in families with adolescents who have substance use problems. Any distrust that caregivers have for adolescents is reinforced by their involvement in substance use. A-CRA seeks to improve communication between family members as a way to enhance relationships. Parents have told us that they have enjoyed the benefits of better communication after participating in A-CRA treatment.
- **Promote abstinence from marijuana, alcohol, and other drugs.** A-CRA helps promote abstinence by working with adolescents to modify the conditions that promote substance use. Therapists are taught to help adolescents reduce use according to their ability because there are individual differences in development, consequences of use, and environment. Treatment is not denied to those who cannot remain abstinent. Sometimes initial treatment goals begin with areas identified from the Happiness Scale that are not substance-related (e.g., legal issues, parent relationship), but typically any goals selected by the adolescent will eventually involve a substance use treatment goal. Although all of the A-CRA procedures are useful in achieving abstinence, certain procedures are more obvious in addressing this goal. For example, a procedure called the Functional Analysis of Substance Use helps adolescents identify (a) marijuana, alcohol, or other drug-using behaviors; (b) the antecedents to marijuana, alcohol, and other drug use; and (c) the positive and negative consequences of their use.

The goals of the A-CRA sessions with the *caregivers* are to:

- **Motivate their participation in the A-CRA process.** The A-CRA clinician's role is to help caregivers understand that they have an ongoing, important role in helping their adolescent overcome a problem and to motivate the caregivers to participate in the therapy process.
- **Help the adolescent reduce or eliminate alcohol and other drug use and associated harm.** A-CRA procedures teach family members behavioral skills aimed at discouraging an adolescent's drug use. The goal is to help caregivers understand how their behavior impacts the adolescent's substance use so that they will be motivated to change their own behavior to promote the adolescent's abstinence.
- **Provide information to the caregivers about effective parenting practices.** The information is based on the research of Bry (1998), Catalano (1998), and Hops (1998) and includes measures to keep the adolescent from relapsing.

A-CRA Therapist Style

Therapists' interactions with adolescents and caregivers are positive and enthusiastic. The therapist is always looking for opportunities to reinforce behaviors that can lead to and support decreased substance use. In contrast to some historical substance use treatment approaches, A-CRA therapists do not use confrontation. The CRA approach is certainly appropriate when working with adolescents, since they are usually attending substance use treatment because of coercion (subtle or otherwise) from parents, school officials, or the juvenile justice system. It is also developmentally appropriate for adolescents, whose resistance often will increase when addressed in a confrontational manner. If adolescents believe they have the power in the counseling situation, they may be more willing to work with a therapist.

It is also important for therapists to become familiar and comfortable with all the A-CRA procedures so that during a session they can choose the procedure that will be most helpful to the client at that time. We believe this approach also helps with therapeutic engagement because rather than imposing a structure or order of procedures that may or may not address current issues with the client, it responds to the client's needs. It is also important to note that attaining comfort with the procedures is a process that may take 6 months to a year.

Target Population

A-CRA was originally designed as an outpatient intervention to be delivered in weekly sessions. The target population was described as adolescents appropriate for an outpatient or intensive outpatient level of care as defined by the American Society of Addiction Medicine's patient-placement criteria (1996). While A-CRA was designed as an outpatient intervention and evaluated as such in the CYT study, since that study the treatment has been successfully implemented in different settings including residential treatment, schools, and sites receiving referrals from adolescent drug courts. A-CRA also has been implemented in several sites with CSAT funding with transitional age youth, aged 18 to 24. A large number of treatment organizations have implemented A-CRA with adolescents and young adults and have collected data during treatment and at follow-up. These data have been used to examine implementation quality and outcomes across different groups. Based on these studies and the flexibility of A-CRA, we believe that A-CRA is appropriate for females and males, for those from various ethnic groups, and for a range of ages. A-CRA also can be used to address substance use problems for those with co-occurring disorders. More information will be provided about implementing A-CRA with these different groups in Unit 3, Chapter 1 (p. 225).

Before beginning this or any treatment program, we recommend adolescents first participate in a comprehensive biopsychosocial assessment to determine the appropriate level of care placement. This assessment should determine the severity of their substance use by considering *DSM-5* diagnostic criteria, any co-occurring problems or disorders, and the clients' recovery environments. The Cannabis Youth Treatment study and many of the CSAT-funded implementation initiatives used the Global Appraisal of Individual Needs (GAIN; Dennis, Titus, White, Unsicker, & Hodgkins, 2003). Other settings where A-CRA has been delivered are juvenile detention homes, group homes, and client homes. Although at the time of this writing there is limited funding for providing substance use treatment in schools, we think schools provide a good setting for early intervention. As such, A-CRA delivered in schools may help prevent the development of problems associated with alcohol and drug use, including entry into the juvenile justice system. We also believe that there is a place for residential treatment in the continuum of care because of multiple problems or the need to be removed from a very poor recovery environment. Examples might include situations in which there is other use in the home or the adults are selling drugs.

Organization of the Manual

The manual is made up of three units. The first unit provides background information for implementing A-CRA. It includes practical information about how a session would flow, how often clients would have a session, and the timing of all the procedures that make up A-CRA. The second unit has chapters that describe each A-CRA procedure and serves as a how-to guide to implement a particular procedure, usually with some sample dialogue. The last unit provides details about individualizing A-CRA for clients who bring different clinical issues with them to therapy; discharge recommendations; the selection, training, and supervision of A-CRA therapists and supervisors; and a review of the research to date on A-CRA. Some readers may prefer to read this section first, but others may want to spend time reading about how to deliver the treatment and read this section at a later date. Finally, there is the reference section and an appendix with helpful resources.

UNIT 1: CHAPTER 2: Guidelines for Implementing A-CRA

Rationale for Implementing a Wide Variety of Procedures

One of the important topics for treatment researchers is to identify how specific evidence-based treatments cause desired treatment outcomes. Research has shown that simply retaining clients in treatment for 90 days or more will on average result in better treatment outcomes. However, if retention is the sole key to successful treatment outcomes, then it should not matter what treatment is being provided. Garner and his colleagues (2009) examined whether clients' receipt of different A-CRA procedures made a difference in their substance use outcomes. They found that exposure to different A-CRA procedures was related to reduction in substance use and associated problems when controlling for treatment retention. This finding suggests that it is not just important to retain clients in A-CRA treatment but to provide them a variety of A-CRA procedures. Indeed, the research suggested that adolescents who received 10 or more A-CRA procedures during their treatment period and participated in at least seven treatment sessions were more likely to be in recovery at follow-up. Based on these findings, one of the statistics we have provided to the management of sites that implement A-CRA is the percentage of their treatment participants who receive Target A-CRA; namely, at least 10 unique A-CRA procedures over at least seven sessions.

Session Flow and Content

A-CRA is Flexible and Procedure-Based

Some evidence-based approaches are designed so that clinicians are asked to complete specific activities in each session. That is, the corresponding treatment manual describes what the clinician is going to do in the first session, the second session, and so on. Clinicians go into each session knowing exactly what will be discussed that day or what forms will be completed. Other therapy approaches are very nondirective, and the clinician is skilled in asking questions that, for example, help clients understand what their motivations for change are and how they might go about changing. A-CRA is situated somewhere between these two types of approaches. It is more directed than the latter approach but still a very flexible therapy. The framework is behavioral and procedure-based. A-CRA has a menu of 19 procedures, and clinicians learn how to introduce a given procedure at the appropriate time during a session. The selection of an appropriate procedure is dependent upon a clinician's assessment of the client's needs at the time. There is a suggested sequencing of procedures in the first four sessions that is described later in this chapter, but the clinician has great leeway in the order that procedures are introduced. It can be more difficult to learn A-CRA than a session-based approach, but clinicians have reported that they like A-CRA's flexibility, in part because this flexibility allows the clinician to individualize treatment for clients (S. H. Godley, White, Diamond, Passetti, & Titus, 2001).

Begin (and End) with Reinforcers

The most important aspect of A-CRA delivery is that the clinician is constantly listening for information or clues about what reinforces or motivates each client. The clinician approaches clients with the understanding that alcohol or drug use is serving a reinforcing function in their lives and that it is important to help them find positive activities and goals that can replace the function that alcohol and drugs serve. When we talk about reinforcers, we include a broad range of desires and activities that could be immediate or long term. For example, some clients would like to graduate from high school, others might want to spend more enjoyable time with their family, and others just want to get off probation. The consequences of a client's substance use behavior are often obvious to clinicians, and thus there may be a desire to clarify the connections for the client. However, the A-CRA approach facilitates discussions so that clients see these connections themselves, as opposed to having the clinician confront them about the negative consequences of their behaviors. There are many ways to discover what clients' reinforcers are, including asking open-ended questions about what they like or hope to do. Several of the A-CRA tools also provide opportunities to learn more about a client's reinforcers, as illustrated in the sample therapy dialogues in this manual.

It is also important to understand that reinforcers can change over time. While clients may first attend treatment because of court or probation mandates, as treatment progresses their reinforcers may become more internal. For example, they may say they want to stay sober because they have more energy or want to please their parents.

Importance of Role Plays

Role plays are used whenever teaching new skills to give clients frequent opportunities to practice and improve skills based on constructive feedback.

The following are important components of good role plays:

- Role plays should be two-sided. That is, there is a back and forth exchange between the clinician and client while the clinician plays the part of the person the client will talk to in real life.
- The role play is stopped after a relatively brief interchange (less than two minutes) so that the clinician can provide feedback to the client on the brief interchanges.
- At the end of each role play, the clinician compliments the client for specific components of the skills that were performed correctly.
- At the end of each role play, clinicians work to help the client improve the targeted skill by giving one or more suggestions for improvement.
- The clinician asks what the client did or did not like about his or her performance in the role play.
- Role plays are repeated more than once, each time varying responses, so that the client learns how to respond in realistic situations, which can often be challenging. The client is encouraged to use additional or new techniques when repeating role plays.

Reverse role plays are helpful when teaching certain skills. These are role plays in which the clinician pretends to be the client and the client pretends to be the person that he or she wants to talk to in a real-life situation. For example, the clinician could pretend to be the client, and the client could be a teacher whom the client will approach about a problem in the classroom. Reverse role plays allow clinicians to model good use of a skill (e.g., communication, assertive refusal skills). They also help the clinician learn how the person the client is going to talk with typically acts so that they can accurately portray that person. Finally, playing the person the client plans to talk to gives the client a perspective on how the other person might feel. Reverse role plays are always followed by regular role plays in order to give clients multiple opportunities to practice the targeted skills.

Basic Session Guidelines

There are general guidelines for conducting an A-CRA session. The overall style is behavioral or cognitive behavioral. As noted above, there is an emphasis on discerning the client's reinforcers and providing verbal reinforcement when possible. Clinicians also are expected to project a positive, upbeat, and supportive approach. In most sessions, clinicians are expected to use A-CRA procedures appropriately during a significant portion of the session. As with any treatment, the clinician's general clinical skills are related to enhancing treatment engagement and effectiveness. These skills include demonstrating warmth and understanding and being nonjudgmental. The clinician will also maintain the session focus so that once a procedure is started, there is time to complete it. Also, the clinician will try to ensure the logical progression from one procedure to another. Finally, A-CRA clinicians skillfully guide the session so that there is an appropriate balance between the amount of time the clinician and the client each talk.

Contact Frequency and Duration

The first A-CRA manual described a fixed-length intervention that was implemented during the CYT study. Clinicians were asked to make every effort to complete ten 1-hour sessions individually with the adolescent, two 1-hour sessions individually with the adolescent's caregivers and two 1.5-hour sessions (approximately) with the adolescent and caregivers together. Additionally, the duration of treatment was recommended to be 12 to 14 weeks. Since the model was first evaluated based on this duration and number of sessions, this might be considered the minimally acceptable parameters for faithful implementation of the model.

However, individual clinicians and programs may add additional sessions based on client and family needs. Differences by treatment setting and modality are described in a subsequent chapter, but some examples might be helpful here. In one implementation of A-CRA, the federal government required a 3-month period of outpatient treatment, followed by a 3-month period of Assertive Continuing Care (ACC), which includes the delivery of A-CRA procedures. Therefore, the planned implementation of A-CRA was closer to 6 months in duration. The length of treatment varies when A-CRA is implemented in residential treatment because the procedures can be used during the full residential stay and then incorporated into a continuing care phase when the client returns to the home environment. A-CRA also might be implemented differently in school-based settings as a consequence of the school calendar and the class-period length. Additionally, the clinician may have the advantage of having more access to an adolescent client during a school year. In this situation, each session might be shorter and the overall treatment duration may be longer, with the addition of check-in continuing care sessions when the adolescent has completed the treatment.

One of the frequent questions we are asked during training and implementation is, "Can we have more sessions with the caregivers?" In most cases, the term "caregivers" means parents, but caregivers could also refer to grandparents, guardians, or other adults who play a significant caring role in the client's life. Initially, when we were training clinicians in A-CRA, many of them had never worked with parents or had worked with them only in group-education classes. So the highly structured sessions offered guidance regarding how to make the best use of minimal sessions with parents. Additionally, some clinicians told us they had considerable difficulty with getting parents to attend *any* sessions, often because the parents worked multiple jobs and cared for other children. We set a minimum number of caregiver sessions so that clinicians would have an achievable target for these important sessions. However, we have always told clinicians that if they think more sessions are clinically indicated and wanted by the client and caregivers, then they can add additional caregiver or family sessions.

Timing of Procedures

A suggested sequence of A-CRA procedures follows for the first 4 weeks of a 12 to 14-week outpatient treatment episode. This sequence is just *suggested* because you may adjust treatment content as needed to enhance the therapeutic alliance, increase motivation to change, or address pressing clinical needs. For example, if the client raises an issue that provides an opportunity to teach a procedure, you should address the need presented rather than rigidly staying with a session plan. Or if you plan to conduct a Functional Analysis of Substance Use but a client mentions a problem (e.g., money is needed for an upcoming healthy social event), you can introduce the Problem Solving procedure. Focusing on issues presented by the client enhances engagement and motivation for change, which is a primary goal of A-CRA.

Interaction between the clinician and the client during the presentation and practice of procedures also enhances engagement and reinforces learning. You can return to the Functional Analysis of Substance Use procedure later in the session if time permits or in the next session.

These guidelines can be changed based on the modality. In intensive outpatient or residential treatment settings, material might be covered more quickly. In these settings there might also be more time for practice, to notice and praise a client using a new skill in a real-life situation, or to ask the client to practice skills instead of providing punishment or deducting points after a rule infraction. For example, if two clients begin to disagree in a residential setting and raise their voices, it would be appropriate to work with them to practice their communication skills. If a client is having difficulty figuring out how to get transportation to a probation appointment, the problem solving skills could be used to help decide on the best solution.

A-CRA supervisors note that this flexible approach to using procedures can increase the difficulty of training clinicians in A-CRA procedures. It takes time and practice for clinicians to learn how to seamlessly introduce procedures into sessions as opportunities occur. Instead of saying, "OK, today I want us to do problem solving," it would be preferable to teach the steps of problem solving after a client has mentioned a problem (which most will). Clinical supervision that incorporates reviews of recorded therapy sessions will be helpful to the training process. As clinicians become more comfortable with the procedures, they can introduce or review them according to each client's needs. When first learning the procedures, it is also common for clinicians to have notes to help them remember all the procedure components.

Materials

Because of the flexible nature of A-CRA, you should be prepared to use a variety of procedures and have materials available to meet the needs that the client presents during a session. The descriptions of the procedures include the materials needed for each one, such as clipboards, pens, handouts, and copies of clinical forms (found at the end of each procedure section).

Offer the client a snack and a drink at the beginning of every session, if your organization's budget permits. Suggestions for snacks include chips, granola bars, fruit bars, candy, cookies, and bottled water or fruit juices. It is more practical to offer snacks packaged as one serving (not a whole bag of chips or a package of cookies). Offering the snacks serves as a primary reinforcer to help engage the client.

Suggested Sequencing of Sessions for Outpatient Treatment

Session 1: Depending on organizational procedures, the first clinical session may follow an agency intake during which disclosures and releases of information forms will be reviewed and signed. There may be a brief overview of treatment during the agency intake. If possible, during the latter part of the agency intake, clinicians should meet with the client and caregivers to introduce themselves, begin to build rapport, provide a brief overview of the A-CRA treatment, and answer questions.

If clinicians are not able to meet with caregivers during the agency intake, they would do so briefly during the first clinical session and would provide a brief overview of A-CRA at that time. When caregivers and clients are both present in a session, it is important to involve them all by talking to or directing questions to everyone in the room. Once clinicians review the necessary information with the caregivers, they explain that the rest of the session will be spent with the client.

Your goal for the rest of the session (with the client alone) is to develop rapport while also providing some important information. Be sure to praise clients for participating in treatment and try to make them feel comfortable by saying something like, "I'm really glad you came today; I look forward to working with you!" Provide or review a detailed overview of A-CRA. Help set positive expectations by describing how A-CRA has been found to be a successful treatment in research studies. Provide an overview of some procedures and begin to identify some of the client's reinforcers or rewards. Provide information about the length of treatment sessions, the number and type of sessions, the utility of alcohol or drug testing, and the role of video or audio recording (which will be used for supervision or certification). Often, it is appropriate to use the Happiness Scale as a basis for conversation and to find out what is important to the client. The session would end with a homework assignment and scheduling the time and place for the next session.

Procedures to Complete by Session 4: Each session will follow a similar format and will include the following:

- Offering a snack or drink, if the agency budget permits.
- Rapport building (praise attendance, ask open-ended questions about the client's week).
- Checking on homework completion.
- Checking on the progress of goals listed on the Goals of Counseling form once completed.
- Asking about relationships with friends, social activities, relationships with family members.
- Teaching or reviewing procedures as appropriate (using role plays).
- Agreeing on a homework assignment related to the session content.
- Scheduling the time and place for the next session.

By the end of Session 4, the clinician typically will have completed a Functional Analysis of Substance Use, a Functional Analysis of Prosocial Behavior, at least one Happiness Scale, and a Goals of Counseling form. Encouragement of prosocial behaviors also begins during the first four sessions by using the Functional Analysis of Prosocial Behavior and Increasing Prosocial Activity procedures.

Remaining Sessions: These sessions follow a similar format but do not require that skills be taught in a standard sequence. Topics and skills that should be covered in these sessions include:

- Communication Skills
- Problem Solving Skills
- Additional Happiness Scales
- Additional Goals of Counseling
- Increasing Prosocial Activity
- Drink/Drug Refusal
- Systematic Encouragement
- Relapse Prevention
- Anger Management
- Alcohol and drug testing (if part of the program)
- Any other A-CRA procedure as needed (e.g., Couple Relationship Skills, Job Seeking Skills, Medication Adherence and Monitoring, Sobriety Sampling)

Last Session: This session includes the review of treatment goals and termination of services (see discharge recommendations in Unit 3, Chapter 2 [p. 234]).

Sequence and Content of Caregiver Sessions

Sessions 1 and 2: The A-CRA clinician meets with the caregivers *without* the client present. In preparation for these sessions, it is important to initiate contact with caregivers as early as possible to schedule the first caregiver session (which occurs around Week 3). The clinician:

- Begins the session with standard rapport-building exchanges.
- Describes the goals of A-CRA treatment.
- Through conversation, identifies caregiver reinforcers and uses them to encourage caregiver participation.
- Describes the four behaviors that research has shown caregivers can do to help prevent the client from relapsing.
- Reinforces positive behaviors of parents or caregivers that support the client and help prevent relapse.
- Presents the Communication Skills procedure.
- Presents the Problem Solving procedure.
- Reinforces attendance at the session and encourages future attendance.
- Schedules the time and place for the next session.

Sessions 3 and 4: The A-CRA clinician meets with the caregivers and the client *together*. These sessions also should occur relatively early in treatment. The clinician:

- Reinforces attendance at the session and encourages future attendance.
- Helps the client and caregivers identify and talk about the things they like or appreciate about each other.
- Has the client and caregivers complete and review the adolescent and caregiver versions of the Relationship Happiness Scales.
- Reviews communication and problem solving skills with the client and caregivers.
- Practices relationship-building and communication techniques (e.g., how to solve problems, how to ask for things, how to receive things, how the caregiver can say no by offering alternatives, and how to remember to be nice).

See Table 1 for a quick reference for the sequencing of procedures. *Note that any procedure can and should be repeated as needed.*

Table 1. Timeline of A-CRA Treatment Sessions, Treatment Procedures, and Participants

Time Frame	Procedures/Other
Client Only Sessions	
Ongoing	• Offer a snack or drink, if the agency budget permits • Use rapport-building techniques (praise attendance, ask open-ended questions about their week) • Check on homework completion • Check on the progress of goals listed on the Goals of Counseling form once completed • Ask about relationships with friends, social activities, relationships with family members • Teach or review procedures as appropriate (using role plays) • Agree on a homework assignment related to the session content • Schedule the time and place for the next session
Week 1	• Overview of A-CRA (also provide a brief overview for parents in the first session)
Weeks 1–4	• Functional Analysis of Substance Use Behavior • First Happiness Scale • First Goals of Counseling • Functional Analysis of Prosocial Behavior • Increasing Prosocial Activity
Any Session	• Communication Skills • Problem Solving Skills • Additional Happiness Scale • Additional Goals of Counseling • Increasing Prosocial Activity • Drink/Drug Refusal • Systematic Encouragement • Relapse Prevention • Anger Management • Alcohol and drug testing (if part of program) • Other A-CRA procedures as needed (e.g., Couple Relationship Skills, Job Seeking Skills, Medication Adherence and Monitoring, Sobriety Sampling)
Last Session	• Review of treatment goals and termination of services (see Unit 3, Chapter 2 [p. 234] for discharge recommendations.)
Caregiver Only Sessions	
Weeks 3–4	• Caregivers' Overview (overview of A-CRA, identify caregivers' reinforcers, four parenting practices) • Communication Skills Procedure training and role play practice • Problem Solving Procedure training and role play practice
Caregiver Client Sessions	
Weeks 6–12	• Caregiver Client Relationship Skills (share appreciation statements, complete the Relationship Happiness Scale, review and practice communication and problem solving skills, teach the Daily Reminder to Be Nice form)

Additional Clinical Considerations

Referrals for Other Needed Services

There are extensive data from adolescent treatment studies indicating that many adolescents requiring substance use treatment services have additional problems. It is important to assess for these problems as part of the initial biopsychosocial assessment so that they can be adequately addressed during treatment. Unit 3, Chapter 1 (p. 228) describes how A-CRA procedures can be helpful for addressing some co-occurring problems, but it is appropriate for you to refer the adolescent (and family members) to other service providers when they have needs that cannot be adequately addressed by A-CRA. For example, if you suspect that an adolescent has a mental health problem that might benefit from medication, you would provide a referral to a family physician, a pediatrician, or a psychiatrist.

Frequently, we have been asked about using A-CRA with other treatment models, like Trauma-Focused CBT. A-CRA can be used in conjunction with other evidence-based models, but it is important that the other treatment is similar to CRA as far as being positive and supportive. Furthermore, when there are two separate clinicians delivering the models, there must be good communication between them (with the proper releases) to ensure that they understand what is being addressed in each therapy.

Sometimes as treatment progresses, it becomes apparent that a client has more severe problems than originally thought, and these problems may require a higher level of care (e.g., residential treatment). In this case, and if residential treatment is available, the appropriate referral should be made. There are often waiting lists for these services; if this is the case, the A-CRA clinician should continue to provide treatment to the client on an outpatient basis until there is an opening in the higher-level treatment program.

When the Client or Caregiver No-Shows

For clients to benefit from treatment, they have to attend. When clients miss a treatment session, it is critical for you to attempt to reengage them in treatment as soon as possible. Likewise, if caregivers miss a session, you need to make additional efforts to engage them. The initial contact is usually a telephone call, but may include a home visit, if necessary and possible. If the client has been required to attend treatment by a probation officer, school official, or another authority figure, contact with this official to prompt the client to attend may also be helpful.

Many of the suggestions below are based on the *Motivational Enhancement Therapy Manual* used in Project MATCH (W. R. Miller, Zweben, DiClemente, & Rychtarik, 1995). As illustrated, clinicians are expected to be aggressive in their efforts to engage both the client and the caregivers in the treatment process. The following are some detailed steps accompanied by some sample dialogue.

1. **Try to contact the client and caregivers by phone immediately, and keep trying until you reach them.**

Respond immediately when a client or caregiver misses a scheduled appointment. Try to reach them by telephone, text, or other electronic means, and when you do, cover these points:

- Clarify the reasons for the missed appointment.
- Affirm the client or caregiver; provide reinforcement for having agreed to participate in treatment.
- Express eagerness to see the client again.

- Remind the client about the reinforcers already discussed for quitting substance use or, in the case of caregivers, the reasons they want the client to quit using substances.
- Express optimism about the prospects for change.
- Reschedule the appointment.

Here is an example of a telephone call from a clinician to an adolescent who has missed a session:

Clinician: *Hello John! How are you doing?*

Adolescent: *Fine.*

Clinician: *Good. I was just calling because you missed your appointment today. Was there anything wrong that led to your missing the appointment?*

Adolescent: *Well, my mom wasn't home, and I didn't have a ride, so I couldn't come.*

Clinician: *OK. I know you really wanted to work on your relationship with your mom, and I think we can work on making things work out between you two in therapy. I really look forward to starting back on this problem during one of our sessions. Is there anything I can do to help you out with getting to therapy?*

Adolescent: *No, not really. My mom just needs to take me.*

Clinician: *OK. If you need anything, just ask. How are you feeling about therapy now?*

Adolescent: *I really don't feel like coming all the time.*

Clinician: *Well, I realize it isn't always easy to come to therapy and try something like this. It's actually pretty common for people to have a hard time coming to therapy at first. What is something you don't really like about coming to therapy?* [Clinician explores obstacles.]

Adolescent: *Nothing really. It just takes up a lot of my time.*

Clinician: *It does take up time. One good thing is that it only lasts a few more weeks and then we will be done. I know you had a few reasons why you came here in the first place and some problems because of alcohol and drugs. What are those things?* [Clinician helps identify potential motivators.]

Adolescent: *I went because my probation officer sent me. I got in trouble with him, and my mom doesn't really like me smoking weed, either.*

Clinician: *What would you like to see happen differently between you and your mom or probation officer?*

Adolescent: *I just want them to stop bothering me.*

Clinician: *I think we can work on that. I would really like to see your mom and probation officer off your back, too. Do you think we could go ahead and reschedule your appointment?*

Adolescent:	*OK. How about Monday night?*
Clinician:	*Sounds good. Is 6:00 still good?*
Adolescent:	*Yeah.*
Clinician:	*Great. I really look forward to seeing you and working on what to do to get your mom and probation officer to stop bothering you.*

If no reasonable explanation is offered for the missed appointment (e.g., illness, transportation breakdown), explore with the client whether the missed appointment reflects any of the following:

- Uncertainty about whether treatment is needed (e.g., "I got everything I needed from residential treatment" or "My child doesn't really have a problem").
- Ambivalence about making any changes.
- Frustration or anger about having to participate in treatment (e.g., because school requires it).

Also, if transportation was the stated reason and a caregiver is needed to provide transportation, then it might also be important to have a conversation with that caregiver as well.

You should not act surprised about poor attendance or confront clients about their motivation. Instead, suggest that it is normal to express reluctance by not showing up or being late and encourage them to express any concerns about participation. Elicit motivational statements from the clients or caregivers by having them review the negative consequences (with peers, family, school, law enforcement, etc.) that brought them to treatment in the first place. Then ask them to review how you can assist in preventing these things from happening again. If speaking with caregivers, talk about the goals they have for their adolescent or the problems their adolescent's use creates.

2. If the client or caregiver does not have a phone, make a home visit and conduct the procedures there.

If you suspect flagging motivation, you may need to offer home visits to prime attendance, if your employer allows them. A home visit is also an option if you have difficulty making contact by telephone or if the family does not have a telephone. The purpose of this visit is to show the client and caregivers that you are genuinely interested and to encourage attendance at a session. You can go through the procedures outlined above and work through any problems with transportation or other obstacles. Some adolescents prefer to have sessions at their school, which is another option to explore.

Another useful technique is to send out greeting cards to motivate attendance and encourage reengagement in treatment. A handwritten message from the clinician provides a very personal contact for the client.

3. If the client does not respond to the procedures, consider contacting a caregiver and the referral source to see whether they can help prompt attendance.

If the caregiver does not attend sessions, consider contacting the referral source for help or consider inviting an alternative caregiver.

Alcohol and Drug Testing

In training sessions, we always begin a discussion of alcohol and drug testing by asking the trainees, who are from different organizations and U.S. states or other countries, a few questions: (a) Do they test for alcohol or drug use as part of their treatment? (b) How often do they test and do they do so on a regular or random basis? (c) What do they do if the test shows no alcohol or drug use? (d) What do they do when the test has a positive result for alcohol or drugs? (e) Are results routinely shared with juvenile justice or other referring entities?

Organizational alcohol and drug testing policies are quite varied. Sometimes, it is clear that organizations have long-standing practices regarding the use of these tests but have not revisited those practices in years. Our goal for asking the questions is to stimulate thought about the appropriate use of these tests, especially in the context of A-CRA, which relies on identifying reinforcers and taking a positive approach.

We are sometimes concerned that treatment providers have become so closely allied with court services that court authorities rely solely on the provider's testing results to determine court sanctions. We believe this practice has the potential to undermine the clinician-client relationship. We think that the best approach is for A-CRA treatment providers to conduct their own tests and use the results in the context of treatment and for court services to conduct their own tests for their uses. A good strategy to address this situation is to meet with judges, probation supervisors, and probation officers to educate them about the A-CRA model. This information will enable them to better understand the role of treatment and the use of alcohol and drug testing in the model. Court service personnel are less likely to expect treatment providers to use testing results in a punitive manner if they understand the use of these tests in treatment. These key stakeholders will also be better able to support treatment overall if they have an understanding of the treatment model.

In general, a negative (no drugs found) test provides the opportunity to reinforce abstinence, whereas a positive test provides additional information to the clinician that can be used to prompt appropriate A-CRA procedures (e.g., Relapse Prevention, Problem Solving). If drugs are detected, the clinician would conduct a nonjudgmental review of the context of use and would help the client identify a healthier plan in the event that a similar risky situation was encountered in the future.

General Recommendations for Alcohol and Drug Testing with A-CRA

- If clients are going to be alcohol and drug tested, they should be informed during the first session and told how the tests will be used in treatment.
- Onsite tests are ideal because they allow for immediate feedback. These tests are improving all the time, but onsite tests are usually considered to provide only preliminary analytical results. Gas chromatography/mass spectrometry (GC/MS) is usually preferred for a confirmatory analysis. These tests are typically done in a laboratory. An onsite test may have limited value in assessing decreasing drug use (as opposed to total abstinence) and does not provide the confirmatory analyses that may be required by a court or other source. If a client denies use but tests positive with an onsite test, consider sending a second urine sample to a certified laboratory to verify the onsite test using GC/MS.
- If a client refuses to submit to a test, it is important for the clinician to continue the session because the most important goal is to treat the client.
- If a client is on probation, the probation officer may conduct the urine test rather than the clinician.

- There is no need for testing when a client freely admits to using, unless the particular test being used is one that provides measures of substance use levels.
- If testing has been mandated by probation, parole, or a court agency, obtain appropriate signed disclosures before revealing the test results to that agency.

Recommendations for Providing Feedback Based on Results

- To individualize urine test results:
  - Focus on the specifics of the client's situation.
  - Focus on what can be done to avoid triggers and lapses.
  - Ask how the test results could affect their goals.
- When the test results indicate that *no* alcohol or drugs are present, provide strong positive reinforcement and social support. Review aspects of the client's living environment that have been conducive to abstinence. Encourage continued development of drug-free activities. Probe for problems with cravings or emotional distress during this time. Find out how the client coped successfully with these problems. Ask, "What is your biggest motivation for not using?"
- When test results indicate that alcohol or drugs *are* present, review the context of the client's use. Remain nonjudgmental. Examine external and internal triggers associated with the use, and generate potential solutions to resist use if a similar circumstance is encountered in the future. Talk with the client about goals for reducing substance use. Encourage the client to commit to changing using behavior, and help the client identify personal motivators for staying away from alcohol or drugs. Review triggers, coping methods, and other Relapse Prevention procedures described in Unit 2, Chapter 9 (p. 111). Also consider using the Sobriety Sampling procedure (Unit 2, Chapter 10 [p. 117]).
- If the client denies using despite positive results:
  - Do not criticize. Rather than being confrontational, play detective and ask questions. For example, "What do you make of this discrepancy?" or "What do you think is going on here?"
  - Point out that perhaps a positive test could have consequences (e.g., probation problems, losing a job) even if the client did not use.
  - Ask the client how you can help.
  - Reiterate that being around others who are using alcohol or drugs is a high-risk situation with negative consequences.
  - Consider completing the Relapse Prevention procedure with the client.

UNIT 1: CHAPTER 3: The Importance of General Clinical Skills

Rationale for Focusing on General Clinical Skills

Why is it important to talk about fundamental clinical skills when clinicians are being trained to deliver an evidence-based treatment like A-CRA? Studies have shown that it is fairly common to find differences in client outcomes across clinicians, and these differences are not related to differences in clinicians' ages, genders, ethnicities and races, educations, or experiences (W. R. Miller & Moyers, 2014). Instead, some of the differences seem to be attributable to a clinician's therapeutic style and the quality of the relationship between the clinician and the client, otherwise known as "common factors" of therapy (Laska, Gurman, & Wampold, 2014; Wampold, 2010). Importantly, researchers have also determined that it is worthwhile to evaluate clinicians and provide feedback on these various factors so that the clinicians can improve (S. D. Miller, Hubble, Duncan, & Wampold, 2010; Norcross & Wampold, 2011; Wampold, 2010). Some aspects of these common factors that appear relevant to A-CRA are highlighted below.

What Are the General Clinical Skills?

Research shows that strong therapeutic relationships and alliances can make valuable contributions to treatment outcomes (Norcross & Wampold, 2011). Within the addiction field specifically, not only is a positive therapeutic alliance associated with better treatment outcomes but with treatment engagement and retention as well (P. S. Meier, Barrowclough, & Donmall, 2005). In terms of defining the "therapeutic relationship," this working alliance is often referred to as the bond between clinicians and their clients *and* the agreement between them in terms of the tasks and goals of treatment (Wampold, 2010). Although we do not know precisely which factors are necessary for a positive and strong therapeutic relationship, there are several prime candidates.

For the purposes of implementing A-CRA, clinician characteristics such as being *warm and understanding* and *nonjudgmental* are viewed as contributors to a strong therapeutic relationship. In part, these characteristics are highlighted because the opposite "negative processes," including being hostile and critical, have been shown to be ineffective aspects of therapeutic relationships (Norcross & Wampold, 2011). Additionally, positive clinician interpersonal skills are associated with better treatment outcomes (Norcross & Wampold, 2011). We also know that clinicians with higher levels of empathy tend to have clients with better treatment retention and lower levels of drinking (W. R. Miller & Baca, 1983; Moyers & Miller, 2013). So it is not surprising, then, that considerable research finds a nonconfrontational, nonjudgmental style to be more effective than a confrontational one within the substance abuse field (W. R. Miller, Wilbourne, & Hettema, 2003). The same holds true for the therapy field more generally: A rejecting, critical, and blaming clinician style is associated with poorer treatment outcomes (see Norcross & Wampold, 2011).

When implementing A-CRA, we also look for clinicians to *maintain the session focus* and to *be appropriately active*. Regarding the former, this entails staying on track and completing an A-CRA procedure once it has been started with a client, as opposed to switching back and forth among several procedures. Since many of the A-CRA procedures involve teaching the client specific skills, a coherent presentation of the entire skill in one sitting is worthwhile, especially when the clinician makes time to also incorporate examples that are directly relevant to the client's current situation. However, there are exceptions to the expectation that a clinician stay on track with a procedure, such as when a clinical emergency becomes apparent. Examples of such emergencies are suspected self-harm or suicidal behavior, a concern about the client being dangerous to self or others, or abuse or neglect that requires reporting. As far as the related construct of being appropriately active, normally one would hope to see a good balance in conversation between the clinician and the client; neither individual should dominate the session. This applies to the family sessions as well, in which the clinician should allow roughly equal speaking time for the caregivers and the client.

As noted earlier, one aspect of a good therapeutic alliance is for the clinician and client to be in agreement regarding the treatment goals (Norcross & Wampold, 2011; Wampold, 2010). The A-CRA treatment program in general, and several procedures in particular, focuses on collaborative clinician-client efforts that entail having both individuals actively working on the same goals. As part of this process, A-CRA supports a clinical style that is directive but, as noted above, not overly domineering. Clinicians seem to be more effective when they exhibit a proper balance between rigidity and flexibility in terms of their approach to structuring a session (Norcross & Wampold, 2011). More specifically, extremely rigid clinicians run the risk of appearing low in empathy, while extremely flexible clinicians have been known to deliver treatments that no longer adhere to the treatment model; they lack treatment fidelity (Norcross & Wampold, 2011). In a nutshell: A good A-CRA clinician is one who can competently deliver the A-CRA procedures while at the same time exhibiting the extremely valuable clinical skills that work to promote a solid therapeutic relationship.

UNIT 2: A-CRA Procedures

The chapters in this unit provide detailed descriptions with sample dialogue of the 19 A-CRA procedures. *The Happiness Scale and the Goals of Counseling are combined in one chapter because these procedures are usually completed together.* The Happiness Scale may be used on its own to gauge the client's satisfaction, but the Goals of Counseling are based on responses to a client's answers on a Happiness Scale.

Also note the frequency with which role plays are used to teach new skills. Since role plays are so important, the components of a good role play are repeated below:

- Role plays should be two-sided. That is, there is a back and forth exchange between the clinician and client while the clinician plays the part of the person the client will talk to in real life.
- The role play is stopped after a relatively brief interchange (less than two minutes) so that the clinician can provide feedback to the client on the brief interchanges.
- At the end of each role play, the clinician compliments the client for specific components of the skills that were performed correctly.
- At the end of each role play, clinicians work to help the client improve the targeted skill by giving one or more suggestions for improvement.
- The clinician asks what the client did or did not like about his or her performance in the role play.
- Role plays are repeated more than once, each time varying responses, so that the client learns how to respond in realistic situations, which can often be challenging. The client is encouraged to use additional or new techniques when repeating role plays.

Reverse role plays are helpful when teaching certain skills. These are role plays in which the clinician pretends to be the client and the client pretends to be the person that he or she wants to talk to in a real-life situation. For example, the clinician could pretend to be the client, and the client could be a teacher whom the client will approach about a problem in the classroom. Reverse role plays allow clinicians to model good use of a skill (e.g., communication, assertive refusal skills). They also help the clinician learn how the person the client is going to talk with typically acts so that they can accurately portray that person. Finally, playing the person the client plans to talk to gives the client a perspective on how the other person might feel. Reverse role plays are always followed by regular role plays in order to give clients multiple opportunities to practice the targeted skills.

UNIT 2: CHAPTER 1: Overview of A-CRA for Clients

Rationale

The A-CRA Overview happens in the first clinical session, and it is designed to help engage clients so that they will want to return and participate in treatment. During this session, you will explain what will happen during treatment and describe how treatment might be helpful. Part of the engagement process is identifying some of the client's reinforcers and explaining how treatment will help the client gain access to those reinforcers.

Learning Objectives

The learning objectives are to help clients:

- Feel comfortable with the treatment approach.
- Learn what A-CRA treatment will include.
- Feel that treatment will be helpful.
- Identify motivations for changing alcohol or drug-using behavior.

Timing, Audience, and Delivery Method

The A-CRA Overview occurs in the first session. It occurs primarily with the client, but often caregivers will be invited to attend part of the session to hear a brief description of the treatment (if this has not already taken place). Caregivers learn what A-CRA consists of, including the expectation that they will be asked to attend some later sessions. The A-CRA Overview will be repeated in more detail for the caregivers when they have their first individual session.

Materials

No specific materials are needed for the Overview, but it is helpful to have available materials for specific procedures that are commonly used during the first session along with the Overview. These include a Functional Analysis of Substance Use form (p. 74), a Happiness Scale (p. 41), and a Goals of Counseling form (p. 43).

General Notes for the Clinician

Since this is the first clinical session, it is important to review all assessment information prior to the session. The assessment will provide information about potential reinforcers for the client and information about co-occurring problems. It is also important to review consent and release of information documentation to ensure that the agency's required paperwork has been completed.

The initial conversation with each client is critical in the rapport-building process. Most clients who drop out of treatment do so in the earlier sessions. During the first two sessions, focus on engagement. Get the client excited about working with you and about the treatment in general. *Do not let filling out forms overshadow the rapport-building process.*

Emphasize that you are glad to see the client. Praise the client for completing the assessment or for participating in previous treatment. For example, if the client was in residential treatment or intensive outpatient treatment before transferring to regular outpatient treatment, ask, "Why did you decide to come to treatment?"

Set positive expectations for change. For example, you might say, "A-CRA is a really good treatment and has worked for a lot of kids like you" and "I'm glad we get to work together." Acknowledge the effort it took to come to treatment that day: "I'm glad you came—I want you to get something out of this" or "You can learn things that will be helpful for you." Note that it takes a lot of courage to come to treatment. You can say, "Anybody can get high; it takes real courage and character to quit!" Acknowledge some discomfort on your part and tell the client, "I feel uncomfortable too at this point. We are in this together."

Explain that you will focus on what the client wants to do in treatment. Emphasize the client's independence. Give the client the power to pick and choose the focus of sessions. Let the client guide and move in the desired direction. The goal is to give the client some sense of control during the therapy session. Tell the client, "I'm not going to ask you to do anything you don't want to do." You might also say, "How can I best help you?"

Be patient; do not push clients when they are resistant. Ask open-ended questions as opposed to ones that require a short yes-or-no answer, such as "Do you like your mom?" Rather, you might say, "Tell me a little bit about your relationship with your mom." Ask open-ended questions about why clients came to treatment and let them talk. Good examples of open-ended questions or conversation starters include:

- Tell me a little bit about yourself.
- Tell me what brought you here today.
- What do you think about being here?
- How do you hope to benefit from these sessions?
- Tell me more about what's going on in school.
- How would you describe how you are feeling today?
- What's going on today?

Many adolescents are not very verbal, so be patient as you wait for responses and be willing to probe for additional information. Let them know that you are there because you want to help. You might say, "We're going to teach you skills you need to know; then you won't need me anymore. I'm just a guide. This isn't forever." Emphasize that the process is time-limited, that is, "We have a limited time to work together, so we need to try to accomplish our business during the time allotted."

Try other ways to build rapport. For instance, you could try shooting baskets with a young client to build rapport. Feel free to provide food and a drink to a client. The snacks are not only potentially reinforcing; they also help keep energy levels up while the client is working on treatment issues.

The five components described below do not need to be covered all at once. In particular, it is common to begin to identify reinforcers later in the session after you have learned more about the client.

Procedural Steps

1. **Describe basic objectives of A-CRA (help find a healthy, reinforcing lifestyle . . .).**
2. **Outline at least two A-CRA procedures that will be a part of treatment.**
3. **Set positive expectations that treatment will be helpful.**
4. **Describe the duration of treatment with emphasis that it is time-limited.**
5. **Start to identify reinforcers and rewards.**

6. **End the session with a homework assignment.**

Detailed Description

1. **Describe basic objectives of A-CRA (help find a healthy, reinforcing lifestyle . . .).**

Describing the objectives of A-CRA treatment can be done succinctly. There are three important parts to the description: (a) noting that the treatment is designed to help the client lead a healthy, reinforcing lifestyle without the use of alcohol and drugs, (b) explaining that learning how to live this healthy lifestyle will involve trying out other enjoyable activities that do not involve substance use, and (c) mentioning the use of reinforcers that are specific to the client and that will be the motivators for a lifestyle change. While the first two parts of this step might use similar language for most clients, the third part needs to be individualized based on what you learn about the motivators for a particular client. Reinforcers for participation in treatment may be addressed several times during the session as the clinician learns more about the client's reinforcers or motivators. The following is an example of how the clinician might describe the objectives:

Clinician:	*Tracy, the main goal of this program is to help you live a lifestyle without drugs or alcohol, but you still need to be happy with your life. If your life sucks without drugs, then it's likely you'll go back to using drugs, right? So I can help you identify things to do that are satisfying and enjoyable to you that aren't drug and alcohol-related. And then you'll feel less stress and be happier. We have to make sure you get the kind of life you want. And you already have some good ideas about what you want out of life. For example, during your assessment, you said that you really want to get off probation and make your mom more proud of you, and testing drug-free can help with both those goals. That's what this program is about—helping you get what you want out of treatment. What do you think?*
Adolescent:	*That sounds good, but I don't really think I need to be here.*
Clinician:	*I can understand that it doesn't seem like fun to have to come here, but since probation is saying you have to come, we can try to make the best of it—help you learn how to get what you want out of life. Does that make sense? What are your thoughts?*
Adolescent:	*Yeah, I guess I can give it a try.*

2. **Outline at least two A-CRA procedures that will be a part of treatment.**

When outlining at least two A-CRA procedures that will be used during treatment, the clinician needs to (a) explain how these procedures will be used, (b) provide enough detail so the client understands what they are, and (c) relate the use of the procedure to the client's particular situation. See the sample dialogue below:

Clinician:	*There are different skills that we'll be working on in here that will help you get what you want out of treatment, like figuring out how to make your mom proud and getting off of probation. A lot of young people we work with really find that learning better ways to communicate helps them to get along better with their parents, as well as others in their lives, so we'll work on those skills to help you communicate with your mom and P.O. You also mentioned that you have a lot of*

friends who smoke weed. Now I know that's kind of hard when you are out with friends and they are passing stuff around, right? So we'll be working on drug refusal skills to help you with that. What do you think?

Adolescent: *Yeah. Those things might be helpful.*

Clinician: *We'll work on other skills, too. We have 14 or so weeks to work together, so we have time to learn these skills during sessions, and you have time to practice them on your own between sessions. Does that sound OK?*

3. Set positive expectations that treatment will be helpful.

The most important element for setting positive expectations for the treatment is to emphasize that A-CRA has been found effective in scientific studies. While it is important to introduce this concept by using language that can be clearly understood, it is also true that people are used to hearing about research studies in the media these days. A sample explanation of setting a positive expectation follows:

Clinician: *Something to think about is that once you're done with the treatment, you'll have these skills we will have worked on for the rest of your life. And you know, I'm not just making this stuff up. There's been a lot of research done, studies and stuff, on these methods and different interventions that are effective, like the drug refusal skills. These interventions that I'm telling you about have been successful with lots of different kinds of teenagers, teens who have been using various types of drugs and different levels of drugs and alcohol, and teens from all different kinds of backgrounds, including those that are similar to you. It's not like we're saying, "Let's try this stuff and see if it works." No—it's actually been tested already and we know that it works. Do you have any questions?*

4. Describe the duration of treatment with emphasis that it is time-limited.

Durations of treatment may vary somewhat across different treatment organizations, but it is important to provide information about (a) the frequency of sessions (e.g., weekly), (b) the duration (e.g., 3 months), (c) the length of each session (e.g., an hour), and (d) the format of sessions (e.g., a number of sessions with the client alone, with caregivers alone, and with everyone together). See the example that follows.

Clinician: *This program lasts for 3 months. There will be 14 sessions. Ten sessions will be you and me meeting individually, usually once a week for about an hour. Now if something's going on where there's a crisis or something and you really need to talk about it, you can come in another day, too. Also, there will be two sessions that I meet with you and your parents together, and two more when I meet just with your parents. These sessions may last a little longer than an hour. During the sessions with your parents alone, I'll teach them some of the things I'm also going to teach you, such as communication skills, and we'll also have the chance to talk about what they'd like to see happen. For the two family sessions that involve the four of us, we'll be talking about your relationship with your parents and how to make it better. So we'll work on how all of you communicate and you'll have the chance to practice the communication skills with one another. For example, maybe you'll want help telling your mom that you'd like her to recognize some of your accomplishments more, right? How does this sound so far?*

5. Start to identify reinforcers and rewards.

As the clinician identifies reinforcers and rewards during the session, it is important to (a) review at least two reasons why the client wants to stop using alcohol or drugs and (b) emphasize why the reinforcers and rewards are being identified in the first place. If the Overview is happening during the first session with the caregivers alone, it would be important for the clinician to help the caregivers talk about how they would benefit if their child stopped using alcohol and drugs and what the caregivers might get out of attending treatment. An example of this part of the session follows:

Clinician:	*So far, I've been explaining a lot to you and doing a lot of talking, but I want to hear more from you about what's important to you. What are your goals here? What do you want to do?*
Adolescent:	*I want my parents to stop yelling at me and give me more freedom to do what I want.*
Clinician:	*OK, that sounds like a good start. What do you think it will take for that to happen?*
Adolescent:	*My parents never let me go out because they tell me that my friends are bad influences. It's true. I do have a hard time saying no to my friends when they're smoking weed, but I also get bored at home and all I think about is getting high.*
Clinician:	*So it sounds like you want to work on finding some fun things to do outside of the house that maybe don't involve substance use and possibly meet some new people. What do you think?*
Adolescent:	*Yeah, that sounds like it could be good, and this is my opportunity to do things right. But like I said, I know I have a problem saying no to drugs. My mom is thinking about taking me out of school this year and maybe putting me in a residential program because school is where all my problems started.*
Clinician:	*As I mentioned before, we can definitely work on skills to refuse drugs and alcohol from people. And we can work on the other things you mentioned too, like getting better grades and getting a good job. We can set some longer-term goals in those areas and then set some weekly goals, too. And it will all be stuff that you want to work on. I'm not going to tell you what you have to do.*
Adolescent:	*That sounds good, I guess.*

Introduce Another Procedure (If Time Allows)

Typical procedures to do after the Overview during a first session are the Functional Analysis of Substance Use or the Happiness Scale followed by the Goals of Counseling. There is not enough time to do all of these, so it is really up to you to decide which procedure would be most appropriate for a particular client. If the client is quiet and appears treatment resistant, then the Happiness Scale might be a more appropriate procedure to do first.

6. End the session with a homework assignment.

As with every A-CRA session, you end by working with the client to identify the homework assignment. During the first few sessions, you need to briefly explain why homework assignments are important and what they will be like. After several sessions, the client will come to expect that each session will start with a review of homework and end with an agreed-upon homework assignment. Here is how a homework assignment might be introduced:

> **Clinician:** *It's awesome that you are interested in getting good grades and doing well in school and eventually getting a good job. One of the things we will do each week is come up with an assignment that you can work on during the week toward your goal. So for example, it might be to set aside so much time each night for homework, or use a study hall to do homework instead of something else. Can you think of something you might want to work on this week to help with your grades or with one of the other goals we discussed?* [The specific assignment should be spelled out clearly before the session ends. See Unit 2, Chapter 3 (p. 47) for more detail on setting up homework assignments.]

UNIT 2: CHAPTER 2: Happiness Scale and Treatment Plan/Goals of Counseling

Rationale

The Happiness Scale can be used frequently to assess how happy or satisfied the client is in multiple life areas and to monitor changes in happiness over the course of treatment. The Happiness Scale life areas include use or nonuse of alcohol, marijuana, or other drugs; relationships with friends and boyfriends or girlfriends; relationships with parents or caregivers; school; social activities; recreational activities; personal habits; legal issues; money management; emotional well-being; communication; and general happiness. It is a strength-based tool in that it helps identify what is going well in the client's life. It also helps keep treatment client-focused because the client's own ratings help in the selection of treatment goals.

The Goals of Counseling is the A-CRA procedure for developing a treatment plan. It allows clinicians and clients to define treatment goals and activities related to the same domains that are assessed with the Happiness Scale.

Learning Objectives

The learning objectives are to help clients:

- Identify life areas that are going well and not so well (with the Happiness Scale).
- Develop treatment goals and strategies that can be used to achieve the goals.
- Develop a homework assignment that will help make progress toward a goal.

Timing, Audience, and Delivery Method

Both the Happiness Scale and the Goals of Counseling procedures are conducted with the client individually. A Happiness Scale usually should be completed during one of the first two sessions, prior to beginning work on the Goals of Counseling, because it provides important information for setting goals. The clinician and client can revisit the Happiness Scale often during treatment as a way to monitor changes in happiness over the course of treatment. Clinicians have found the Happiness Scale helpful when a client appears resistant to treatment or is simply providing very little information (for whatever reason). The Happiness Scale provides a starting point for discussion in several areas.

It is useful to at least start the Goals of Counseling form on the same day (during one of the first two sessions) as the Happiness Scale because the ratings from the Happiness Scale are used to guide the selection of goals to address. Like the Happiness Scale, the Goals of Counseling can be revisited throughout therapy. New issues that the client wants to address may emerge, or further clarification of old issues may prompt the selection of new goals. Like the Functional Analysis of Substance Use Behavior and the Functional Analysis of Prosocial Behavior, the Goals of Counseling should be thought of as a work in progress. The Happiness Scale and Goals of Counseling forms are described together in this section, but remember that the Happiness Scale can always be used independently as well.

Materials

Procedure-specific materials include a clipboard, pens, and a Happiness Scale (p. 41).

Goals of Counseling materials include a clipboard, pens, a Goals of Counseling form (p. 43), and a completed Happiness Scale (p. 41).

General Notes for the Clinician

Before beginning to use the Happiness Scale or work on the Goals of Counseling, review on your own any available assessment information as well as the Functional Analysis of Substance Use Behavior and Functional Analysis of Prosocial Behavior forms if they have been completed. This review will allow you to suggest goals, activities, and reinforcers based on information the client has already provided.

Treatment organizations usually have specific treatment plan formats that need to be followed to fulfill state licensing or accreditation requirements. In many cases, we have seen that these licensing and accrediting bodies approve of the Goals of Counseling because (a) it is client driven (rather than being prescribed by the clinician), (b) goals are stated in the client's own words, and (c) it uses generally accepted rules for writing goals and strategies. It is worthwhile to have a discussion with clinical management when implementing A-CRA about how the Goals of Counseling could be helpful in creating the existing treatment plan or possibly how the two could be merged.

Note that one of the advantages of completing the Goals of Counseling form is that it does not focus solely on a client's use of marijuana and alcohol as a problem area. As you review the form with the client, it becomes clear that you want to help with problems in multiple areas. This knowledge can help lower the resistance of some clients. As always, maintain a positive approach with the client, finding opportunities for reinforcement.

Procedural Steps

1. Provide an overview of the Happiness Scale and Goals of Counseling.
2. Ask the client to complete the Happiness Scale, and review it together.
   - **Choose two or three Happiness Scale categories that were rated in the high range to discuss first.**
   - **Next, choose two or three Happiness Scale categories that were rated in the middle range to discuss.**
   - **Last, choose two or three Happiness Scale categories that were rated in the low range to discuss, and learn about areas that are of most concern to the client.**
3. Complete the Goals of Counseling form together.
   - **Ask the client to choose areas in which to develop goals. There are advantages to choosing a middle-rated item for goal setting (these items typically are not too hard or too easy to work on). However, the client can pick any goal area of interest.**
   - **Work with the client to devise a step-by-step intervention to accomplish each goal.**
   - **Decide on a time frame for completing each intervention or activity. For interventions requiring skills training, decide when the skills will be taught.**
4. Assign homework.

Detailed Description

1. Provide an overview of the Happiness Scale and Goals of Counseling.

There are different versions of the Happiness Scale, but the one we include here covers 16 areas of life. Clients rate each area on a scale of 1 (totally unhappy) to 10 (totally happy) to indicate how happy or satisfied they are *currently* with each area. These same life areas are repeated on the Goals of Counseling form. The 16 areas of life on the Happiness Scale include the following: marijuana use and nonuse, alcohol use and nonuse, other drug use and nonuse, relationship with boyfriend or girlfriend, relationships with friends, relationships with parents or caregivers, school, social activities, recreational activities, personal habits, legal issues, money management, emotional life, communication, general happiness, and other. The "other" category is any other life area that is important to the client, such as church or music.

When completed as part of the treatment plan, the Happiness Scale provides a baseline measure that indicates which areas of a client's life are most in need of attention. Blank and completed samples of these forms are located at the end of this section. After the Happiness Scales are completed, you will help clients define specific goals and plans for those life areas in need of attention and set time frames in which to meet them. If the Happiness Scale reveals that the client is unhappy in many life areas, it is important not to overwhelm the client by attempting to develop too many goals addressing too many different life areas at once. It is always possible to set new goals as the adolescent is ready to work on them.

The following dialogue is an example of how to introduce the Happiness Scale.

> **Clinician:** *Today, Jim, we are going to work on coming up with the best treatment plan for you. To help us do that, there are two exercises we are going to do together. The first one involves completing a Happiness Scale. The purpose of this exercise is to help us get a clear idea about how satisfied you are* right now *with different areas of your life. It will also help us pinpoint which areas of your life you might want to work on. The second exercise involves completing the Goals of Counseling. On this form, we will list specific goals that you want to reach during treatment and then devise a plan for you to reach those goals.*

2. **Ask the client to complete the Happiness Scale, and review it together.**
   - **Choose two or three Happiness Scale categories that were rated in the high range to discuss first.**
   - **Next, choose two or three Happiness Scale categories that were rated in the middle range to discuss.**
   - **Last, choose two or three Happiness Scale categories that were rated in the low range to discuss, and learn about areas that are of most concern to the client.**

Explain the directions for completing the Happiness Scale. Give the client the form and a pencil as you describe the form. Note that the scale can be given orally if the client is not able to read.

When rating each life area, the client is instructed to use the *current* time frame; that is, how happy they are *today* with each area.

> **Clinician:** *Let's look first at the Happiness Scale. There are 16 categories. As you go through each item on the form, I'd like you to rate how happy you are right now with that part of your life, using a scale of 1 to 10. A rating of 1 in a life area means you are totally unhappy with that part of your life now—about as unhappy as you could be. A rating of 10 means you are totally happy with that part of your life right now—you are totally satisfied and that part of your life doesn't need any changes. All the numbers in between are less extreme; the lower numbers (2 through 5) mean you are unhappier with that area, and the higher numbers (6 through 9) mean you are happier with that area. Let's look at the first one together: marijuana use and nonuse. Using the 1 to 10 scale, how satisfied or*

happy are you right now with that part of your life? You'll see that some of the first questions are about your alcohol and drug use. You can circle "use" or "nonuse" depending on your current situation before rating your happiness on those items.

When reviewing the client's responses, start with life areas that were rated high. This encourages the client to talk and can help build rapport. It also provides an opportunity to learn about what is going well in the client's life and what strengths the client has. Next, discuss areas that have been rated low. In discussing clients' ratings, ask open-ended questions to encourage them to tell more about their different ratings as illustrated with the dialogue below. Then discuss those areas rated in the middle range.

Clinician:	*Let's talk about your ratings. Oh, I see there are a couple that you've rated really high—that means you must be pretty happy with those areas of your life. Tell me why you rated Friends and Social Activities a 9.*
Adolescent:	*I feel like I have some good friends.*
Clinician:	*Can you tell me more about what makes them good friends to you?*
Adolescent:	*They are there for me. I can always count on them to help me out.*
Clinician:	*I'm happy for you. Having good friends is really important. [Clinician asks again about why Social Activities was rated a 9; reinforces answer if appropriate, then moves to a lower rating.]*
Clinician:	*OK, I also see that you rated Legal Issues a 2. A 2 rating means you're pretty unhappy with that part of your life. Tell me a little bit about why you decided on a 2 rating. What made you decide to rate it a 2?*
Adolescent:	*I really don't like that I'm on probation and I have these fines I'm supposed to pay.*
Clinician:	*What would it take for you to improve your rating for Legal Issues from a 2 to a 3 or a 4?*
Adolescent:	*If I can get off probation.*
Clinician:	*That makes sense. What will it take for you to get off probation?*
Adolescent:	*I don't know . . . I guess I have to do what my P.O. says and pay those fines.*
Clinician:	*Well, you and I can talk about that and set some goals in that area, if you like. For now, it might be better to start with a goal for something that you've rated in the middle range so you can see how this works. Let's look at some of those areas.*

3. **Complete the Goals of Counseling form together.**
   * **Ask the client to choose areas in which to develop goals. There are advantages to choosing a middle-rated item for goal setting (these items typically are not too hard or too easy to work on). However, the client can pick any goal area of interest.**
   * **Work with the client to devise a step-by-step intervention to accomplish each goal.**

- **Decide on a time frame for completing each intervention or activity. For interventions requiring skills training, decide when the skills will be taught.**

The same 16 areas of life listed on the Happiness Scale are repeated on the Goals of Counseling form. The first column contains the list of 16 major areas of life from the Happiness Scale. In this column, clients record specific goals related to their chosen problem area. The second column, "Intervention," is for recording the specific steps the client needs to meet each goal. In the third column, "Time Frame," a specified period is recommended to carry out the intervention.

When completing the Goals of Counseling form, it is important to teach clients the following basic guidelines:

- Always state goals or plans *positively*. This means clients should say what they want and will do rather than what they do *not* want and will *not* do.
- Be *specific*. For example, if the client suggests wanting to do "better" at school, ask, "What would it look like if you did 'better' at school?" or "What does that mean to you?"
- Specify *measurable* behaviors. That is, goals and interventions should specify how often (e.g., once a week, every day), on what days, or for how long an intervention will last. This way, progress can easily be monitored.
- Keep statements *simple and straightforward*. Goals and plans to reach them should be in the form of simple statements.
- Ensure that the goal is *under the client's control*. It is not useful to set goals that involve *other* people changing *their* behaviors.

Offer guidance and examples to show the client how goals and interventions can be stated according to these basic guidelines.

To begin, let the client choose only one or two areas of life to work on. It is preferable to begin with a category from the Happiness Scale that was rated in a moderate satisfaction range. Goal setting and devising interventions for a category with some satisfaction are usually easier.

Clinician:	*You've rated School a 5 on the Happiness Scale. You also rated your relationship with your parents as a 6. Both of these are areas that we might set goals in so that you would feel happier about them . . . or there might be another area you have noticed from the Happiness Scale that you would like to improve. What area would you like to set a goal in?*
Adolescent:	*School.*
Clinician:	*OK, can you tell me what would make you happier at school?*
Adolescent:	*I guess I'd like to get better grades.*
Clinician:	*That's neat that you would like to improve your grades. Can you tell me what you mean by "better" grades?* [Clinician helps the adolescent get more specific.]
Adolescent:	*I'd like to get grades as high as I can.*
Clinician:	*What particular grade: an A, a B, or a C? What would you be happy with?* [Clinician helps the adolescent put the goal in measurable terms.]

Adolescent:	*Well, I'd like to get As and Bs.*
Clinician:	*OK, let's see whether we can put that goal down as something we can work on while you are coming here. Remember, the goal should follow the five guidelines we talked about: it should to be positive, specific, measurable, simple and straightforward, and under your control. Go ahead and try stating your goal for school, making it fit all of these rules.*
Adolescent:	*All right. I want to get As and Bs at school.*
Clinician:	*That was good. You stated it positively; it is straightforward and under your control. Let's see if we can make it even more specific and measurable; tell me when you want to get these grades . . . by the end of the quarter, or semester, or when?*
Adolescent:	*I want to get them by the end of this quarter.*
Clinician:	*OK, Jason, sometimes we need to set a middle step to make a goal easier to achieve. What do you think would help you get As and Bs and what subject would you like to start with?*
Adolescent:	*I need to study more and turn in my assignments. I'm doing the worst in math, so I guess we could start there.*
Clinician:	*That sounds good. I agree that studying more would improve your math grade. Can you be more specific about how much more you would study?*
Adolescent:	*I need to do my nightly homework and review each weekend for 2 hours.*
Clinician:	*That is a good goal because it meets all those five criteria we talked about. It's positive, specific, measurable, straightforward, and under your control.*

One of the challenging aspects of setting goals is that clients will often first state the goal in a negative way. It will be helpful for you to help the client rephrase goals in a positive way:

- "I don't want to go to jail" becomes "I want to change my behavior so I can enjoy my freedom."
- "I don't want my mom yelling at me" becomes "I'd like to get along better with my mom."

A second challenging aspect of goal setting is helping the client formulate realistic goals, because often the first goal stated is too far-reaching to be achievable. One strategy to help clients devise reasonable goals is to ask them what they are dissatisfied with in a given area. As they talk, listen carefully. Examples of good open-ended questions to help the client break down complex goals into simpler ones include:

- "How can you get better grades at school? What subjects would you like to improve in?" (Ultimately, the goal is setting a study schedule and working to improve one subject grade.)
- "What do you want in your relationship with your parents?" (Ultimately, a goal could be pleasant conversation with the parent after school.)

- "What would you like to have happen with your legal issues?" (Ultimately, a goal could be regular attendance at meetings with the probation officer.)

Once an attainable goal has been set and recorded in the first column on the Goals of Counseling form, work with the client to devise a reasonable plan (intervention) for reaching the goal. The same guidelines used for stating goals should also be used to devise plans: Be brief, be positive, and use specific (measurable) behaviors. Some goals may require more than one intervention. Open-ended questions such as the following can help the client begin to develop appropriate interventions:

- "What would make this happen for you?"
- "What would make your relationship with this person better?"
- "How do you see that happening?"
- "What can we do to help you reach this goal?"

After the client suggests an intervention, it is always important to talk about possible obstacles that might interfere with the strategy and brainstorm ways to overcome them. The following is an example of how to discuss potential obstacles with an adolescent:

Clinician:	*The next thing we can do is fill out the blank here in the intervention column, that is, the types of things we do to reach the goal. Let's follow the same five guidelines we talked about for setting a goal so we know exactly how you plan to improve your grades. Let's start with what you can do to review each weekend.*
Adolescent:	*Well, that's a tough one. I usually stay out late Friday night, so maybe I could do it on Saturday afternoons.*
Clinician:	*Do you think that will work?*
Adolescent:	*Yeah, I think so.*
Clinician:	*When we talk about how we are going to meet a goal, it is helpful to think about things or obstacles that might get in the way of achieving the goal. Can you think of anything that might get in the way of studying on Saturday afternoon?*
Adolescent:	*Yeah, if one of my friends asks me to go hang out.*
Clinician:	*I can see how you might want to do that, so what are some things you could do in that situation?*
Adolescent:	*I could switch my studying to Sunday.*
Clinician:	*That sounds like a good possibility. Any other ideas?*
Adolescent:	*I could ask my friend if we could hang out after I study.*
Clinician:	*That's another good idea. Any other thoughts?*
Adolescent:	*I could ask my friend to study with me?*

Clinician:	*You've come up with three possible things you could do: Switch your studying to Sunday, ask your friend if you could hang out another day, or ask your friend to study with you. Which one of those possibilities are you most comfortable with or do you think would work the best.*
Adolescent:	*Hmmm . . . maybe switching the studying to another day.*
Clinician:	*OK. Well, it would be good to try it this week, and we can see how it goes. Let's write that plan right here.* [Point to the intervention column.] *And when we meet next we can also talk about if anything got in the way and how that worked.* [Next, they talk about the strategies to ensure he does his homework nightly.]

The next step in completing the Goals of Counseling form is to assign a time frame for each intervention in the last column.

Clinician:	*OK. When trying to reach a goal, you will find it helpful to set a time frame: when you will begin working on it and when you will do a status check to see whether you are doing what you planned to do. When would you like to start studying more?*
Adolescent:	*I might as well start this weekend.*
Clinician:	*Go ahead and write down that date as the start date for studying. When shall we do a status check to see whether you were able to spend the time on the weekend? Can we check on this in your next session?*
Adolescent:	*OK.*
Clinician:	*Well, let's write this time in the time frame column, too, so we will remember to check on that. Sometimes, to help people find options that help in solving problems, we work on problem solving techniques. In your case, we would work on problem solving techniques to find ways to improve your grades. Would you be willing to do that?* [Clinician and adolescent add problem solving techniques to the plan.]

As the Goals of Counseling form is completed, monitor the number of intervention assignments clients will accept for a given week. Be careful not to overwhelm them with too many assignments at the same time.

If you and the client are unable to finish the selected categories of the Goals of Counseling form and you believe the client has the skills to do so, assign a category for the client to complete at home.

4. Assign homework.

Help the client decide on a homework assignment related to accomplishing the goals listed on the Goals of Counseling form. At the next session, review progress toward completion of the goals. Refer to the chapter on the Homework procedure for detailed guidance regarding assigning and reviewing homework (p. 47).

Additional Notes

Common Difficulties with Goal Setting

Before leaving this section, it is worthwhile to review the following common difficulties encountered when completing the Goals of Counseling form (Meyers & Smith, 1995, p. 93–94):

- Not applying the five guidelines for developing goals. Most people talk about their problems in vague, negative, and nonmeasurable ways. For example, "I want to have more fun" or "I want to get along with my parents."
- Designing goals and interventions that are too complex, thus making them confusing and difficult to follow. For example, a goal to make the varsity basketball team as a freshman for an adolescent who does not have outstanding athletic skills would be difficult to achieve.
- Leaving out important steps that are needed to work toward a certain goal. For example, to improve grades, a student would need to increase time spent studying every week, not just one week.
- Including plans that are not really under the control of the client. For example, if a teenage boy wants go out with a specific girl, he cannot control whether she wants to go out with him.
- Placing the client in a high-risk using situation. For example, if you know from the Functional Analysis of Substance Use that a certain person's house is a trigger for substance use, you would steer the client away from planning to study at that house.

As noted earlier, it is recommended that the Happiness Scale be revisited often. Ratings on the scale will probably fluctuate as issues are resolved and new ones appear in the client's life. Thus, it may be necessary or even desirable to revisit the Goals of Counseling form and create new goals as new issues arise in the client's life. The Goals of Counseling form is a work in progress and should reflect a client's needs as they change.

Working with a Resistant Client

The following dialogue illustrates how a clinician might approach filling out the Goals of Counseling form with a resistant client. The adolescent has completed a Happiness Scale in this session, and the clinician and adolescent have already discussed the high and low scores and why the adolescent rated areas the way that he did.

Clinician:	*Thanks, Josh! I appreciate you letting me know how things are going for you. I can help you set some goals in some of these areas. Since you rated school a 5 on your Happiness Scale and your relationship with your parents a 6, would you be interested in setting goals in one of those areas or another area from the Happiness Scale?* [Clinician shows the Goals of Counseling form to the adolescent.]
Adolescent:	*I ain't filling out no damn form, and what makes you think that I don't already have goals of my own?*
Clinician:	*That's cool. We don't need this form. Tell me about the goals that you have. You mentioned that the reason you are unhappy is that you wanted to graduate with all of your friends this year and you don't think you are going to be able to.* [Clinician decides not to use the form. She will conduct the Goals of Counseling part of the session orally.]

Adolescent: *I told you! I want to graduate with my friends.*

Clinician: *What makes you think that you aren't going to graduate?*

Adolescent: *I have been missing a lot of school lately because I got suspended for fighting. I definitely can't miss any more or I won't graduate. My principal already told me that.*

Clinician: *How much have you missed?*

Adolescent: *All together?*

Clinician: *Yes.*

Adolescent: *About 3 weeks total this semester. I was suspended for 1 week and missed a couple of days here and there throughout the year.*

Clinician: *What was going on the days that you weren't suspended?*

Adolescent: *Just slept late and skipping . . . hanging with friends.*

Clinician: *What do you think you have to do to graduate with your friends? What are some of the things that need to happen?* [Clinician tries not to tell client what he does and does not need to do. She tries to have client verbalize steps. This increases the probability that the client will take ownership of or become invested in the steps needed to accomplish the goals.]

Adolescent: *I need to go to school every day for the rest of the year and make sure that I pass my math class, which I am failing.*

Clinician: *Sounds as if you really know what you need to do to get there.*

Adolescent: *Yeah.*

Clinician: *Do you think you will be able to get to class daily and to pass math?*

Adolescent: *I think so.*

Clinician: *You're doing great. You have goals, know what you need to do achieve them, and you are a very smart guy. You seem to have all of this figured out; you know exactly what needs to be done and can see it. I have problems trying to keep all of these things you are telling me straight in my head. It gets overwhelming for me at times. Do you mind if I take notes on what we are talking about to see if there is any way that I may be able to help you with this goal of yours?*

Adolescent: *Yeah, that's OK.*

Clinician: *Thanks. So your goal is that you don't want to have to graduate with any other class than your current class.* [Clinician writes notes as if she needs them herself. She will look at them later with the client to illustrate his plans to work on his goals and refer back to them in future sessions.]

Adolescent: *Yes.*

Clinician: *I like to write goals in a positive way. How would I be able to say that in a positive way?* [Attempts to break down the steps of goal setting.]

Adolescent: *Listen, I don't know what the hell you are talking about.*

Clinician: *How would you tell me your goal in a positive way?* [Continues to deal with resistance, not arguing or confronting.]

Adolescent: *I want to graduate this year with my friends?*

Clinician: *Yes, great! Thank you! Now tell me again the steps you are going to take to get there?*

Adolescent: *Go to school every day and pass math. Damn, how many times do I have to tell you?*

Clinician: *You seem irritated. I'm sorry, I am just trying to get all of this down so I can remember. I really appreciate your help. And how are you going to be able to get there every day?*

Adolescent: *Just get up and go.*

Clinician: *You stated you oversleep a lot. What kind of things will you do to make sure you get up?*

Adolescent: *I am going to set my alarm, try to go to bed earlier, and have my buddy come by the house to give me a ride. And if I'm not up, I can have him wake me up.*

Clinician: *You've got all of this all figured out, don't you? You are a good planner.* [Gives praise and positive reinforcement whenever possible.] *That's good because I would really like to see you graduate with your friends, too. So you will set your alarm, go to bed earlier, and have your friend help get you up.* [Reflects and summarizes.] *What else can you do to make sure you get there?*

Adolescent: *I guess I can have my mom help me get up, too.*

Clinician: *Sounds as if you have several ways in mind to help you get there. And what are your plans for improving your math grades so you won't fail?*

Adolescent: *I don't know. That teacher just doesn't like me. She's a mean piece of work.*

Clinician: *Why doesn't she like you?*

Adolescent: *She just doesn't. She thinks I'm a troublemaker, so she's always on me.*

Clinician: *So what is it about math that you are having problems with? Is it just the teacher?*

Adolescent:	*No. I haven't been doing my homework. I hate math and don't want to do it. At this point, I'm so far behind.*
Clinician:	*So you are feeling pretty overwhelmed at this point?* [Encourages reflection.]
Adolescent:	*Yes.*
Clinician:	*So how can we get that grade up? Let's brainstorm some possible ideas. Can you think of any right off?*
Adolescent:	*I could do my work the way I am supposed to.*
Clinician:	*Good. You mentioned that you were far behind and hate math. What are some ways that we can get you caught up and back on track?*
Adolescent:	*I can go to class and pay attention.*
Clinician:	*Good. Going to class is the first step, isn't it? When you go to class, you're not paying attention?*
Adolescent:	*No. Usually talking to my friends or sleeping.*
Clinician:	*So paying attention would probably help a lot. What else would help?*
Adolescent:	*Doing my homework; asking parents, friends, and teachers for help; and studying the way I should.*
Clinician:	*That is a good plan. Even though you don't get along with your math teacher, would you be willing to share your goal with her—that you may have made mistakes in the past but that you are really ready to work at it now? Possibly asking her what you could do to try to catch up?*
Adolescent:	*I can. But like I told you, she's mean and probably doesn't even want to hear me.*
Clinician:	*All we can do is try. That's something that I can help you with. We can talk about how to get her to hear you. Would you be up for that?*
Adolescent:	*That's cool, I guess.*
Clinician:	*Good. You have a lot of great ideas on how to accomplish this goal of yours. When thinking about goals, sometimes it is important to put time frames on them. Here, let's take a look at the notes I scribbled down on how you want to get to where you want to be.*

The clinician and client look at the Goals of Counseling form. Together, they determine time frames for each step or intervention. The clinician then summarizes the goal, interventions, and time frames discussed.

Revisiting the Happiness Scale

As noted above, it is a good idea to revisit the Happiness Scale often during treatment to monitor the client's ongoing progress in therapy and to provide information for adding new goals or revising current goals. However, it is also important not to attempt to set more than one or two goals with the Goals of Counseling form per session. Setting too many goals and interventions per session may overwhelm clients and make it less likely they will be successful in achieving the goals set. The purpose of this procedure is to help clients increase happiness across different life areas. If a client's ratings go up (become more positive), ask the reasons for the change. Use the change as an opportunity to be positive about the client's improved happiness and to reinforce the work completed so far.

> **Clinician:** *It looks as if there are some things you feel good about. Tell me what's happened in your relationships with your friends that you feel better about.*

If the ratings go down, explore with the client the reasons for the unhappiness, adding new goals to the Goals of Counseling form if necessary. Consider, however, that ratings sometimes get worse at first because the client begins to think more about the situation.

Happiness Scale

Date _____ Client Name_____ Client ID _____ Clinician Name _____

This scale is intended to estimate your *current* happiness with your life in each of the 16 areas listed below. You are to circle one of the numbers (1 to 10) beside each area. Numbers toward the left side of the 10-unit scale indicate various degrees of unhappiness, whereas numbers toward the right side of the scale reflect increasing levels of happiness. Ask yourself this question as you rate each area of life: *"How happy am I today with this area of my life?"* In other words, state according to the numerical scale (1 to 10) exactly how you feel today. Try to exclude yesterday's feelings and concentrate only on today's feelings in each of the life areas. Also, try *not* to allow one category to influence the results of the other categories.

	Completely Unhappy								**Completely Happy**	
1. Marijuana use/nonuse	1	2	3	4	5	6	7	8	9	10
2. Alcohol use/nonuse	1	2	3	4	5	6	7	8	9	10
3. Other drug use/nonuse	1	2	3	4	5	6	7	8	9	10
4. Relationship with boyfriend or girlfriend	1	2	3	4	5	6	7	8	9	10
5. Relationships with friends	1	2	3	4	5	6	7	8	9	10
6. Relationships with parents or caregivers	1	2	3	4	5	6	7	8	9	10
7. School	1	2	3	4	5	6	7	8	9	10
8. Social activities	1	2	3	4	5	6	7	8	9	10
9. Recreational activities	1	2	3	4	5	6	7	8	9	10
10. Personal habits (e.g., getting up in the morning, being on time, finishing tasks)	1	2	3	4	5	6	7	8	9	10
11. Legal issues	1	2	3	4	5	6	7	8	9	10
12. Money management	1	2	3	4	5	6	7	8	9	10
13. Emotional life (feelings)	1	2	3	4	5	6	7	8	9	10
14. Communication	1	2	3	4	5	6	7	8	9	10
15. General happiness	1	2	3	4	5	6	7	8	9	10
16. Other	1	2	3	4	5	6	7	8	9	10

Happiness Scale (SAMPLE)

Date _____ Client Name _____ Client ID _____ Clinician Name _____

This scale is intended to estimate your *current* happiness with your life in each of the 16 areas listed below. You are to circle one of the numbers (1 to 10) beside each area. Numbers toward the left side of the 10-unit scale indicate various degrees of unhappiness, whereas numbers toward the right side of the scale reflect increasing levels of happiness. Ask yourself this question as you rate each area of life: "*How happy am I today with this area of my life?*" In other words, state according to the numerical scale (1 to 10) exactly how you feel today. Try to exclude yesterday's feelings and concentrate only on today's feelings in each of the life areas. Also, try *not* to allow one category to influence the results of the other categories.

	Completely Unhappy						Completely Happy		

1. Marijuana use/nonuse   1 2 3 **(4)** 5 6 7 8 9 10

2. Alcohol use/nonuse   1 2 3 **(4)** 5 6 7 8 9 10

3. Other drug use/nonuse   1 2 3 4 5 6 7 8 9 10

4. Relationship with boyfriend or girlfriend   1 2 3 4 5 6 **(7)** 8 9 10

5. Relationships with friends   1 2 3 4 5 6 7 8 **(9)** 10

6. Relationships with parents or caregivers   1 2 3 4 5 **(6)** 7 8 9 10

7. School   1 2 3 4 **(5)** 6 7 8 9 10

8. Social activities   1 2 3 4 5 6 7 8 **(9)** 10

9. Recreational activities   1 2 3 4 5 6 **(7)** 8 9 10

10. Personal habits (e.g., getting up in the morning, being on time, finishing tasks)   1 2 3 4 5 **(6)** 7 8 9 10

11. Legal issues   1 **(2)** 3 4 5 6 7 8 9 10

12. Money management   1 2 3 4 **(5)** 6 7 8 9 10

13. Emotional life (feelings)   1 2 3 4 **(5)** 6 7 8 9 10

14. Communication   1 2 3 4 5 6 **(7)** 8 9 10

15. General happiness   1 2 3 4 5 6 **(7)** 8 9 10

16. Other   1 2 3 **(4)** 5 6 7 8 9 10

Goals of Counseling

Problem Areas/Goals "In the area of _____ I would like to:"	Intervention	Time Frame
1. Marijuana use/nonuse		
2. Alcohol use/nonuse		
3. Other drug use/nonuse		
4. Relationship with boyfriend/girlfriend		
5. Relationships with friends		
6. Relationships with parents/caregivers		
7. School		
8. Social activities		

43

Goals of Counseling

Problem Areas/Goals "In the area of ___ I would like:"	Intervention	Time Frame
9. Recreational activities		
10. Personal habits (e.g., getting up in the morning, being on time, finishing tasks)		
11. Legal issues		
12. Money management		
13. Emotional life (my feelings)		
14. Communication		
15. General happiness		
16. Other		

_____ (Participant Signature)   _____ (Date)   _____ (Clinician Signature)   _____ (Date)

_____ (Guardian Signature – Optional)   _____ (Date)   _____ (Supervisor Signature)   _____ (Date)

Goals of Counseling (SAMPLE)
NOTE: These would *not* all be assigned at once!

Problem Areas/Goals "In the area of _____ I would like:"	Intervention (Weekly)	Time Frame (Goal)
1. Marijuana use/nonuse **Be abstinent from marijuana for 30 days.**	1. Play video games after school with my two nonusing friends (Sam and Pete). 2. Use drug-refusal skills whenever offered drugs.	1 month
2. Alcohol use/nonuse **Be abstinent from alcohol for 30 days.**	1. Go to an alcohol-free party on Saturday night (Ted's).	1 month
3. Other drug use/nonuse **N/A**	N/A	N/A
4. Relationship with boyfriend/girlfriend **Do two non-drug-related activities each week outside of home (both agree).**	1. Use Problem Solving Skills procedure with girlfriend to identify an enjoyable activity they both like. 2. Try the activity once.	1 month
5. Relationships with friends **Make one new nonusing friend.**	1. Attend church youth group this week.	1 month
6. Relationships with parents/caregivers **Spend 2 hours per week doing a fun activity together (movie, shop, dinner).**	1. Sit down and have a glass of juice with my parents at breakfast time before rushing out the door (do two times per week).	1 month
7. School **Get As and Bs by the end of this quarter.**	1. Do my math homework nightly. 2. Review math each Saturday for 2 hours; if friends ask me to hang out on Saturday, review math on Sunday or a different day.	By end of school quarter Start this weekend Check at next session
8. Social activities **Identify one new fun social activity that I want to do weekly and begin doing it.**	1. Ask my nonusing cousin what he does for fun with other people. 2. Look through newspaper to get ideas; check on the internet.	1 month

Goals of Counseling (SAMPLE)
NOTE: These would *not* all be assigned at once!

Problem Areas/Goals "In the area of _____ I would like:"	Intervention (Weekly)	Time Frame (Goal)
9. Recreational activities **Get punching (speed) bag.**	1. Call Uncle Ned to see if he still has a bag; call the YMCA to see if they have any old ones.	1 month
10. Personal habits (e.g., getting up in the morning, being on time, finishing tasks) **Be on time for school every day.**	1. Set a backup alarm across the room. 2. Turn off computer and go to bed by midnight on school nights.	1 month
11. Legal issues **Make it through the month with no new charges.**	[See intervention/goal #1]	1 month
12. Money management **Save $20 per month.**	1. Do odd jobs for elderly neighbors (e.g., pick up trash, run errands) and put $5 away each week.	1 month
13. Emotional life (my feelings) **Use anger management "cool down" techniques whenever angry.**	1. Try out two possible "cool down" techniques this week (e.g., saying "cool down/relax," walk away quickly) when angry.	1 month
14. Communication **Spend a half hour per day in pleasant conversation with parents.**	1. Use positive communication skills to say a pleasant "goodbye" when leaving for school each day and "hello" when returning home.	1 month
15. General happiness		
16. Other		

_____ (Participant Signature)

_____ (Date)

_____ (Clinician Signature)

_____ (Date)

_____ (Guardian Signature – Optional)

_____ (Date)

_____ (Supervisor Signature)

_____ (Date)

UNIT 2: CHAPTER 3: Homework

Rationale

Teaching new skills and practicing them during sessions is necessary, but it is not sufficient for most clients to generalize these skills to their daily lives. New skills are more likely to become automatic when clients attempt to use them in their natural environment. Reviewing assigned homework at the beginning of a session reinforces the importance of doing the homework and provides the opportunity to discuss any challenges that occurred when trying to complete it. Discussing obstacles encountered and helping clients decide on steps to overcome them can help in the future when the same or different obstacles arise. Reviewing homework can also help set a session agenda. For example, suppose a client's homework was to go to the YMCA to exercise, but her mother refused to transport her after they got into a fight. This might suggest that the clinician should add the training or reviewing of Communication Skills during the session.

Learning Objectives

The learning objectives are to help clients:

- Develop homework or weekly goals to practice new skills that are taught in sessions.
- Explore obstacles that may interfere with completing homework assignments and identify possible solutions.
- Increase the likelihood of completing a task by reviewing homework assignments.

Timing, Audience, and Delivery Method

Each session will typically end with a mutually agreed-upon homework assignment. Each session after the first one will typically begin with a review of the homework assignment from the prior session. Homework is assigned in all three session types: client only, caregiver only, and client-caregiver joint sessions.

Materials

Since homework assignments are related to the skills taught or topics discussed during each session, materials for homework assignments will vary. At times there will be specific forms that clients can take with them, for example, the Daily Reminder to Be Nice (p. 180). In general, it might be helpful for clients to have a written reminder about their homework assignment. If a client has a smartphone, the notes can be entered in the calendar with reminders.

General Notes for the Clinician

Working with the client to generate homework assignments that meet the requirements outlined below is a skill that may take some time to develop. It is important to involve the client in creating the homework assignment. A common mistake clinicians make when first trying this procedure is deciding what the homework assignment should be without really involving the client in the discussion.

The term "homework" has a negative connotation for some clients. It is fine to use another term that might be more acceptable to them. You might call it a "practice exercise," "an experiment," a "weekly goal," or a "challenge" for the week.

Many of the A-CRA procedures naturally lead to homework assignments, including Problem Solving Skills, Communication Skills, Refusal Skills, and Functional Analysis of Prosocial Behavior. Other procedures do not (e.g., Functional Analysis of Substance Use). It is always important to involve the client in developing the homework assignment, but it is also acceptable for clinicians to suggest possible tasks based on what they have learned about the client and the topics discussed during the session.

Tips for promoting successful homework completion include:

- Suggest possible obstacles to discuss when the client cannot think of any.
- Limit homework tasks or an assignment to a few steps to maximize the opportunity for success.
- Make a midweek phone call to check in with the client with reminders of the homework assignment, and reinforce any steps already completed toward completing the homework.
- Involve the caregiver in assisting or helping support the client. If the caregiver is in the waiting room, it might be possible to ask for assistance immediately after a session.

Working with the client to define the homework assignment takes time, so it is important to leave around 10 minutes at the end of the session to the joint development of the assignment, exploring obstacles, and reviewing possible solutions. Likewise, there should be 10 minutes or so allotted at the beginning of sessions to review homework assignments from prior sessions.

If a client does not complete a homework assignment, it is an opportunity to talk about the obstacles encountered and how they might be overcome in the future. This is an example of using a nonjudgmental style with clients, which as we discussed in the General Clinical Skills chapter (p. 19), has been found to be more effective than a confrontational one.

We recommend referring back to this procedure frequently, since homework review or assignment is a part of every session.

Procedural Steps for Reviewing Homework

1. **If other than the first session, ask the client what happened with the homework assignment from the previous week.**
2. **Praise the client for any effort to complete the homework assignment.**
3. **If the homework was attempted, ask the client how it went (including a description of any obstacles), or if the assignment was not attempted, ask for a description of the obstacles to doing the assignment.**
4. **If the client was not able to complete the assignment because of obstacles, help generate possible ways to overcome the obstacles encountered.**
5. **Ask the client to describe what was learned from the assignment or how the assignment helped make progress toward achieving a treatment goal.**

Detailed Description

1. **If other than the first session, ask the client what happened with the homework assignment from the previous week.**

Before asking about homework, it is important to spend a little time making small talk or asking about the client's week as part of rapport building. Sometimes clients will bring up a problem that occurred during the week, and it is tempting to start addressing the problem. Unless it is a very serious problem, it is possible to acknowledge the problem, let the client know that you will save time to talk about it later during the session, and then transition to reviewing the homework.

Clinician:	[After some small talk about the week.] *It is good to see you again, Jack. Thanks for coming in. Hey . . . remember when we were together last time . . . you were really interested in getting a job, so you said that this week you were going to talk to at least three people you know about any job openings they might know about?*
Adolescent:	*Yes, I remember that.*
Clinician:	*How did it go? Were you able to talk to those three people we talked about?*
Adolescent:	*I only talked to two people. I asked my friend Joe if they were hiring where he works at a fast food place and I asked my computer programming teacher if he knew of any jobs where I could use my computer skills.*

2. **Praise the client for any effort to complete the homework assignment.**

Clinician:	*Jack, it is really good that you talked to two people. That is a really good start. We can talk about how that went, OK?*
Adolescent:	*OK.*

3. **If the homework was attempted, ask the client how it went (including a description of any obstacles), or if the assignment was not attempted, ask for a description of the obstacles to doing the assignment.**

Clinician:	*So, tell me about how it went talking with Joe and your teacher.*
Adolescent:	*I hang out with Joe a lot and knew he had a job—so I just asked him if they were hiring. It was harder to bring it up with my teacher, but I figured like we talked about last week—what the hell—what did I have to lose?*
Clinician:	*What you say makes sense. It's easier to talk to a friend and for many of us harder to talk to someone like a teacher. How did it go?*
Adolescent:	*Not so good. Joe said that they weren't hiring where he works, and my teacher didn't have any ideas either . . . so neither thing worked. . . . I was supposed to ask my brother's friend, but I didn't see him this week.*

4. **If the client was not able to complete the assignment because of obstacles, help generate possible ways to overcome the obstacles encountered.**

Clinician:	*I can see how it would be discouraging not to get any leads. Remember how we talked about only doing things that were under your control. You did what you could do . . . asked them for job leads. You couldn't control if they knew any possibilities right now. You know, it can be hard to get a job and it happens a lot that people have to apply to a lot of places before they find something. Does that make sense?*

Adolescent:	*I guess so.*
Clinician:	*So, it sounds like you couldn't ask the third person because you didn't see him, right?*
Adolescent:	*Right.*
Clinician:	*What do you think you could have done to try and contact him even though you didn't see him in person?*
Adolescent:	*I guess I could ask my brother for his phone number.*
Clinician:	*That's a good idea. What else?*
Adolescent:	*Maybe I could ask someone else instead.*
Clinician:	*Excellent! Yes, I think that is also a very good idea, if you can't see or get in touch with the person you initially thought you would ask; then you can think of some other people to ask for job leads. You know, getting a job is a numbers game . . . the more people you talk to about jobs, the more likely you will find out about a possibility.*

5. **Ask the client to describe what was learned from the assignment or how the assignment helped make progress toward achieving a treatment goal.**

Clinician:	*Can you tell me anything you learned from doing this? Anything you learned about getting a job?*
Adolescent:	*Even though they didn't have any jobs to tell me about . . . the people I talked to didn't seem to mind that I was asking them, so that was cool.*
Clinician:	*Yeah, that is an important thing to know—so you don't need to feel like people are going to be bothered or get upset with you when you ask them for job leads.*
Adolescent:	*Yeah.*
Clinician:	*So getting this job is hard work and takes time, but I know that you have talked about wanting to pay off your court fees by getting a job.*

Procedural Steps for Assigning Homework

1. The assignment is based, at least in part, on the client's input.
2. The homework assignment addresses the following five criteria:
    - It is stated positively (that is, clients state what they will do rather than what they will not do).
    - Is specific (this is, the exact behavior that the client will engage in is specified as well as when it will occur).
    - Is measurable (observable).
    - Is simple and straightforward (that is, it does not involve too many steps that would be difficult to remember).

- **Is under the client's control** (that is, it is not dependent on what someone else does but only on what the client can do).
3. **Potential obstacles to the homework assignment are explored and potential solutions generated and practiced.**
4. **The assignment is linked back to the client's treatment plan or reinforcers.**
5. **The client is asked to repeat the assignment back to the clinician at the end of the session.**

Detailed Description

If the client continues to work toward a goal relevant to the homework assigned in the previous session, it is acceptable to work on a similar assignment again. For example, in the scenario above, if Jack still wants to find a job, he can continue with the strategy from the week before or change it up after discussing it with his clinician and reviewing pertinent barriers and solutions. It is also important to have a homework assignment related to a new skill that was taught and practiced during the session. However, it is always necessary to consider what the client can accomplish during a given time period; experiencing the success of completing an assignment is helpful for the client, and having an assignment that is too difficult to achieve will be frustrating.

The following are the steps for assigning homework and are illustrated with dialogue.

1. **The assignment is based, at least in part, on the client's input.**

> **Clinician:** *So, we talked about a lot of stuff that's going on with you this week. You said that you wanted to exercise more regularly—that you thought it would help with your goal of getting on the basketball team. When we practiced communication skills you also said you wished you and your mom talked more. Would you like to work on a homework assignment related to one of these areas or is there something else you were thinking about for homework this week?*

> **Adolescent:** *Yeah, I'd like to make the basketball team, so I guess more exercising.*

2. **The homework assignment addresses the following five criteria:**
   - **It is stated positively** (that is, clients state what they will do rather than what they will not do).
   - **Is specific** (that is, the exact behavior that the client will engage in is specified as well as when it will occur).
   - **Is measurable** (observable).
   - **Is simple and straightforward** (that is, it does not involve too many steps that would be difficult to remember).
   - **Is under the client's control** (that is, it is not dependent on what someone else does but only on what the client can do).

> **Clinician:** *So remember how when we work on homework assignments, it's important to say what you* want *to do and to come up with something that's specific, measurable, and under your control? Do you remember all those parts or do you want me to review them?*

> **Adolescent:** *I think I remember.*

Clinician:	OK. Good. Why don't you go ahead and say what you want your homework to be.
Adolescent:	I want to exercise more—maybe three times a week after school.
Clinician:	OK. That's really good! You said what you wanted to do, so you were positive, and you'll be able to measure three times a week. Let's get it more specific; what kind of exercise are you going to do?
Adolescent:	Does it have to be just one kind?
Clinician:	It's up to you—what you want to do and what you think would work for you. What were you thinking?
Adolescent:	Well, I was thinking of both running and skateboarding.
Clinician:	OK. So, you want to say you will either run or skateboard at least three times a week. To get it even more measurable, how about we say how many minutes at a time?
Adolescent:	OK. Let's say 20 minutes at a time.

3. **Potential obstacles to the homework assignment are explored and potential solutions generated and practiced.**

Clinician:	Let's talk about what's stopped you from running or skateboarding currently, and then we'll figure out a way to address the obstacles so you can exercise this week. Can you think of anything that gets in the way of you exercising?
Adolescent:	Mainly I'm just lazy and would rather hang out with my friends or watch TV.
Clinician:	What do you think you could do to overcome those obstacles?
Adolescent:	I don't know.
Clinician:	Would it help if you had regular times to exercise so that you know you will still have plenty of time to be with your friends and watch TV? Also, another idea is to see if you have friends that want to exercise with you.
Adolescent:	I don't want to ask any friends right now, but it might help to have a regular time of the week.
Clinician:	When would those times be?
Adolescent:	Well, since basketball practice will be after school, maybe I could exercise after school.
Clinician:	What days make sense? Like, would you want to exercise on Friday after school or maybe that's more a day when you want to hang out with friends.
Adolescent:	Yeah, I think Monday, Tuesday, and Thursday will work best.

Clinician:	*Sounds good. Can you think of anything that might get in the way of exercising on those days?*
Adolescent:	*No, I should be able to do this.*
Clinician:	*What about the weather? What if it's raining and you can't get outside to run or skateboard?* [Often clients are not used to thinking about obstacles and may have difficulty posing obvious ones. It is important to spend time thoroughly discussing obstacles, so if the client can think of only one, the clinician should bring up some potential additional obstacles.]
Adolescent:	*Maybe I could switch my exercise time to another day?*
Clinician:	*So, if you plan to exercise after school on Monday, Tuesday, and Thursday . . . what would be good alternate days in case of rain?*
Adolescent:	*Either Saturday or Sunday when I get up.*
Clinician:	*That sounds good—you have two alternative days that way.*

4. **The assignment is linked back to the client's treatment plan or reinforcers.**

Clinician:	*So, it sounds like this homework assignment can help you toward your goal of getting on the basketball team because you will be getting in better shape and it will be hard to smoke weed while you are running or skateboarding. . . . What do you think?*
Adolescent:	*Yeah, that's true.*

5. **The client is asked to repeat the assignment back to the clinician at the end of the session.**

Clinician:	*OK, let's review the assignment because that will help you remember.*
Adolescent:	*I'm going to either run or skateboard three times a week, on Monday, Tuesday, and Thursdays.*
Clinician:	*That's right. . . . Do you remember how long you wanted to exercise each day?*
Adolescent:	*20 minutes.*
Clinician:	*What do you think about putting that in your phone—to remind you? I know it helps me to put reminders in my phone.*
Adolescent:	*I can do that. . . .*
Clinician:	*How about we do that now . . . so it's taken care of?*
Adolescent:	*OK.*

A list of sample homework assignments is on the next page.

Homework Assignments (SAMPLE)

I will . . .

- Get three job applications at the mall on Wednesday and bring them to the next session.
- Check on the status of all submitted job applications on Wednesday after school (around 4 p.m.).
- Say "No, thanks" assertively if asked to smoke with friends this weekend. If that doesn't work, I will change the subject or leave the situation.
- Ask Mom on Wednesday night (using communication skills) to go the mall on Saturday.
- Complete and ask Mom to complete at least one column of the Daily Reminder to Be Nice every day this week or until the next session.
- Complete three pages of the Leisure Questionnaire by Sunday at 3 p.m., and complete the rest of the LQ on Tuesday at 4 p.m. (before appointment).
- Ask five neighbors by Thursday to play kickball this Friday after school.
- Go hiking with Dad this Sunday afternoon at 2 p.m. (could get more specific on where).
- Talk to the drama coach after school on Monday about joining the drama team.
- Practice the first part of communication skills (understanding statement) at least three times this week when talking with Mom and Dad.
- Create a list of 10 fun, healthy, nonusing activities on Saturday afternoon and try at least one of those activities by the next session (Tuesday).
- Stay away from high-risk situations for one week (be specific on high-risk situations). If triggers arise, I will go for a walk, call a sponsor, or play basketball with nonusing friends.
- Complete handout on triggers on Tuesday evening at 8 p.m.
- Create a list of five positive reinforcers on Sunday at 4 p.m. and share the list with the counselor at the next session.
- Be on time to school (by 8 a.m.) and attend all classes every day this week.
- Go to the library at 4 p.m. two days this week (Tuesday and Thursday) to work on homework, and check out two books to take home.
- Complete Anger Management form on Wednesday afternoon at 5 p.m.
- Attend three AA meetings this week (one on Monday, Wednesday, and Friday) at 6 p.m. for additional support.

UNIT 2: CHAPTER 4: Systematic Encouragement

Rationale

Treatment goals usually require the completion of multiple tasks. It can be difficult for a client to take the first step toward a new or avoided activity due to previous negative experiences, uncertainty about how to obtain contact information, or not knowing what to say. Systematic Encouragement is often used when a client wants to sample a new activity but needs some guidance (e.g., a new recreational activity to compete with alcohol or drug use), is avoiding an activity that really needs to be tackled (e.g., the client needs to make weekly contact with probation officer and is making weekly excuses for not doing so), or needs to schedule an appointment (e.g., with a probation officer, for birth control, or for STD testing). Often clients lack the skills needed to figure out all the steps involved or are overwhelmed by the multiple steps required to complete the task. However, if clients have help in identifying the necessary steps and actually complete the first one or two steps during a session, they will be more likely to finish the remaining steps and successfully complete the task.

For example, suppose a client decides that she would like to get tested for STDs and talk to someone about choosing a birth control method. However, she is not sure where to go, how to make an appointment, or what it would cost. During a session, the clinician can help her identify appropriate questions, locate contact information, role play a call to the appropriate health clinic, and then actually have her make the call and gather the information while in the session. Homework would be related to the goal and might include attending an appointment, which would be planned at some time prior to the next session, if possible. Additional steps would be addressed in a similar fashion until the client was able to reach her goal of getting tested for STDs and deciding on a birth control method.

Learning Objectives

The learning objectives are to help clients:

- Break a task down into achievable steps.
- Practice making a contact via a role play to make it easier to complete the contact.
- Complete the first step in a task (e.g., making a phone call for an appointment) so it is easier to complete the remaining steps.
- Review obstacles and possible solutions to improve skills at overcoming obstacles when they occur.

Timing, Audience, and Delivery Method

Systematic Encouragement can be used in any session. It is not a stand-alone procedure and is generally woven in with another procedure like Increasing Prosocial Activity, Goals of Counseling, and Job Seeking Skills. It can be used with clients and their caregivers. Systematic Encouragement begins with an explanation of how it is best to break a task into steps. For example, if the client needs to make a phone call or have a conversation with someone else to set up an appointment or get information to complete a task, then the clinician will help the client role play the phone call or conversation first. Finally, the clinician and client complete the first steps of a multistep task.

Materials

Materials needed are dependent on the steps to be completed, but in most cases access to a phone, smartphone, or computer or tablet with internet capability is required. Clients may contact health or social service providers by calling, text messaging, e-mailing, or actually going to the facility or agency.

General Notes for the Clinician

It is important to look for opportunities to use Systematic Encouragement because this procedure will increase the likelihood that your client can successfully complete tasks. After reviewing the sample dialogue, watch for the tasks from other procedures that are often appropriate for the use of Systematic Encouragement. Some typical uses of Systematic Encouragement with procedures are listed at the end of this chapter (p. 60).

Procedural Steps for Systematic Encouragement

1. **Encourage the client to use time during the session to take the first step toward sampling an activity that involves multiple steps and would be difficult for the client to identify and carry out.**
2. **Use session time to write an e-mail or text or to role play the conversation between the client and a contact person prior to the actual call or visit, and give the client specific feedback about what was done well as well as how it could be improved.**
3. **Use time during the session to perform the first step, which could entail making a telephone, e-mail, or text message contact or accompanying the client to an appointment or visiting a facility.**
4. **Discuss with the client the next step toward the goal or activity when a contact was successfully made, or discuss the next step if the client was not able to make the desired contact (e.g., only got a voice message and did not speak with the contact person).**

Detailed Description

1. **Encourage the client to use time during the session to take the first step toward sampling an activity that involves multiple steps and would be difficult for the client to identify and carry out.**

   It is up to the clinician to use clinical judgment and knowledge of the client's previous experiences and abilities to know when a task might benefit from Systematic Encouragement during a session.

Clinician:	*So, you said that for a goal in the area of health, you wanted to get tested for STDs and also begin using birth control. How about we think through the steps involved in getting an appointment like that and then take the first step or two here in the session? How does that sound?*
Adolescent:	*OK, that sounds good. I wasn't really sure where to go.*
Clinician:	*Let's figure out where to go first, and then we can work on making an appointment. We can practice, and then you can actually call from my office while you are here.*

Adolescent: *OK.* [The clinician and the adolescent first work on finding an appropriate referral.]

2. **Use session time to write an e-mail or text or to role play the conversation between the client and a contact person prior to the actual call or visit, and give the client specific feedback about what was done well as well as how it could be improved.**

Clinician: *Now that you've decided to go the health department, let's figure out how to get an appointment. Let's look at that part of their web page together.* [Clinician and client look at the website and determine that it is best to call for an appointment.] *How about we practice calling and asking for an appointment?*

Adolescent: *OK.*

Clinician: *What do you think you might say?*

Adolescent: *"I'd like an appointment."*

Clinician: *That's a good start, but I think they have a lot of different kinds of appointments at the health department—like for immunizations and other services, so you may want to be more specific, like say that you would like to see someone about STD testing and birth control. Let's try it again. I'll pretend to be the receptionist.* [As receptionist.] *"Hello, County Health Department."*

Adolescent: *"Hello, I'd like an appointment to talk about STD testing and birth control."*

Clinician: [As receptionist.] *"I'll transfer you to the correct department."* [Clinician as receptionist in correct department.] *"Can I help you?"*

Adolescent: *"Hello, I'd like an appointment to talk about STD testing and birth control."*

Clinician: [Clinician as receptionist in correct department.] *"I can help set that up, but first I need to ask you some questions."* [Clinician may know what the questions are from previous experience or could ask questions she thinks might be asked.]

Clinician: [After the role play] *You did a very good job of asking for the appointment and thinking on your feet when I asked you those questions. You were polite and friendly too. I don't really know if you will be asked any additional questions, but it is good to be prepared, and it is usually about stuff you will know—like your birthdate. What did you like or not like about how you did in the role play?*

Adolescent: *I like that it's pretty simple just to ask for an appointment. I was a little nervous when you said you had to ask me additional questions.*

Clinician: *Well, as I said, you did well. We find it helps to practice more than once, so how about we practice one more time before you make the call for real?*

Adolescent: *OK.* [They practice the call again.]

3. **Use time during the session to perform the first step, which could entail making a telephone, e-mail, or text message contact or accompanying the client to an appointment or visiting a facility.**

Clinician:	*You did a very good job practicing. Are you ready to call the health department now and really set up the appointment?*
Adolescent:	*Yes.*
Clinician:	*Let's talk about when you would want the appointment—so it works out for you.* [They discuss days of the weeks and times that would work.] *OK, I think you are ready to call now.* [Adolescent calls and schedules an appointment.]

4. (a) **Discuss with the client the next step toward the goal or activity when a contact was successfully made.**

Clinician:	*Great job with the phone call! How did that go for you?*
Adolescent:	*It was easier than I thought it would be. She said I could come in for an appointment on Thursday after school.*
Clinician:	*Great! Nice work. Let's talk about how you'll get to the appointment and what you'll need to bring with you.* [Clinician and client discuss details of attending appointment and explore obstacles. The next step is the homework assignment.]

(b) **Discuss the next step if the client was not able to make the desired contact.**

Clinician:	[The client calls and gets a voice recording, and they are about out of time in the session.] *Oh, too bad we were not able to get anyone. How about we make a plan for when you will try again to call and get an appointment?*
Adolescent:	*OK.*
Clinician:	*When would be a good time for you to call?*
Adolescent:	*I could try when I get home.*
Clinician:	*That's a good idea. What if you don't get anyone then, when is another time?*
Adolescent:	*After school tomorrow?*
Clinician:	*Can you think of anything that might get in the way of calling after school tomorrow?* [They discuss barriers and possible solutions.]

Procedural Steps for Reviewing the Next Steps in Subsequent Session

1. **Check in with the client to find out whether the next steps that were agreed to in the prior session were followed, ask how it went, and inquire about any next (remaining) steps.**
2. **Ask about obstacles and address them if needed, reinforce any efforts, and ask what the client learned from the experience.**

Detailed Description

Remember that this part of Systematic Encouragement is essentially the same as described in the section on reviewing the homework assignment (Unit 2, Chapter 3 [p. 47]) in the next session or a session following the scheduled activity or appointment.

1. **Check in with the client to find out whether the next steps that were agreed to in the prior session were followed, ask how it went, and inquire about any next (remaining) steps.**

Clinician:	*So, last week during the session, you made an appointment to go the health department on Thursday to talk about STD testing and birth control? How did that go?*
Adolescent:	*Pretty good. They were able to give me a test then and make an appointment for me to see a doctor about birth control.*
Clinician:	*Sounds like you made very good progress. What did you think about the appointment?*
Adolescent:	*I'm glad to have the testing over with. They said I didn't have anything.*
Clinician:	*That's good news. How did that feel?*
Adolescent:	*Oh . . . I was really relieved.*
Clinician:	*That's a great feeling! I'm going to ask you about any challenges you had in a minute, but I also want to know how the appointment ended, are there any next steps you need to take?* [They discuss any next steps and will plan some next steps before the end of the session.]

2. **Ask about obstacles and address them if needed, reinforce any efforts, and ask what the client learned from the experience.**

Clinician:	*You know, it is important for us to talk about any obstacles or challenges you might have had, so we can figure out ways to address them. Did you have any challenges making it to the appointment?*
Adolescent:	*No, I took the bus like we discussed. I was pretty nervous and almost didn't go, but I ended up just getting on the bus and going.*
Clinician:	*Great job! I know that wasn't easy for you and I'm really proud of the efforts you're making to reach your goals.* [They also talk about how what she learned might be helpful in the future.]

   Or, if the client did not follow through with the appointment, the discussion would go this way:

Clinician:	*So, last week during the session, you made an appointment to go the health department on Thursday to talk about STD testing and birth control? How did that go?*

Adolescent: *I wasn't able to go. I had too much to do and I was afraid it would take up too much time.*

Clinician: *OK, can you tell me a little more about that.*

Adolescent: *Well, I had to come here, and I had to go to probation this week—I just didn't think I could go to another appointment, and it takes so long to get there on the bus.*

Clinician: *Maybe we can talk again about why you wanted to go to the appointment and other ways you might be able to get there?* [They review reasons the client wanted to go and problem solve ways to get there.]

Additional Note and Typical Uses of Systematic Encouragement

- Remember that with any goal or homework assignment it is always helpful to ask what the client learned from the experience or how the assignment helped the client make progress toward achieving an overall treatment goal.
- Refer to these other procedures for additional opportunities to weave in Systematic Encouragement:
    o Job Seeking Skills (when clients need to call to make job inquiries).
    o Prosocial Activity (when clients are gathering information about the activity they want to try out—costs, hours available, etc.).
    o Drink/Drug Refusal (when clients want to reach out to a potential support person).
    o Relapse Prevention (when clients want to set up an early warning monitor).

UNIT 2: CHAPTER 5: Functional Analysis (FA) of Substance Use Behavior

Rationale

This procedure is used to uncover information about the client's typical substance use behavior. The FA of Substance Use is used to discover the client's triggers for marijuana, other drug, or alcohol use. Triggers are thoughts, feelings, or behaviors that precede a using episode and are instrumental in leading the client to use. By specifying the chain of events that lead to use, the client is made aware that the use of illicit drugs or alcohol does not just happen. Rather, many small decisions lead up to the substance use behavior and are, therefore, within the client's control.

A second key purpose for conducting an FA of Substance Use is to clarify the positive and negative consequences of substance use that occur immediately afterwards and those that may occur in the long term. Clients can realize that motivations exist to stop using and there are healthier ways to obtain some of the "pleasures" from alcohol or substance use. Information gleaned from this process is never used in a confrontational manner; instead, it is used to help clients describe the consequences of their substance use in their own words.

Functional analyses are based on structured interviews that help identify the antecedents and consequences of a specific behavior. The specific behavior of interest can fall into one of two categories: a problematic behavior, such as poor anger management, self-harm, or substance use; or a prosocial behavior or activity that the client enjoys, such as skateboarding or playing the guitar. While this chapter focuses on the Functional Analysis (FA) of Substance Use, the next chapter (p. 76) describes the Functional Analysis (FA) of Prosocial Behavior.

Learning Objectives

The learning objectives are to help clients:

- Begin to uncover what is powerful enough to cause the client's behavior to change by analyzing the typical using situation.
- Realize that motivations to stop using already exist.
- Identify the triggers for substance use and their associated high-risk situations.
- Identify and clarify substance use behavior.
- Identify the short-term positive consequences of using.
- Identify the long-term negative consequences of using.
- Discuss how what was learned can be applied to positive behavior change.

Timing, Audience, and Delivery Method

This procedure is often completed in Session 1 or 2, but it should be completed by the fourth session. The FA of Substance Use can be revisited in later sessions and can be considered a work-in-progress as the client's behaviors and needs change.

Materials

Procedure-specific materials include a clipboard, pens, and two FA of Substance Use forms (p. 74). Occasionally, clinicians use a white board and markers instead of the paper forms.

General Notes for the Clinician

Recognize that it is important throughout treatment to elicit positive expectations for change. Part of this entails repeatedly finding even small actions or statements that can be praised to enhance the client's motivation for participating in the intervention. Likewise, it is important to maintain a positive and enthusiastic tone of voice. These practices also help to foster a therapeutic connection with the client.

The steps outlined below explain how to conduct an FA of Substance Use with the client at the start of therapy. However, it may be useful to revisit the FA of Substance Use process periodically throughout therapy, as the client's behaviors and needs change.

Review and clarify assessment information with clients before starting this procedure so that they do not have to retell everything that was covered in the assessment. Forms are used to help conduct both types of Functional Analyses. Importantly, try to engage the client in a conversation about a typical using situation versus just filling out the form. This will help to guide the conversation so the form can be completed but avoids making the form the focal point. Clients may not be willing to share information about their use until a certain level of trust and rapport has been established with their clinician. It is better to come back to the FA of Substance Use at a later session than to risk alienating a client by pushing too hard for information that may be difficult to recall or that the client is not yet ready to discuss.

When the opportunity presents itself, use praise during the FA of Substance Use to promote engagement and to move the client in the right direction. For example:

> **Adolescent:** *I'm not getting high as often as I used to.*
>
> **Clinician:** *That's excellent news, Johnny. How do you feel about that accomplishment?*
>
> **Adolescent:** *Good, I guess.*
>
> **Clinician:** *Great! Congratulations! What an accomplishment!*

At the end of the session (and every session), praise the client for working with you. Communicate that the client has provided useful information and has worked hard.

Procedural Steps

1. **Provide a concise and coherent rationale for completing the FA of Substance Use, which includes the following:**
   - **A description of some of the information that would be collected.**
   - **A general overview of plans for the information collected.**
   - **An explanation of the FA of Substance Use form.**
   - **An explanation of how the information could be used throughout treatment.**
2. **Explain that a common (typical) episode will be used, and help the client identify the common episode.**
3. **Ask questions to help the client outline both external and internal triggers.**
4. **Clarify the using behavior further (if needed) by asking the four basic questions:**
   - **What did you usually use (e.g., drug of choice or more than one drug if typically used together)?**
   - **How much do you usually use?**
   - **How often do you use? (Frequency)**

- **Over how long a period of time do you usually use? (Duration)**
5. **Discuss positive and negative consequences of the behavior.**
6. **Give examples of how the information will be used, praise the client for participating in the session, and make a homework assignment based on some of the information learned by doing the FA.**

Detailed Description

The remainder of this section contains a detailed overview for conducting an FA of Substance Use with a client. Before you begin this procedure, review the client's assessment information. This will help you comment on and link any relevant information from the assessment as you complete the items on the FA of Substance Use form. It also communicates to clients that the assessment was not wasted time and that you are familiar with and understand their situation.

Explain the purpose of the FA of Substance Use, bringing any relevant assessment information into the conversation. Introduce the client to the FA of Substance Use form; hand the client a copy to follow along with during the process.

The FA of Substance Use consists of three basic parts: identifying external and internal triggers for the behavior, documenting the behavior, and identifying the positive and negative consequences of the behavior. Point out the connections between the three steps of an FA of Substance Use: triggers lead to behaviors that in turn lead to consequences. During the introduction of the FA of Substance Use, you will need to explain terms, such as triggers and consequences. Try to avoid using professional jargon that could interfere with the rapport-building process.

Information from the FA of Substance Use is recorded on a form that can be placed in the clinical record for future reference. This form reflects the basic steps of the analysis noted above. Use the FA for Substance Use Behavior (Initial Assessment) form. Blank and sample completed copies of the FA of Substance Use form are included at the end of this section. We recommend that you deemphasize the act of filling in the form because many clients are turned off by any activity that resembles schoolwork. You might tell clients that you are taking notes about what they are saying so that you can remember it and that you will share it with them so they can correct it if it is not accurate.

1. **Provide a concise and coherent rationale for completing the FA of Substance Use, which includes the following:**
   - **A description of some of the information that would be collected.**
   - **A general overview of plans for the information collected.**
   - **An explanation of the FA of Substance Use form.**
   - **An explanation of how the information could be used throughout treatment.**

Here is an example of how a clinician might introduce the FA of Substance Use:

> **Clinician:** *I'd like you to help me understand more about your use. I have this form called a Functional Analysis of Substance Use Behavior. It will help guide our discussion. Could you help me? Here's a copy for you. We're going to talk about the types of things that typically lead up to you using marijuana. We call these triggers. These might be things that happen to you or things you feel inside yourself. Then, we will also talk about the positive and negative consequences of your marijuana use. This information can help us figure out healthier ways for you to get the*

good things that you like from using alcohol or drugs. It is important for you to enjoy life but to do it in a way that keeps you healthy and out of trouble.

2. Explain that a common (typical) episode will be used, and help the client identify the common episode.

After providing the rationale for the procedure, the clinician focuses on helping the client identify a common using episode. Focusing on the typical episode will provide more useful information to help the client make changes in patterns of use. Most alcohol or substance users have a typical pattern of use.

Clinician:	*Can you tell me a story like it is a scene in a movie about a typical time that you use? Like, where are you and who are you with and what happens?*
Adolescent:	*Well, last Friday I got high right after school when I got home.*
Clinician:	*OK. So is that a typical time when you get high or was that different?*
Adolescent:	*Well, most of the time I go to my friend's house at night and get high. We smoke weed.*
Clinician:	*OK. Let's stick with that nighttime situation at your friend's house, then, as we do this exercise, since that is the more typical situation.*

3. Ask questions to help the client outline both external and internal triggers.

Triggers are thoughts, feelings, or behaviors that precede a using episode and are instrumental in leading a client to use. Reiterate that triggers lead to behaviors, which in turn lead to consequences. (In fact, you may want to write this on a board or clipboard before or after completing the FA of Substance Use.) *External triggers* are associated with a client's environment (whom they are with when they use, where they typically use, when they typically use), whereas *internal triggers* are associated with a client's internal states (what clients think about, feel physically, feel emotionally before they use). Table 2 presents a sample of the section of the form about triggers.

Table 2. Triggers

External	Internal
1. Who are you usually with when you use? *Friends, sister, sister's boyfriend*	1. What are you usually thinking about right before you use? *Getting high and hanging out with friends while everyone gets silly and laughs a lot*
2. Where do you usually use? *Friend's house (Sue)*	2. What are you usually feeling physically right before you use? *Don't know*
3. When do you usually use? *Nighttime*	3. What are you usually feeling emotionally right before you use? *Bored*

Explore with the client the chain of events that led to the alcohol or drug use. Ask the client to give you an example of a typical using episode. By addressing a typical, concrete situation, you can ask specific questions about the event, but the client's responses usually can be applied to many situations. If you need additional information about external triggers, the following questions can be used:

- "*Who* are you with typically?" (Particular friends, groups of friends, or relatives may serve as triggers to use—clients do not have to give names, if they are uncomfortable doing so. The most important information to gather is the relationship of those people to the client and to label them for consistency's sake, e.g., Friend A, Friend B.)
- "*Where* do you usually use?" (At home? At a friend's house? In the woods behind the school? At school dances? This question presents a great opportunity to point out high-risk situations.)
- "*When* do you usually use?" (Are there particular days or times of the day that the client uses?)

If it appears the client uses more than one substance and has more than one pattern of use, it is important to focus on only one (possibly the most common or the most problematic) for the first FA of Substance Use. If a client always uses two substances in a typical episode, then both could be noted in the FA. However, if different substances are typically used in different patterns, it is possible that there are different triggers and different consequences for these different substances, and another FA of Substance Use might be completed. Importantly, it is best to complete only one FA of Substance Use per session, so if needed, additional FAs could be completed in subsequent sessions. More commonly, clinicians obtain the necessary information for another substance and pattern without having to complete an entire second FA of Substance Use, since the client is already familiar with the objective of the procedure and the process can be abbreviated.

Clinician:	*OK, let's talk about triggers. Do you know what a trigger refers to?*
Adolescent:	*Yes.*
Clinician:	*OK, please explain it to me.*
Adolescent:	*Yeah, it's like a thing on a gun.*
Clinician:	*What do you mean?*
Adolescent:	*Well, you pull it and it goes off.*
Clinician:	*OK, a trigger on a gun is like a trigger for drug use. A trigger is something that leads to a behavior. For example, a trigger to getting high may be hanging out with friends who get high. Maybe the smell of marijuana leads to wanting to get high. Does this make sense?*
Adolescent:	*Yes.*
Clinician:	*What are some of your triggers? What triggers you to get high?*
Adolescent:	*I don't know. I guess the people I'm around, 'cause everyone I know smokes weed.*
Clinician:	*So everyone you know smokes weed?*
Adolescent:	*Yeah, every day.*

Clinician:	*Hmmm, every day. You said before that usually you get high at night, is that right?*
Adolescent:	*Yeah. Nighttime.*
Clinician:	*I know you said everyone you know smokes weed. Whom do you smoke with?*
Adolescent:	*My friends, my sister, my sister's boyfriend.*
Clinician:	*Where do you usually go to get high?*
Adolescent:	*Friend's house.*
Clinician:	*Which friend's house?*
Adolescent:	*Sue's.*

Next, ask the client specific questions about internal triggers. With a client who is having difficulty expressing thoughts or feelings, you might try using visual imagery, for example, "Why don't you close your eyes and imagine where you usually use marijuana." Set up the scene where alcohol or illicit drug use occurs, and use imagery to help the client finish describing the whole episode. For example, if the client typically uses in the bedroom, you could start by asking the client to visualize the bedroom. Then go through what happens next. Another helpful approach with adolescents (because of their emotional and cognitive developmental level) is to provide several examples of the type of information desired. The following are probes that can be used to identify internal triggers.

- "What are you usually *thinking* about right before you use?"

  Identifying the thinking process is critical because clients need to see that, at some point, they make a decision to use: using is not an automatic process. Thoughts also provide information on the client's defense system and valuable insight into the feelings associated with using. For example, a client might say, "I usually think about how much fun it would be to get high with my friends."

- "What are you usually *feeling physically* right before you use?"

  Bodily sensations can suggest different states of emotional arousal. For instance, a tight feeling in the chest, sweaty palms, and restlessness may suggest anxiety.

- "What are you usually *feeling emotionally* right before you use?"

  Identify how the client feels before using. For instance, it is important to know whether use is linked to an emotional reaction such as anger, frustration, or despair. Then you can spend more time on teaching adaptive behaviors in response to stress. Examine both positive and negative emotional states. What emotional statements trigger using behavior? For example, a client who uses because of depression is making a statement about that depression when using. In addition, you need to know whether a client is using primarily because of a need to affiliate with peers.

Here is an example of a dialogue about internal triggers:

Clinician:	*OK. Thanks for sharing that information on the external triggers. You're doing great. I'd like to ask you more about the internal triggers you may have.*
Adolescent:	*OK.*
Clinician:	*Internal triggers are those that involve your thoughts and feelings about getting high. What are you usually thinking about right before you use?*
Adolescent:	*I think about getting high and hanging out with friends.*
Clinician:	*OK. It sounds as if you like to spend time with friends. Tell me a little more about the getting high part.*
Adolescent:	*Well, I look forward to us all being together and how we pass a blunt around and then all get silly and laugh and have fun.*
Clinician:	*What are you feeling physically right before you use?*
Adolescent:	*I don't know.* [It is acceptable not to get all the information initially; some clients will be better able to describe details later in treatment.]
Clinician:	*OK. Do you know what you're feeling emotionally right before you use?*
Adolescent:	*I feel bored—there's nothing to do.*
Clinician:	*Oh, you feel bored? I wonder if we could talk about this more.*
Adolescent:	*OK.*
Clinician:	*Does getting high help you to feel less bored?*
Adolescent:	*Yes.*
Clinician:	*OK, you're doing great. This is really helping me get to know you better. Now I want to talk about what you use, how much, and typically how long.*

4. **Clarify the using behavior further if needed by asking the four basic questions:**
   - **What did you usually use (e.g., drug of choice or more than one drug if typically used together)?**
   - **How much do you usually use?**
   - **How often do you use? (Frequency)**
   - **Over how long a period of time do you usually use? (Duration)**

As you move from the triggers to the using behavior itself, you have another opportunity to impress on the client the crucial connection between these triggers and using. Say, "Tell me about what goes on when you use." In addition, as you talk with the client about use, you will probably gather explicit details on patterns of use.

While focusing on the typical use situation identified above, gather explicit details on the client's use of the substance. The information collected should be as specific as possible.

Here are more examples:

Clinician: *OK, you're doing great. Now I'd like to ask a few questions to make sure I clearly understand your use pattern. You said that you usually use weed, is that right?*

Adolescent: *Yeah, mostly. Sometimes I drink.*

Clinician: *Oh, do you usually drink when you smoke weed?*

Adolescent: *Naw, that's usually a party thing.*

Clinician: *OK. Thanks for telling me. Let's talk about your marijuana use today, because it sounds like that is what you usually use. We can talk about drinking another day. When you get high, how much weed do you use at a time and how do you use it, for example, in a joint or blunt?*

Adolescent: *One or two blunts.*

Clinician: *Could you clarify: one or two?*

Adolescent: *Two.*

Clinician: *You said that you use at Sue's. Do you get high every day?*

Adolescent: *It's more like every other day.*

Clinician: *OK. You said you smoke about two blunts, how long does that usually take?*

Adolescent: *We smoke two blunts in about two hours.*

Clinician: *Once again thanks for reviewing this with me; you are doing great. I appreciate you being open and honest with me. That's cool. Next, let's talk about positive and negative consequences of getting high.*

Table 3 presents a sample of the section of the FA form about behavior.

Table 3. Behavior

Behavior
1. What do you usually use?   *Marijuana*
2. How much do you usually use?   *Two blunts*
3. How often do you use?   *Every other day*
4. Over how long a period of time do you usually use?   *A couple of hours*

5. Discuss positive and negative consequences of the behavior.

Although alcohol and drug use can lead to long-term negative outcomes, clients certainly must be experiencing short-term positive outcomes to continue using. For instance, smoking marijuana may make clients feel more relaxed, may make them feel more affiliated with peers, or may help them temporarily forget their problems. It is important for you to acknowledge these positive benefits. When you show an understanding that alcohol and drugs have served a purpose in their lives, it helps build rapport. It is true that these benefits are short lived, but they are enough to reinforce continued use.

The clinician's goal is to help a client find the same reinforcers in a positive way. It often catches a client's attention when a clinician starts talking about the positive aspects of marijuana use. The approach is not judgmental, and therefore it can help engage the client in treatment. You may want to briefly mention that later you will help the client find healthier ways to achieve some of these positive consequences.

While focusing on the typical-use situation, encourage the client to talk about the positive aspects of using the substance. You can begin this procedure by saying, "I'm going to ask you something you may find surprising: What are the things you like about smoking weed?" Here are some additional ways to probe for short-term positive consequences of using:

- What do you like about using with [whom]?
- What do you like about using [where]?
- What do you like about using [when]?
- What are some of the pleasant thoughts you have while you are using?
- What are some of the pleasant physical feelings you have while you are using?
- What are some of the pleasant emotional feelings you have while you are using?

For example:

Clinician:	*When I say consequence, what do you think I mean?*
Adolescent:	*Well, something that happens afterward.*
Clinician:	*OK, yes. It's the result of a behavior, right?*
Adolescent:	*Yeah.*
Clinician:	*OK. Well, usually there are both positive and negative consequences of smoking marijuana. Could you tell me more about what you think the positive consequences of getting high are? What are some pleasant thoughts you have while you are high?*
Adolescent:	*I think about chilling and my future.*
Clinician:	*Can you tell me what you mean by that? What does "chilling" mean?*
Adolescent:	*I feel relaxed.*
Clinician:	*OK. You mean that your body feels more relaxed—like physically?*

Adolescent:	*Yeah.*
Clinician:	*OK, I understand. You mentioned that you think about your future. What are you thinking about your future?*
Adolescent:	*Mainly, I don't want to have to think about it . . . how I should be studying all the time and get into college.*
Clinician:	*Sounds like thinking about your future stresses you out and you want to avoid worrying about it?*
Adolescent:	*Yes, I like that I feel mellow and don't worry about my future.*
Clinician:	*I see. Also, can you tell me what you like about getting high with your friends, your sister, and her boyfriend?*
Adolescent:	*It's cool to hang out with them—they're older than me.*
Clinician:	*Oh, I get it. What do you like about getting high at Sue's house?*
Adolescent:	*Her mother is never around. So it's cool there.*
Clinician:	*Is there anything you like about getting high at night?*
Adolescent:	*It's cool to just hang out and chill.*

Up to this point, the FA of Substance Use has served to lay the groundwork for showing the client the long-term negative consequences that result from the using behavior just outlined. Now turn your attention specifically to the problems associated with the client's use of marijuana, other drugs, or alcohol.

Focusing on the specific situation outlined at the beginning of the process, explore with the client the problems that are associated with using behavior. The client may not have a negative consequence for each category; however, it is important to probe each area in a positive and supportive manner. For instance, "Can you think of people you've had a problem with because of your marijuana use?" If the client is having difficulty providing an example, you may want to offer some, such as those below from the client's assessment information. You might ask, "What are the negative results of your use regarding each of these?"

- Family members
- Friends
- Physical problems
- Emotional problems
- Legal consequences
- School problems
- Job problems
- Financial problems
- Other problems

The goal is for the client to see the connection between substance use behavior and negative consequences. Although clients may not always be willing to acknowledge the relationship between substance use and negative consequences, they may see the connection. Clients often mention problems, and you may want to help them make the connection between substance use and a problem. For example, "Do you see that there is a connection between your legal problems and your use of marijuana?"

Some clients may completely resist verbalizing any negative consequences of their substance use. It is important for the A-CRA clinician to accept the client's resistance and not confront the client. The FA of Substance Use form and requests for specific information can be revisited at a later session, after the relationship between the clinician and client has had time to develop.

Here is an example of a dialogue about negative consequences:

Clinician:	*OK. Now that I understand what the positive consequences of using are, I'd like to ask you about some of the negative or bad consequences. For example, how does getting high negatively affect your relationship with family members?*
Adolescent:	*Well, my mother gets on my back, and my father takes privileges away.*
Clinician:	*It sounds as if getting high causes problems between you and your parents.*
Adolescent:	*Yeah, I guess so.*
Clinician:	*How does getting high affect your friendships?*
Adolescent:	*My girlfriend wants me to stop using.*
Clinician:	*It sounds as if she really cares about you and wants you to stop using.*
Adolescent:	*Yeah.*
Clinician:	*How else does smoking affect you negatively? Tell me about any negative physical effects you have from using.*
Adolescent:	*Like forgetting things?*
Clinician:	*Yes, what else?*
Adolescent:	*I often get dry mouth.*
Clinician:	*Yes, dry mouth and memory problems are associated with marijuana use. Do you have any other negative physical feelings?*
Adolescent:	*Sometimes I get tired.*
Clinician:	*Emotionally or physically tired?*
Adolescent:	*Both, like I want to just lie around the house.*
Clinician:	*Like you don't want to do much?*

Adolescent:	*Yeah. I don't want to do anything.*
Clinician:	*Do you feel any negative consequences with other parts of your life, like with your school or job, or legally?*
Adolescent:	*Yeah. I got suspended from school for smoking outside the school.*
Clinician:	*So it sounds as if getting high affects your life in school.*
Adolescent:	*Yeah, I got suspended, and now I have to come here.*
Clinician:	*Do you think getting high has affected you legally?*
Adolescent:	*What do you mean by legally?*
Clinician:	*I mean getting probation and going to court.*
Adolescent:	*OK, yeah. I'm on probation because I got caught smoking.*

Table 4 presents a sample section of the FA form about consequences.

Table 4. Consequences

Short-Term Positive Consequences	Long-Term Negative Consequences
1. What do you like about using with friends? [who] *They are older.*	1. What are the negative results of marijuana use? (behavior/activity in each of these areas):
2. What do you like about using at Sue's house? [where] *Sue's mother isn't home.*	a. Family members: *Mother gets on back; father takes away privileges*
3. What do you like about using at night? [when] *It's cool to hang out and chill.*	b. Friends: *Girlfriend wants me to stop using*
4. What are some of the pleasant *thoughts* you have while you are using? *Chilling/my future*	c. Physical feelings: *Forgetting things, tired, dry mouth*
5. What are some of the pleasant *physical feelings* you have while you are using? *Feel relaxed*	d. Emotional feelings: *Feel lazy*
6. What are some of the pleasant *emotional feelings* you have while you are using? *Feel mellow*	e. Legal situations: *Probation, having to go to court*
	f. School situations: *Suspended from school*
	g. Job situations: *Not working*

6. **Give examples of how the information will be used, praise the client for participating in the session, and make a homework assignment based on some of the information learned by doing the FA.**

After completing the FA of Substance Use, summarize for the client the information gathered through the process to ensure that the full picture of the use (what leads up to it, what follows) is clear. Do not forget to use positive reinforcement or to praise clients for their work and participation in the session.

This process also provides the client an opportunity to develop insight into the triggers and consequences involved in use. Most important, the information gained from the FA of Substance Use provides the framework for the Goals of Counseling work that will follow. As illustrated in the earlier sample dialogue, much information can be gathered that will be useful in later sessions. For example, you can see in the positive consequence column that several elements are reinforcing this client's marijuana use. He likes to hang out with older kids and feels relaxed when using. It also appears that he has provided worthwhile information about his girlfriend that can be used later. It seems clear that he sees her as reinforcing his abstinence. It is also important, as part of this procedure, for you to provide the client with some specific examples of how the information will be used in treatment.

Clinician:	*Thanks for doing this exercise with me. What are some things you learned?*
Adolescent:	*Marijuana helps me relax and I like hanging out with older people.*
Clinician:	*Yes, it also seems like you are worried about your future, too, and it helps you not think about that. Do I have this right?*
Adolescent:	*Yeah, that's about it.*
Clinician:	*What about the negative consequences of your use?*
Adolescent:	*My mom doesn't like it and I've gotten in trouble at school and have some legal consequences.*
Clinician:	*I think you also mentioned that you girlfriend doesn't really like it, right?*
Adolescent:	*Yeah, she gets upset with me.*
Clinician:	*This information will be helpful. It sounds like we need to find some other ways for you to relax. We have this Problem Solving technique that I can teach you. Lots of the people we work with find it really helpful. Maybe we can help you not be so concerned about your future. Also, as we work together to reduce your use, then others will not be so upset with you. What do you think?*
Adolescent:	*That would be good.*
Clinician:	*Great! OK. Let's work together on a homework assignment that is related to what we learned from the FA of Substance Use.* [They work on the assignment using the components of the Homework procedure.]

Additional Note

- The FA of Substance Use combined with the clinical intake assessment provides detailed clinical information that can be used going forward to structure the treatment in a way that is individualized to the client's particular triggers and consequences.

Functional Analysis of Substance Use Behavior
(Initial Assessment)

External Triggers	Internal Triggers	Using Behavior	Short-Term Positive Consequences: Good Things (rewards)	Long-Term Negative Consequences: Not So Good Things
1. **Who** are you usually with when you use?	1. What are you usually **thinking** about right before you use?	1. **What** do you usually use?	1. What do you like about using with (who)?	1. What are the negative results of your using in each of these areas:
			2. What do you think about using (where)?	a) Interpersonal:
			3. What do you like about using (when)?	b) Physical:
2. **Where** do you usually use?	2. What are you usually **feeling physically** right before you use?	2. **How much** do you usually use?	4. What are the pleasant **thoughts** you have while using?	c) Emotional:
				d) Legal:
			5. What are the pleasant **physical feelings** you have while using?	e) Job:
3. **When** do you usually use?	3. What are you usually **feeling emotionally** right before you use?	3. Over **how long** a period of time do you usually use?	6. What are the pleasant **emotions** you have while using?	f) Financial:
				g) Other:

Adapted from *Clinical Guide to Alcohol Treatment: The Community Reinforcement Approach* (Meyers & Smith, 1995)

Functional Analysis of Substance Use Behavior (SAMPLE)
(Initial Assessment)

External Triggers	Internal Triggers	Using Behavior	Short-Term Positive Consequences: Good Things (rewards)	Long-Term Negative Consequences: Not So Good Things
1. **Who** are you usually with when you use? *Everyone I know smokes weed: friends, sister, sister's boyfriend*	1. What are you usually **thinking** about right before you use? *Getting high and hanging out with friends*	1. **What** do you usually use? *Marijuana*	1. What do you like about using with **friends** (who)? *They are older than I am*	1. What are the negative results of your use in each of these areas:
2. **Where** do you usually use? *My friend's (Sue's) house)*	2. What are you usually **feeling physically** right before you use? *I don't know*	2. **How much** do you usually use? *One or two blunts every other day*	2. What do you think about using at Sue's house (where)? *It's cool there; her mom is never around* 3. What do you like about using at night (when)? *It's cool to just hang out and chill*	a) Interpersonal: *Mom gets on my back, Dad takes away my privileges; problems with my girlfriend— she wants me to stop using* b) Physical: *Forget things, dry mouth, tired*
3. **When** do you usually use? *Nighttime*	3. What are you usually **feeling emotionally** right before you use? *Bored*	3. Over **how long** a period of time do you usually use? *Over a couple of hours*	4. What are the pleasant **thoughts** you have while using? *Chilling/my future* 5. What are the pleasant **physical feelings** you have while using? *Feel relaxed* 6. What are the pleasant **emotions** you have while using? *Feel mellow*	c) Emotional: *Feel lazy* d) Legal: *On probation; having to go to court* e) Job: *Not working*

Adapted from *Clinical Guide to Alcohol Treatment: The Community Reinforcement Approach* (Meyers & Smith, 1995)

UNIT 2: CHAPTER 6: Functional Analysis (FA) of Prosocial Behavior

Rationale

The Functional Analysis (FA) of Prosocial Behavior is an important contribution to the substance use treatment field. Unlike many treatment approaches that focus solely on the negative consequences of substance use to motivate a treatment participant to change, the A-CRA intervention uses positive, enjoyable activities as motivators to change (Azrin, Donohue, Besalel, Kogan, & Acierno, 1994; Azrin, McMahon, et al., 1994; Meyers & Smith, 1995). However, before pleasurable activities can be used as motivators, they have to be behaviorally defined.

Begin this procedure by asking the client to describe enjoyable activities that do not typically involve using alcohol or drugs. Next, narrow down to one specific enjoyable activity that the client does without alcohol or drugs that can reasonably be increased in frequency. Help the client identify the triggers and consequences of this behavior. Finally, work with the client to make a detailed plan for when, where, and how the activity will be completed before the next session (homework).

Learning Objectives

The learning objectives of this procedure are to help clients:

- Identify pleasurable nonusing (prosocial) behavior.
- Identify positive triggers for prosocial behavior.
- Identify the short-term negative consequences of prosocial behavior.
- Identify the long-term positive consequences of prosocial behavior.
- Identify a homework activity related to increasing prosocial activity and commit to trying it.

Timing, Audience, and Delivery Method

This procedure typically is completed within the first four treatment sessions and may be revisited as needed during treatment.

Materials

Procedure-specific materials include a clipboard, pens, two Functional Analysis of Prosocial Behavior forms (p. 89), and activity exercises such as the What Else Can I Do? and Activities That May Interest You handouts below (starting on p. 86). Also see the Leisure Questionnaire (p. 95) and the 2X2 Activity Brainstorming Exercise (p. 101) in the Increasing Prosocial Activity chapter.

General Notes for the Clinician

Continue to maintain a positive and enthusiastic tone of voice to establish a positive atmosphere for change. Find even small things to praise to keep the client's motivation high for participating in the intervention.

The FA of Prosocial Behavior, like the FA of Substance Use and the Goals of Counseling, is a work in progress, not a one-time process. It may be worthwhile to revisit the FA process periodically during the treatment episode as the client's behaviors and needs change.

This procedure always works in tandem with the Increasing Prosocial Activity procedure, which is described in the following chapter (p. 91).

Procedural Steps

1. **Provide the rationale for the procedure in a concise manner, and include:**
   - **A description of some of the information that will be collected and an explanation of the purpose of the exercise; namely, to identify healthy and rewarding nonusing behaviors to increase the likelihood that the client will choose the healthy behavior over substance using behavior.**
   - **A general overview of how the information will be used.**
   - **A brief explanation of the FA of Prosocial Behavior form.**
2. **Focus on one enjoyable activity and clarify the following (the description, frequency, and duration of the activity are written in the middle column of the form):**
   - **That the client has enjoyed the activity at least once in the preceding 6 months.**
   - **That the client typically does the activity without using alcohol or drugs.**
   - **That the client has the opportunity to increase the frequency of the activity (if it is not done more than three times per week already).**
   - **The duration (how long does the activity last?).**
3. **Outline both internal and external triggers associated with the activity.**
4. **Outline positive and negative consequences of behavior.**
   - **Identify the short-term negative consequences of the prosocial behavior.**
   - **Identify the long-term positive consequences of the prosocial behavior.**
5. **Summarize and give examples of how the information will be used during treatment by using specifics learned during the FA.**
6. **Jointly develop a homework assignment related to the desirable activity.**

Detailed Description

The remainder of this section contains a detailed overview for conducting a FA of Prosocial Behavior with an adolescent and sample dialogue.

1. **Provide the rationale for the procedure in a concise manner, and include:**
   - **A description of some of the information that will be collected and an explanation of the purpose of the exercise; namely, to identify healthy and rewarding nonusing behaviors to increase the likelihood that the client will choose the healthy behavior over substance using behavior.**
   - **A general overview of how the information will be used.**
   - **A brief explanation of the FA of Prosocial Behavior form.**

Clinician:	*Denzel, now we're going to look at some of the positive activities in your life that don't involve using drugs or alcohol. One of the things we do while working together is try to help you increase the things in your life that are positive, the things that make you happy. These are activities that you can do that do not involve alcohol or drugs, because it is important that you have a happy life and have friends you can do healthy activities with. Tell me a little bit about how you spend your spare time. I'd like to talk about interests you have other than getting high. What activities do you really enjoy?*
Adolescent:	*I like biking and movies.*

Clinician:	*OK, good. Tell me what you like about those activities.*
Adolescent:	*Well, I like being outside and being able to get places quicker on my bike.*
Clinician:	*Sure, that makes sense. Tell me what you like about watching movies.*
Adolescent:	*Well, I just like watching movies.*
Clinician:	*OK, well, let's talk more about those activities and see if there is one that you would like to increase—that you've done recently—but maybe would like to do more. And, we can pick one that you don't usually do when you are using alcohol and drugs.* [The clinician gives the adolescent the Functional Analysis of Prosocial Behavior form (p. 89).] *This form is called a Functional Analysis of Prosocial Behavior; it's very similar to the form we filled out about your marijuana use. I'd like you to follow along with me as we go through the questions. Does that sound OK with you?*
Adolescent:	*Yeah.*
Clinician:	*OK, good. Let's get started.*

2. **Focus on one enjoyable activity and clarify the following (the description, frequency, and duration of the activity are written in the middle column of the form):**
   - **That the client has enjoyed the activity at least once in the preceding 6 months.**
   - **That the client typically does the activity without using alcohol or drugs.**
   - **That the client has the opportunity to increase the frequency of the activity (if it is not done more than three times per week already).**
   - **The duration (how long does the activity last?).**

Even though the details about what the behavior is and its frequency is in the middle of the FA of Prosocial Behavior form, it is *very important* to identify an appropriate prosocial activity *before* beginning to identify triggers and consequences so that you can be sure the activity can be increased and that the chosen activity does not typically involve alcohol and drugs.

If clients have difficulty identifying enjoyable prosocial behaviors they have done in the past, you can use the following exercises to help jog their memories. Ask the clients to read through lists of age-appropriate activities for their community and have them circle the ones they have done in the past 6 months. Examples of such lists, called What Else Can I Do? and Activities That May Interest You, are included at the end of this section (p. 86). The first simply lists activities available in the local area, and the second provides lists of categories of fun things to do by the name of businesses and their addresses and phone numbers. These lists can be developed by working with adolescent groups wherever they are found—in community centers, schools, or treatment settings. Also, you might use the Leisure Questionnaire (p. 95) or the 2X2 Activity Brainstorming Exercise (p. 101), found in the Increasing Prosocial Activity chapter, which follows this one.

It is also possible that you may be working with clients who cannot identify enjoyable nonusing activities because it has been such a long time since they were alcohol or drug free. In these situations, you can still use the above tools to identify an activity for the client to sample (and this becomes the homework assignment). Then, the following week, you can do an FA of Prosocial Behavior using the sample activity as the prosocial activity.

Clinician:	*So, it would be good to pick an activity that you've enjoyed in the last 6 months, but also one that you could do more often. Could you tell me a little bit about when you last biked and watched movies and how often you do each?*
Adolescent:	*I biked last week—and I bike about once a week. I watch movies on TV pretty often, like most days.*
Clinician:	*When you say "biking," are you talking about like a regular bike or a motorbike?*
Adolescent:	*I just mean a regular bike —not a motorbike.*
Clinician:	*I see—one you have to sweat on a bit, huh? That's good exercise. So tell me whether or not you have typically used alcohol and drugs while biking or watching TV?*
Adolescent:	*I don't use much alcohol or drugs if I'm going for a long bike ride. If I'm hanging out with friends while watching a movie on TV, we might use.*
Clinician:	*Hmmm. It sounds like biking might be a good activity to try and increase. What do you think? Is this something you would like to do more of? We could also talk about something else if you would rather.*
Adolescent:	*I would like to increase my biking because I want to get in better shape.*
Clinician:	*OK, that makes sense. You also said you like to get places quickly. What else do you like about biking?*
Adolescent:	*I like exploring places that the bike trails go to and just being outdoors.*
Clinician:	*OK, great! You said you bike about once a week. How long are your bike rides?*
Adolescent:	*Usually for an hour.*
Clinician:	*OK. You're doing very well! It sounds as if you really enjoy biking.*
Adolescent:	*Yeah, it's cool.*

3. Outline both internal and external triggers associated with the activity.

As you did with the FA of Substance Use, ask about external and internal triggers. The conversation can flow more naturally by asking the client to tell you a story about a typical bike ride. If needed, you can follow up with the following specific questions.

- "Who are you usually with when you [activity]?"
- "Where do you usually [activity]?"
- "When do you usually [activity]?"

Then move to internal triggers.

- "What are you usually thinking about right before you [activity]?"
- "What are you usually feeling physically right before you [activity]?"
- "What are you usually feeling emotionally right before you [activity]?"

It is important to help a client make the distinction between a trigger that leads to drug use and a trigger that leads to prosocial behavior. Certain feelings or events may trigger both using behavior and prosocial behavior. For instance, feeling tired may prompt a person to smoke marijuana at one time and to go for a walk at another time. Help the client discern what other factors lead to substance use rather than taking a walk. Once this is determined, it may be helpful to shift the focus of the session to refusal skills or problem solving skills, as appropriate.

Here is a sample exchange to determine triggers for the biking prosocial behavior mentioned in the example above:

Clinician:	*Like we did when we were talking about substance use, let's try to figure out the triggers and consequences for you to ride your bike. Can you like pretend it's one of the movies you like to watch and tell me a story about a typical bike ride? And like we did before, can you try to include who you were with, where you started, what you were thinking . . . details like that?*
Adolescent:	*OK. Well, usually I am home when I start biking, because that's where my bike is. I feel like I want to get out of the house and do something different. Sometimes I call Joe to see if he wants to bike with me, sometimes I don't.*
Clinician:	*And I remember that Joe is one of your nonusing friends, so that's good. I'm getting the picture. What time of day do you usually bike?*
Adolescent:	*In the late afternoon—usually after 4:30—while it's still light outside.*
Clinician:	*OK. Where do you usually bike?*
Adolescent:	*In North Philadelphia, on Broad Street.*
Clinician:	*OK. I've heard there is a lot of drug dealing going on around there.*
Adolescent:	*Yeah, it's true. I'm from the neighborhood though—so I know what to stay away from.*
Clinician:	*Like what do you mean?*
Adolescent:	*Well, if there is a big group of teens on a corner—I'm not gonna go there—I just need to keep my eyes out. Temple University is a good place to ride around. It feels pretty safe there.*
Clinician:	*Sounds good. So it sounds like you ride by yourself or with Joe?*
Adolescent:	*It can be either. I like to ride with friends if some are around, but I don't always have someone to ride with.*

Clinician:	*Well, biking sounds like a fun activity that could be one of the things you do to help make your life satisfying. It's also nice that it is something that you sometimes do with your friends, but it's also good that it doesn't hold you back from doing something you enjoy if no one is available to ride with you. What are you thinking about before you go out and ride?*
Adolescent:	*Well, I think about how I want to get out of my house, get with my friends, and ride around and see what's going on.*
Clinician:	*OK. Do you remember what you feel before you bike? You mentioned wanting to get out of the house and do something different. Is there a certain physical feeling you have?*
Adolescent:	*No.*
Clinician:	*Let's think about that a little more. Sometimes people feel antsy or tired before they exercise—do you feel one of these or something else?*
Adolescent:	*Well, I don't feel tired. I'm really ready to get out of the house and not be cooped up. It's more like I have extra energy.*
Clinician:	*OK, got it. What would you say about your emotional feelings? Can you identify any of these feelings—like sad, happy, anxious?*
Adolescent:	*I feel bored, I guess.*

As with the FA of Substance Use, one form is completed for a specified activity. For instance, suppose a young woman says that she really likes dancing. She attends dance class once every two weeks and goes dancing with friends on the weekend. The Functional Analysis of Prosocial Behavior form can be filled out by specifying her enjoyment of dance class. Then without necessarily filling out another form, you can see whether she can generalize from the first process and provide similar information for another pleasurable activity (e.g., dancing with friends on the weekend).

4. **Outline positive and negative consequences of the activity.**
   - **Identify the short-term negative consequences of the prosocial behavior.**
   - **Identify the long-term positive consequences of the prosocial behavior.**

Note that with the FA of Pro-Social the negative consequences are now viewed as short-term and the positive consequences are long-term—the opposite of how these consequences are viewed in the FA of Substance Use. Sometimes enjoyable activities also have unpleasant aspects. Although the unpleasant aspects of a fun activity are usually immediate and brief, they can sometimes keep a client from doing them. Unpleasant aspects of fun activities could be that the activity costs money or is difficult to get transportation to. But it also could be that the client does not have any friends to share the activity with, has to get up early to do it, or has difficulty finding time to do it. Listen to any negative aspects of the activity and determine how much of an obstacle or threat they are. Are the negative aspects serious enough to keep a client from engaging in the prosocial behavior? Problem solving techniques may need to be used to help the client figure out ways to solve problems that present barriers or result in negative consequences of engaging in the behavior.

Thus, it is important to acknowledge the negative aspects of the activity before moving on to the positive consequences. Be sure to brainstorm ways to overcome these obstacles. If, for example, the client would enjoy going to the library but does not have a library card, help the client obtain a card. For example, ask, "How can we get a library card?" Do not assume that the client will understand and undertake the steps involved in successfully completing the task. This is an excellent time to use the Systematic Encouragement Procedure to help the client take the first steps toward engaging in an enjoyable activity. Be sure to review the client's experience at such an event at the next session.

If the client cannot think of any negative aspects to the enjoyable activity, here are some questions that could be asked:

- "What do you dislike about [activity] with [whom]?"
- "What do you dislike about [activity] [where]?"
- "What do you dislike about [activity] [when]?"
- "What are some of the unpleasant thoughts you have while you are [activity]?"
- "What are some of the unpleasant physical feelings you have while you are [activity]?"
- "What are some of the unpleasant emotional feelings you have while you are [activity]?"

If after asking the questions the client still has difficulty identifying the negative consequences, you might ask what prevents the client from doing the activity more often. It is also appropriate for you to suggest some common possible consequences to provide the client an opportunity to think about whether these negative aspects apply.

The following is an exchange about negative consequences of the prosocial behavior:

Clinician:	*OK, now I'd like to ask you about the negative aspects of biking. It is important to identify these because sometimes they can keep us from doing something that we want to do. But if we know what they might be, then we can plan ways to address them. Is there anything that you dislike about biking?*
Adolescent:	*Yeah, when I catch a flat.*
Clinician:	*Yeah, that would not be fun! How about biking in North Philadelphia? Is there anything you dislike about where you bike?*
Adolescent:	*Well, sometimes when I'm not in my own neighborhood, I don't know the people that are around.*
Clinician:	*OK, thanks for being honest with your answer; you're doing very well! Is there anything else you dislike about when you bike?*
Adolescent:	*No.*
Clinician:	*OK. When you are biking, do you ever have unpleasant thoughts?*
Adolescent:	*Yeah, that a car might hit me.*
Clinician:	*So it makes you uncomfortable, maybe a little nervous about whether you can trust people you don't know or the drivers in cars?*
Adolescent:	*Yeah, that's right.*

Clinician:	How about any unpleasant physical feelings you may have?
Adolescent:	Yeah, like being thirsty, hungry, and sweaty.
Clinician:	That happens. I understand. Do you have any unpleasant emotional feelings?
Adolescent:	Yeah, I get scared that a car will hit me.
Clinician:	That is scary; have you ever been hit?
Adolescent:	No.
Clinician:	Good! OK, you did a great job with this part! We will need to talk about ways you can overcome these obstacles. [Later, the clinician will help the client develop plans for overcoming obstacles, as described in the Homework chapter (p. 47).]

Spend time probing this topic so that there is no question about what the client finds reinforcing. You might say, "It looks as if you are into dancing [or whatever activity has been mentioned]. What do you like about dancing?" Behaviors or activities that are reinforcing in many different areas of the client's life, such as those listed below, are good candidates for behaviors that can compete with using drugs.

"What are the positive results of [activity] in each of these areas?"
- Family members
- Friends
- Physical feelings
- Emotional feelings
- Legal situations
- School situations
- Job situations
- Financial situations
- Other situations

The following dialogue is an example of probing to find the positive consequences of an activity:

Clinician:	Do you think there are positive consequences of biking?
Adolescent:	What do you mean?
Clinician:	I mean that because you like to bike, do you think that there are positive parts of biking? For example, do you think that it makes your mom happy that you are biking, so it's good for your relationship?
Adolescent:	Yeah, she's happy because it keeps me off the corner.
Clinician:	OK, great! Do you think that it has affected your relationship with friends?
Adolescent:	Yeah, I see more people when I bike, and a lot of them don't use.
Clinician:	OK, good. Do you think that there are positive physical consequences of biking?

Adolescent:	*Yeah, I can ride farther now, so I think I'm getting in better shape.*
Clinician:	*Oh, great! You mentioned earlier that you want to get in better shape and you've already noticed that starting to happen. How about emotionally?*
Adolescent:	*I feel as if I have more energy.*
Clinician:	*Energy sounds more like a physical feeling. When I say emotional, I'm thinking about whether you feel happy, sad, bored, or something like that. What emotion do you think you feel?*
Adolescent:	*OK. Well, I'm happy because I like the feeling of moving faster than when I walk.*
Clinician:	*Good. How about legally? Has biking had any positive consequences on your legal situation?*
Adolescent:	*Yeah, it keeps me out of trouble.*
Clinician:	*Yes, that is a positive consequence!*
Adolescent:	*[Laughs.]*
Clinician:	*OK, has it had a positive effect on school?*
Adolescent:	*No, I don't think so.*
Clinician:	*Well, you mentioned that you felt as if you had more energy—what is the connection between that high energy and getting homework done?*
Adolescent:	*Well, by the time I get home, I'm pretty tired, so I don't always feel like doing my homework then.*
Clinician:	*Oh, I see. That sounds like a negative consequence that we should talk more about. Does biking help you any with getting a job?*
Adolescent:	*Well, I could ride my bike to work.*
Clinician:	*That's right! Good thinking! How about financially? Would biking have positive financial consequences?*
Adolescent:	*Um, yeah. I could ride it to work and save money.*

5. **Summarize and give examples of how the information will be used during treatment by using specifics learned during the FA.**

After completing the Functional Analysis of Prosocial Behavior form, provide the client an opportunity to summarize the information gathered through the process and then add additional information to help see the links between triggers, the behavior, and the consequences.

Clinician:	*So what did you learn from this FA of Prosocial Behavior? When we talked about triggers and consequences, did anything stand out for you that you might not have noticed before?*
Adolescent:	*Well, we talked about what I already knew. I like getting out of the house and riding through the neighborhood. It helps me get physically fit.*
Clinician:	*Yes, that's right. Thank you for being patient as we went through this exercise. Do you remember some of the things that you said are negative about riding bikes?*
Adolescent:	*Oh yeah. I don't always know if I'm around safe people and I get concerned about the cars.*
Clinician:	*Yes, those are real concerns that you need to be aware of. We can talk about some ways to reduce those possibilities by learning some Problem Solving Skills as we work together in treatment because we don't want them to keep you from doing something you really enjoy. We'll also talk more about increasing the number of times you bike a week, so you can get in even better shape. It sounds like increasing your time biking definitely would be helpful in reducing your substance use and helping you get off probation.*

6. Jointly develop a homework assignment related to the desirable activity.

Work together with the client on a homework assignment. The homework assignment should involve the enjoyable activity used in the FA of Prosocial Behavior. Refer to the Increasing Prosocial Activity (p. 91) and Homework (p. 47) procedure chapters. The homework assignment should specify the frequency and the amount of time the client will engage in the activity. Any obstacles to completing the activity should be explored and methods to address each obstacle outlined. At the next session, review any obstacles the client encountered while trying to complete the homework assignment, since this process provides the opportunity to learn from experiences in the client's natural environment.

If clients appear unsure of their ability to perform these types of tasks, it would be a good idea to make some of the initial steps during the session (e.g., call to find out when a facility is open or what the cost of admission is, talk with a caregiver about helping with transportation). In other words, use Systematic Encouragement (see Unit 2, Chapter 4 [p. 55]).

The information gained from the FA of Prosocial Behavior provides additional material for ongoing work with the Goals of Counseling. Work continually with the client to increase the amount of time engaged in prosocial activities that do not involve substance use.

Remember to provide positive reinforcement or praise clients for their work and participation in the session.

What Else Can I Do? (SAMPLE—Midwest)

Skateboard
Go out to eat
Go to the movies
Go shopping
Rent a movie
Walk around the mall
Watch TV
Go camping
Lift weights
Do aerobics
Ride a motorcycle
Play baseball
Jog
Go to Six Flags
Ride a bike
Join a youth group
Play hockey
Barbecue
Go on a picnic
Play volleyball
Play golf
Walk
Listen to music
Go to a sporting event
Play football
Skydive
Play softball
Play cards
Attend a play
Be in a play
Travel
Go camping
Ride horseback
Plant flowers
Paint your room
Go to a science center
Shovel snow

Ride a hot air balloon
Attend a car show
Play pool
Box
Go bungee jumping
Take flying lessons
Talk on the phone
Go to a zoo
Go to a museum
Play a board game
Make a pizza
Go to a concert
Learn to cook
Go canoeing
Write a letter
Read a book
Find a hobby
Go skiing
Visit grandparents
Go to a library
Mow the lawn
Learn something new
Draw
Paint
Write a poem
Rearrange your room
Get a job
Help a neighbor
Bathe a pet
Test drive a car
Hike
Learn archery
Play miniature golf
Sunbathe
Play ping pong
Make/decorate pottery
Go to an amusement park

Go to an airshow
Watch airplanes
Visit caves
Write a story
Ride Metrolink
Take a computer class
Sing
Play soccer
Play an instrument
Collect baseball cards
Write a song
Go snowboarding
Get a makeover
Do your nails
Look at the stars
Play tennis
Swing
Pick flowers
Put up new posters
Help clean the house
Learn to take pictures
Make a scrapbook
Organize your closet
Make candles
Try new foods
Go dancing
Try a new dance
Go fishing
Take an art class
Go to batting cages
Go to a carnival
Swim
Go to the driving range
Start a journal
Play a video game
Go to car races

Do gymnastics
Make stained glass
Try karate classes
Try paintball
Go rock climbing
Get ice cream
Go ice skating
Play racquetball
Take carriage/sled rides
Go to a waterpark
Take a nap
Start a collection
Get a different haircut
Go boating
Try jet skiing
Exercise
Run an errand
Go hunting
Write rap music
Take a class
Play basketball
Join a sports team
Play laser tag
Study for driver's test
Go to the YMCA
Wash the car
Ride go-carts
Go sledding
Go to the park
Scuba dive
Make a snowman
Use a computer
Rollerblade
Go bowling
Work at a craft
Walk the dog

What Else Can I Do? (SAMPLE—Northeast Urban Area)

Be on student council
Visit Statue of Liberty
Visit the Liberty Bell
Go to Sesame Place
Fix a car
Surf the internet
Go to Dorney Park
See a Phillies game
Play video games
See a Flyers game
See a 76ers game
Go to Dave & Busters
Go to the circus
Attend summer school
See a Broadway show
Go to New York City
Take horse/buggy ride
Play basketball
Shovel snow for
    elderly/sick person
Speak to a group about
    being drug-free

Buy stereo equipment
Listen to music
Learn to swing dance
Learn to ballroom dance
Deliver newspapers
Work on an ice cream truck
Join Neighborhood Watch
Get your hair treated/permed
See an Eagles game
Go to Club McDonald's
Go to club dances
Help with grocery shopping
Learn to knit
Go to the ballet
Learn to play the piano
Learn to play the guitar
Fix a bike
Laugh and smile
Attend the youth
    empowerment project
Shop for elderly/sick person

Watch Discovery Channel
Play tennis
Watch MTV or VH1
Recite a rhyme
Eat Chinese food
Study for driver's permit
Babysit
Go to Great Adventure
Go to the mountains
Go to family game rooms
Learn to crochet
Talk to neighbors
Train for a triathlon
Learn to read music
Erase graffiti
Go to Washington DC
Fix a radio
Hug someone
Play at PAL (Police
    Athletic League)

Play baseball
Play hopscotch
Run track
Go to a park
Go rafting
Make grits
Braid your hair
Go to the beach
Ride a bicycle
Learn to sew
Ride a unicycle
Ride a dirt bike
Go jogging
Bake a cake
Watch TLC
Go to a gallery
Play water polo

Run up the art
    museum steps

Activities That May Interest You (SAMPLE)

Aircraft Flight Instruction

Metro-East Airport (Shafer Field)	2070 Triad Rd., St. Jacob	644-5411
Langa Air, Inc.	10 Terminal Dr., East Alton	895-8911

Amusement Places

Aladdin's Castle	133 St. Clair Sq., Fairview Hts.	632-1027
Family Fun Tyme	8 Gateway Dr., Collinsville	344-7747
Family Fun Tyme	1 Schiber Ct., Maryville	288-7747
G & B Amusement Co.	6930 W. Main, Belleville	397-7609
Games People Play	699 S. Bluff Rd., Collinsville	345-0885
Time Out	131 St. Clair Sq., Fairview Heights	632-1027
Time Passages Arcade	321 Broadway, Alton	465-1270

Amusement Parks

Six Flags	I-44 & Allenton Rd., Eureka, MO	938-4800

Antiques

Alton Landing Antiques	110 Alton St., Alton	462-0443
Antique Emporium	100 E. Warren, Bunker Hill	585-3929
Broadway Antiques	217 E. Broadway, Alton	465-0423
Belleville Antique Mall	208 E. Main, Belleville	234-6255
Richard's Antiques	2 N. Main, Wood River	254-5793
Maryville Antique Mall	2114 S. Center, Maryville	345-5533
MC Antiques and More	126 E. Chain of Rocks, Granite City	797-2581
Pywacket Antiques	215 E. Central, Benld	835-2970
Wagon Wheel Antiques	National and Academy, Pocahontas	669-2918

Aquariums (Public)

Mid-America Aquacenter	416 Hanley Industrial Ct., St. Louis, MO	647-9594

Aquariums

Aqua Pets	5733 Godfrey Rd., Godfrey	466-3474
Oceans Windows Pets	2755 E. Broadway, Alton	462-6353
The Swamp	2324 Nameoki Rd., Granite City	451-1852

Archery Ranges

Bullseye Archery	405 E. U.S. Hwy. 40, Troy	667-8616
Town Hall Archery Shop	Hwy. 15 and 59th St., Belleville	235-9881

Functional Analysis of Prosocial Behavior (_____)
activity

External Triggers	Internal Triggers	Prosocial Behavior	Short-Term Negative Consequences: Not So Good Things	Long-Term Positive Consequences: Good Things (rewards)
1. **Who** are you usually with when you (activity)?	1. What are you usually **thinking** about right before you (activity)?	1. **What** is the nondrinking activity?	1. What do you dislike about (activity) with (who)?	1. What are the positive results of (activity) in each of these areas: a) Interpersonal:
			2. What do you dislike about (activity) (where)?	
2. **Where** do you usually (activity)?	2. What are you usually **feeling physically** right before you (activity)?	2. **How often** do you engage in it?	3. What do you dislike about (activity) (when)?	b) Physical:
			4. What are the unpleasant **thoughts** you have while (activity)?	
3. **When** do you usually (activity)?	3. What are you usually **feeling emotionally** right before you (activity)?	3. **How long** does it usually last?	5. What are the unpleasant **physical feelings** you have while (activity)?	c) Emotional:
			6. What are the unpleasant **emotions** you have while (activity)?	d) Legal: e) Other:

Adapted from *Clinical Guide to Alcohol Treatment: The Community Reinforcement Approach* (Meyers & Smith, 1995)

89

Functional Analysis of Prosocial Behavior (biking) (SAMPLE)

activity

External Triggers	Internal Triggers	Prosocial Behavior	Short-Term Negative Consequences: Not So Good Things	Long-Term Positive Consequences: Good Things (rewards)
1. **Who** are you usually with when you **bike**? *Either by myself or with friends*	1. What are you usually **thinking** about right before you **bike**? *Getting out of the house, meeting friends, riding around, seeing what's going on*	1. **What** is the nondrinking activity? *Biking*	1. What do you dislike about **biking with friends**? *When I get a flat*	1. What are the positive results of (activity) in each of these areas:
2. **Where** do you usually **bike**? *Broad St. in North Philly*	2. What are you usually **feeling physically** right before you **bike**? *Extra energy, don't want to be cooped up in the house*	2. **How often** do you engage in it? *Once per week*	2. What do you dislike about **biking** in **North Philly**? *Sometimes I don't know the people around me.*	a) Interpersonal: *My mom is happy because it gets me off the corner; I see more people when biking*
3. **When** do you usually **bike**? *Late afternoon, usually after 4:30*	3. What are you usually **feeling emotionally** right before you **bike**? *Bored*	3. **How long** does it usually last? *A few hours*	3. What do you dislike about **biking in the evening**? *I can't think of anything I dislike about it*	b) Physical: *I can ride longer distances*
			4. What are the unpleasant **thoughts** you have while **biking**? *I think that I might get hit by a car*	c) Emotional: *I'm more energetic*
			5. What are the unpleasant **physical feelings** you have while **biking**? *I get thirsty, hungry, and sweaty*	d) Legal: *Keeps me out of trouble*
			6. What are the unpleasant **emotions** you have while **biking**? *I get scared that a car might hit me*	e) Other: *Keeps me out of trouble at school; could ride my bike to work if I got a job; I could save money by riding my bike to places*

Adapted from Clinical Guide to Alcohol Treatment: The Community Reinforcement Approach (Meyers & Smith, 1995)

UNIT 2: CHAPTER 7: Increasing Prosocial Activity

Rationale

Increasing the client's time and involvement in prosocial activities is one of the key hypothesized mechanisms of change underlying the Community Reinforcement Approach, so Increasing Prosocial Activity is a procedure to use often. The key to this procedure is identifying a prosocial activity to increase or try out and making a specific plan to optimize the likelihood that the client will complete the activity. It requires a lot more attention to detail than simply suggesting to clients that it would be good for them to find activities to replace alcohol or drug use or even identifying activities they might like to try. It involves actually making the plan of what they will do and discussing ways to overcome obstacles that might interfere with completing an activity.

Learning Objectives

The learning objectives of this procedure are to help clients:

- Understand the importance of having a satisfying life, including a healthy social and recreational life.
- Understand the importance of replacing alcohol and substance using behavior with competing positive behavior.
- Identify an existing activity to increase or a new activity to try out.
- Make a plan that will likely succeed in increasing or trying out the target behavior.

Timing, Audience, and Delivery Method

This procedure should be completed within the first four treatment sessions in conjunction with the FA of Prosocial Behavior, and then used frequently throughout treatment either in combination with other procedures or by itself.

Materials

If paired with another procedure, have handy any form for that procedure (e.g., a completed FA of Prosocial Behavior). Also, have available the What Else Can I Do? and Activities That May Interest You handouts from the previous chapter (p. 86) and the Leisure Questionnaire (p. 95) and 2x2 Activity Brainstorming Exercise (p. 101) at the end of this chapter.

General Notes for the Clinician

The Increasing Prosocial Activity procedure is often used with the FA of Prosocial Behavior. It may also be used with Problem Solving and Goals of Counseling. However, it can also be used to increase prosocial activity with the help of exercises described below without being tied to another procedure.

When clients say there is "nothing to do" besides use drugs or they simply have trouble generating different ideas, you can have them review the activity lists found at the end of the previous chapter (p. 86), or use the Leisure Questionnaire (p. 95) or the 2X2 Activity Brainstorming Exercise (p. 101) at the end of this chapter to help stimulate new thoughts.

Another approach is to ask, "What is something you really enjoyed doing in the past that did not involve alcohol or drugs," "What is something that you have always wanted to do," or "What is something you have seen someone else try that you thought was pretty cool?"

Procedural Steps

1. **Discuss the importance of a satisfying life, including a good social and recreational life.**
   - **Note that it is important to replace substance use with healthy, rewarding, and nonusing behaviors and to have a number of fun drug-free activities from which to choose.**
   - **Provide some specific reasons why it is important to have a satisfying life and social and recreational life.**
   - **Relate a satisfying life to some of the client's own goals and reinforcers for being in treatment.**
2. **Identify one existing activity to increase in frequency or a new activity to try out.**
   - **The activity should be one that can be completed before the next session.**
   - **It should not have been associated with substance use in the past.**
   - **The link between the prosocial activity and what the client described as positive consequences from substance use should be noted.**
3. **Devise a detailed plan for increasing the frequency of the existing activity or trying out a new one.**

Detailed Description

The remainder of this section contains a detailed overview for Increasing a Prosocial Activity with a client and sample dialogue

1. **Discuss the importance of a satisfying life, including a good social and recreational life.**
   - **Note that it is important to replace substance use with healthy, rewarding, and nonusing behaviors and to have a number of fun drug-free activities from which to choose.**
   - **Provide some specific reasons why it is important to have a satisfying life and social and recreational life.**
   - **Relate a satisfying life to some of the client's own goals and reinforcers for being in treatment.**

The sample dialogue below is based on an adolescent completing a Leisure Questionnaire. In this situation, the adolescent had already increased one activity based on the FA of Prosocial Activities but needed to add some other satisfying activities to his life to compete with his alcohol and drug use.

Clinician:	*Jose, thanks for completing the Leisure Questionnaire. It looks like there are a lot of activities that interest you. Can you remember some of the activities that you checked that you were interested in doing?*
Adolescent:	*Visiting relatives, well, I really like to visit my grandma, and I like singing and being involved in music.*
Clinician:	*Those do sound like fun activities. Do you remember why we talked about how it was important to find these kinds of activities?*
Adolescent:	*Yeah, so that I have things to do that don't involve alcohol and drugs.*

Clinician:	You got it! I really want these to be activities that you like, that are fun, that give you good connection to other people. If you have a variety of fun things to do, you will be less likely to use if you encounter an old trigger. Right?
Adolescent:	Yeah, I guess so.
Clinician:	And one of your goals is to get off of probation, and if you are busy with doing positive activities you'll be less likely to get in trouble and jeopardize your probation. Does that make sense?
Adolescent:	Yeah, it does.

2. **Identify one existing activity to increase in frequency or a new activity to try out.**
   - **The activity should be one that can be completed before the next session.**
   - **The activity should not have been associated with substance use in the past.**
   - **The link between the prosocial activity and what the client described as positive consequences from substance use should be noted.**

Clinician:	Tell me a little bit more about how much you currently visit your grandma or sing and play music?
Adolescent:	I don't have a regular time to visit my grandma—just whenever my mom goes over—I go. I'm not really singing now or playing music, but I'd like to.
Clinician:	So one of these is an activity you could increase and the other one is a new activity that you could try out, is that right?
Adolescent:	Yeah.
Clinician:	Well, why don't we concentrate on one of those before our next session? We can come back to the other one at another time. Would you like to choose one of these or would you like to do something else?
Adolescent:	Well, I've really wanted to try out music.
Clinician:	OK. We can work on that. What were you thinking about? Like, do some of your friends have a band or is there a singing group at your school?
Adolescent:	A few of my friends are in a band and maybe I could talk to them.
Clinician:	That sounds like a good idea. Are these friends who use alcohol and drugs while they are playing or performing?
Adolescent:	Maybe, I'm not sure.
Clinician:	Well, that would be important to know, because we don't want to put you in a position where everyone around you is using. We'd rather you be in a place where no one is. Is there another situation where you could try singing? I heard that they have a group at the Boys' Club. Would you be interested in finding more out about that?

Adolescent:	*Yes.*
Clinician:	*OK. Let's do that.* [The clinician and client use the computer to look up more information about the singing group at the Boys' Club, and the client decides he wants to try that. Note that the clinician is using the Systematic Encouragement procedure here.]
Clinician:	*We've talked about how you've liked getting high because it's something fun to do with other people; it gives you a good connection with them. Do you think singing with people your age at the Boys' Club might do the same thing?*
Adolescent:	*I don't know, but it's worth a shot.*

3. **Devise a detailed plan for increasing the frequency of the existing activity or trying out a new one.**

Clinician:	*So it looks like it is possible to join this group at any time, and we saw on their website that they meet every Wednesday night. How would you feel about going to their meeting this week?*
Adolescent:	*I could try. I think it would be cool to see what is about.*
Clinician:	*OK, well like we always do with homework, we need to talk about any obstacles that could get in the way of you going on Wednesday night.* [The clinician explores obstacles with the client, and they figure out possible methods to overcome them.] *So can you summarize for me what the plan is?*
Adolescent:	*I'm going to walk to the Boys' Club Wednesday night and see what the singing group is about. I'm going to tell you how it goes when we get together for our next session.* [They also review plans for addressing obstacles, and the clinician links the assignment back to a reinforcer for sobriety. If the clinician was still not convinced that the client would follow through and attend, it would be reasonable to continue with the Systematic Encouragement procedure, such as by having the client call the leader of the singing group during the session about keeping an eye out for him that Wednesday.]

The Leisure Questionnaire and 2X2 Activity Brainstorming Exercise

Copies of the Leisure Questionnaire and the 2X2 Activity Brainstorming Exercise follow. The Leisure Questionnaire is pretty straightforward. If the client has decent reading skills, review the instructions orally and then have the client complete the form. The questionnaire can be completed either during the session or as a homework assignment prior to a session that concentrates on Increasing Prosocial Activity. Once the form is completed, help the client narrow down the activity to one that the client rated as Very Much or Much in terms of level of interest.

The 2X2 Activity Brainstorming Exercise is much more interactive and is also a good group activity. The boxes can be drawn on a whiteboard or poster board or a large sticky note in the office, and clients can fill it in with a marker so that they can be active as well. Explain that some activities can be done alone or with others. Some activities are free and some cost money. Begin to fill in the form with some examples and then encourage clients to brainstorm ideas. Once numerous possibilities are generated, help clients circle the activities that they actually would like to do and then start the planning process.

Leisure Questionnaire

For every activity listed on the left, mark the space on the right that best describes how interested you are in that activity when you are *not* using alcohol or drugs.

YOUR amount of interest

	Very Much	Much	A Little	Not At All
1. Decorating and painting around the house	☐	☐	☐	☐
2. Finding bargains at sales and auctions	☐	☐	☐	☐
3. Astrology, horoscopes, the zodiac	☐	☐	☐	☐
4. Visiting caves, waterfalls, scenic wonders	☐	☐	☐	☐
5. Making jewelry, baskets, statues	☐	☐	☐	☐
6. Breeding or training animals for shows or competition	☐	☐	☐	☐
7. Planning trips, excursion and outings	☐	☐	☐	☐
8. Attending circuses and rodeos	☐	☐	☐	☐
9. Going to church groups and church social activities	☐	☐	☐	☐
10. Growing house plants	☐	☐	☐	☐
11. Raising pets	☐	☐	☐	☐
12. Geocaching	☐	☐	☐	☐
13. Doing things with your parents or grandparents	☐	☐	☐	☐
14. Doing things with your neighbors	☐	☐	☐	☐
15. Flower or vegetable gardening	☐	☐	☐	☐
16. Visiting the library	☐	☐	☐	☐
17. Visiting the zoo	☐	☐	☐	☐
18. Making or watching home videos	☐	☐	☐	☐
19. Blogging or vlogging	☐	☐	☐	☐
20. Reading books	☐	☐	☐	☐
21. Jogging, calisthenics, gymnastics, physical activity	☐	☐	☐	☐
22. Woodworking activities	☐	☐	☐	☐
23. Playing a musical instrument	☐	☐	☐	☐
24. Dancing	☐	☐	☐	☐
25. Going to parades, fireworks shows, public spectacles	☐	☐	☐	☐
26. Attending parties	☐	☐	☐	☐
27. Walking in parks or around the neighborhood	☐	☐	☐	☐

	Very Much	Much	A Little	Not At All
28. Attending after-school activities	☐	☐	☐	☐
29. Doing crossword or jigsaw puzzles	☐	☐	☐	☐
30. Meeting new friends	☐	☐	☐	☐
31. Reading detective or mystery stories	☐	☐	☐	☐
32. Writing letters to friends and relatives	☐	☐	☐	☐
33. Reading or studying history	☐	☐	☐	☐
34. Visiting museums, art galleries, or monuments	☐	☐	☐	☐
35. Making or designing clothing	☐	☐	☐	☐
36. Playing bingo and similar games	☐	☐	☐	☐
37. Traveling to see historic sights and places	☐	☐	☐	☐
38. Going to flea markets, bazaars, or yard sales	☐	☐	☐	☐
39. Visiting amusement and theme parks	☐	☐	☐	☐
40. Ice or inline skating	☐	☐	☐	☐
41. Working on the church, school, business, or neighborhood newspaper or newsletter	☐	☐	☐	☐
42. Writing stories, poems, articles, or songs	☐	☐	☐	☐
43. Donating time to church work and projects	☐	☐	☐	☐
44. Painting, sketching, or drawing	☐	☐	☐	☐
45. Looking for new people to date	☐	☐	☐	☐
46. Entering contests	☐	☐	☐	☐
47. Visiting with friends	☐	☐	☐	☐
48. Going to dog, cat, horse, or other animal shows	☐	☐	☐	☐
49. Traveling	☐	☐	☐	☐
50. Talking or texting with friends	☐	☐	☐	☐
51. Going to restaurants	☐	☐	☐	☐
52. E-mailing friends or hanging out in chat rooms	☐	☐	☐	☐
53. Doing lawn and yard work at home	☐	☐	☐	☐
54. Learning about stocks, bonds, or other investments	☐	☐	☐	☐
55. Playing chess, checkers, bridge, etc.	☐	☐	☐	☐
56. Going rock climbing	☐	☐	☐	☐
57. Buying or making things to sell for profit	☐	☐	☐	☐
58. Flying kites	☐	☐	☐	☐

	Very Much	Much	A Little	Not At All
59. Checking family trees, genealogies, tracing your kin	☐	☐	☐	☐
60. Making models and miniatures	☐	☐	☐	☐
61. Bicycle riding	☐	☐	☐	☐
62. Singing with others	☐	☐	☐	☐
63. Going to the beach or river	☐	☐	☐	☐
64. Learning about ceramics, porcelain, or glass	☐	☐	☐	☐
65. Acting in plays or doing sets, props, or lighting	☐	☐	☐	☐
66. Watching team sports (baseball, hockey, etc.)	☐	☐	☐	☐
67. Learning about or doing design and decoration	☐	☐	☐	☐
68. Riding motorcycles or off-road vehicles	☐	☐	☐	☐
69. Lawn sports such as volleyball, badminton, Frisbee	☐	☐	☐	☐
70. Collecting stamps, coins, dishes, dolls, sports cards, etc.	☐	☐	☐	☐
71. Participating in social media	☐	☐	☐	☐
72. Fixing things around the house	☐	☐	☐	☐
73. Doing henna art	☐	☐	☐	☐
74. Going to movies or plays	☐	☐	☐	☐
75. Playing golf or minigolf	☐	☐	☐	☐
76. Fixing up, refinishing, or collecting old furniture	☐	☐	☐	☐
77. Going fishing or hunting	☐	☐	☐	☐
78. Playing paintball, airsoft, or laser tag	☐	☐	☐	☐
79. Downloading new apps	☐	☐	☐	☐
80. Being in political groups and activities	☐	☐	☐	☐
81. Browsing in stores, at estate sales, etc.	☐	☐	☐	☐
82. Playing games like pool, shuffleboard, horseshoes, etc.	☐	☐	☐	☐
83. Playing team sports (football, softball, soccer, etc.)	☐	☐	☐	☐
84. Attending concerts or other music performances	☐	☐	☐	☐
85. Winter sports such as skiing, sledding, etc.	☐	☐	☐	☐
86. Visiting or creating websites	☐	☐	☐	☐
87. Attending church or Bible study	☐	☐	☐	☐
88. Playing board games like Scrabble, Monopoly	☐	☐	☐	☐
89. Playing video games	☐	☐	☐	☐

	Very Much	Much	A Little	Not At All
90. Babysitting or other work with children	☐	☐	☐	☐
91. Charity or volunteer work for the sick or needy	☐	☐	☐	☐
92. Watching television or streaming videos	☐	☐	☐	☐
93. Boating or canoeing	☐	☐	☐	☐
94. Hiking, camping, picnicking outdoors	☐	☐	☐	☐
95. Cooking or baking	☐	☐	☐	☐
96. Photography (taking or editing pictures)	☐	☐	☐	☐
97. Playing cards	☐	☐	☐	☐
98. Target, trap, or skeet shooting	☐	☐	☐	☐
99. Sewing, knitting, crocheting, needlepoint, etc.	☐	☐	☐	☐
100. Working on cars or other vehicles	☐	☐	☐	☐
101. Playing tennis, handball, squash, racquetball, etc.	☐	☐	☐	☐
102. Doing art and crafts	☐	☐	☐	☐
103. Swimming, skin diving, and other water activities	☐	☐	☐	☐
104. Collecting bottles, old glass, etc.	☐	☐	☐	☐
105. Learning about other countries and cultures	☐	☐	☐	☐
106. Collecting shells, rocks, specimens, nature objects	☐	☐	☐	☐
107. Reading or watching science fiction	☐	☐	☐	☐
108. Reading romantic novels and love stories	☐	☐	☐	☐
109. Going to fairs or carnivals	☐	☐	☐	☐
110. Listening to music	☐	☐	☐	☐
111. Taking courses on new topics	☐	☐	☐	☐
112. Civic and service clubs, lodges, community groups	☐	☐	☐	☐
113. Going to a coffee house	☐	☐	☐	☐
114. Watching auto races, demolition derbies, etc.	☐	☐	☐	☐
115. Watching individual sports (boxing, tennis, weightlifting, etc.)	☐	☐	☐	☐
116. Sailing	☐	☐	☐	☐
117. Architecture (designing, studying, building, etc.)	☐	☐	☐	☐
118. Taking quizzes online	☐	☐	☐	☐
119. Aerobics (exercises, dancing, etc.)	☐	☐	☐	☐
120. Keeping a journal	☐	☐	☐	☐

	Very Much	Much	A Little	Not At All
121. Making audio or videotape recordings of events, movies, concerts, parades, etc.	☐	☐	☐	☐
122. Skateboarding	☐	☐	☐	☐
123. Going shopping	☐	☐	☐	☐
124. Going horseback riding	☐	☐	☐	☐
125. Going to a car show	☐	☐	☐	☐
126. Rearranging your room, organize your closet	☐	☐	☐	☐
127. Learning archery	☐	☐	☐	☐
128. Putting on makeup or doing your nails	☐	☐	☐	☐
129. Winter activities (building a snowman, snowball fight, etc.)	☐	☐	☐	☐
130. Going to an airshow	☐	☐	☐	☐
131. Getting a manicure or pedicure	☐	☐	☐	☐
132. Stargazing	☐	☐	☐	☐
133. Helping clean the house	☐	☐	☐	☐
134. Making a scrapbook	☐	☐	☐	☐
135. Candle or soap making	☐	☐	☐	☐
136. Go to the batting cages	☐	☐	☐	☐
137. Going to the golf driving range	☐	☐	☐	☐
138. Playing ping-pong	☐	☐	☐	☐
139. Sunbathing	☐	☐	☐	☐
140. Taking and editing selfies	☐	☐	☐	☐
141. Going for ice cream or frozen yogurt	☐	☐	☐	☐
142. Taking a nap	☐	☐	☐	☐
143. Riding go-carts	☐	☐	☐	☐
144. Studying for the driver's exam	☐	☐	☐	☐
145. Going to the YMCA	☐	☐	☐	☐
146. Washing the car	☐	☐	☐	☐

If you have any other interests or hobbies that were not listed, please list them here:

A. _____

B. _____

C. _____

D. _____

E. _____

F. _____

G. _____

H. _____

From the checklist you have just completed (items checked off on previous pages and items written above), pick your five favorite (strongest or least disliked) interests, and next to each one, estimate how much time you now spend engaged in that interest in a typical week.

Favorite Interests	Hours/Days in Typical Week
1. _____	_____
2. _____	_____
3. _____	_____
4. _____	_____
5. _____	_____

2X2 Activity Brainstorming Exercise

With Money/With Others	With Money/Without Others
Without Money/With Others	Without Money/Without Others

UNIT 2: CHAPTER 8: Drink/Drug Refusal

Rationale

It is important to help clients practice refusing alcohol and drugs because there are others around them who will ask them to use. It is likely that many of the people who ask them to use will be people they have used with in the past and thus may be triggers for using.

Learning Objectives

The learning objectives of this procedure are to help clients:

- Identify potential social supports for abstinence and enlist their support.
- Identify individualized high-risk situations to help the client avoid the situations completely or create a plan to avoid using substances in these situations.
- Learn and practice different ways to assertively refuse drinks or drugs.

Timing, Audience, and Delivery Method

This procedure can be completed in any session. It will be useful for clients who are still using alcohol or drugs or who are concerned that they might be asked to use and do not know how to refuse. It would also be helpful to review this procedure before clients place themselves in high-risk situations. Finally, it is a good procedure to use after clients slip or relapse. Often, after completing the Behavioral Chain of Events described in the Relapse Prevention chapter that follows (p. 111), it is evident that a review and practice of these skills will help address problematic links in the chain.

Materials

You should have a completed FA of Substance Use form (helpful for identifying high-risk situations) and the Resisting Pressure to Use handout (p. 110).

General Notes for the Clinician

It is helpful to have other clients or at least one other person available to help practice the assertive refusal skills because they can make it appear more realistic.

Procedural Steps

1. **Identify and enlist social support by:**
   - **Noting the importance of having people who support the client's abstinence.**
   - **Asking the client to identify several people who would be supportive.**
   - **Having the client describe how he or she would ask a person to support sobriety, then role play the request.**
2. **Review high-risk situations:**
   - **If the client mentions an upcoming high-risk situation, discuss the triggers and a plan for addressing them.**
   - **Note that the client needs to be aware of high-risk situations for substance use, and provide the rationale for knowing about these situations.**
   - **Discuss relevant triggers and make plans to address them.**

3. **Teach, review, and practice assertive refusal skills.**
4. **Help the client role play assertive refusal skills with appropriate feedback.**

Detailed Description

The remainder of this section contains a detailed overview for conducting Drink/Drug Refusal with a client and includes a sample dialogue.

1. **Identify and enlist social support by:**
   - **Noting the importance of having people who support the client's abstinence.**
   - **Asking the client to identify several people who would be supportive.**
   - **Having the client describe how he or she would ask a person to support sobriety, then role play the request.**

Clinician:	*You know, it's very important to have people in your life that support your goal of abstinence. Do you have someone in your life who you think will support your decision to quit weed?*
Adolescent:	*Yeah, I think so.*
Clinician:	*Sounds like you're not sure. If you have someone, that's great! Let's talk about this some more because it's important to have people you can turn to when you're feeling triggered. I can help you identify someone that will support you. Are you OK with that?*
Adolescent:	*I guess so.*
Clinician:	*Good! So let's write down the names of people that you think are potential supports for your abstinence. You want to think of people you can contact or who will be with you when you're in high-risk situations. We can talk about each one and figure out whether or not they would be a good support.*
Adolescent:	*Well, there's my mom.*
Clinician:	*Yes, she is definitely supportive. We'll put her name down. It would also be good to put down someone who's a friend or who might be with you at a party or a place where you think you might want to use. There may be times when you wouldn't want to call your mom and would be more comfortable talking to someone your own age.*
Adolescent:	*I'm not sure about that, but I have this friend, Jordan, who I think would support me. And then there is my girlfriend.*
Clinician:	*That sounds good! When we set up a support system, we want to talk to all these people ahead of when we might need them. That is, we want to tell them that you know there will be times when you are in a situation where you might have a trigger to use and that you'd like them to remind you of your goal during those times . . . that you might want to call and talk to them in those situations. Does that make sense?*

Adolescent:	*Yeah.*
Clinician:	*So, like we always do, let's practice what you would say to them because that will make it easier. Can you give it a try? Why don't we first pretend that you are talking to Jordan?*
Adolescent:	*OK. Would I call him?*
Clinician:	*Well, that depends. Do you see him every day? Could you ask him in person? It's fine to call him if you think that works best.*
Adolescent:	*I usually see him at school, so I could talk to him there. I could say, "Jordan, you know I'm in treatment 'cause of my probation and I need to stay away from weed now. Could you help with that?"*
Clinician:	*That's a good start. Can you be more specific with how you want Jordan to help you? Pretend you are talking to him again and I will pretend to be Jordan.*
Adolescent:	*Jordan, if I get in a situation where I have a strong craving to smoke weed, will you be willing to remind me that I need to pass since I want to get off probation?*
Clinician:	[As Jordan.] *Yeah, I'm willing to help you.*
Adolescent:	*Thanks, Jordan.*
Clinician:	*That sounds good! Maybe next time you could mention that you would like to be able to call him on the telephone at those times, if he is not with you.* [They continue to practice until the adolescent has a good grasp on what he needs to say. If the adolescent cannot come up with the words to discuss the needed support, the clinician can shape this behavior with role playing.]
Clinician:	*So, you are going to have this same conversation with your mom and girlfriend as well, right? When do you think you can talk to each person?* [They decide on when the adolescent will talk with each person, and if the conversation is going to occur by phone, the clinician makes sure the adolescent has the correct phone numbers in his phone.]

2. **Review high-risk situations:**
   - **If the client mentions an upcoming high-risk situation, discuss the triggers and a plan for addressing them.**
   - **Note that the client needs to be aware of high-risk situations for substance use, and provide the rationale for knowing about these situations.**
   - **Discuss relevant triggers and make plans to address them.**

There may be times during sessions when clients mention an upcoming situation that you recognize from the assessment or the FA of Substance Use as a high-risk situation. At those times it is appropriate to work on a plan together to address the triggers—including a discussion of any obstacles and how they would be overcome. However, even if clients do not present with a particular high-risk situation, it is important to review and prepare for any that may occur.

Clinician: *Now that you have a list of people who would support you, let's talk about some situations that might be high risk for you. So it seems that you are pretty upset about your girlfriend breaking up with you. I'm sorry that happened to you. I know you really liked her. It's normal for something like that to catch you off guard and affect you. You know, sometimes when people are really angry or sad about something that has happened in their lives, it can be a trigger for using. We didn't really talk about that kind of situation with your FA of Substance Use, and maybe it doesn't apply to you, but do you find yourself thinking more about using because you are feeling bad about the breakup?*

Adolescent: *Well, I just want to hang out with my friends more—since I'm bored.*

Clinician: *I get that. . . . So when you hang out with your friends what do you do together?*

Adolescent: *We like to go skateboarding and just go to someone's house and hang out.*

Clinician: *Would either of those activities be what we might call "high risk" where you might be likely to use? I remember from your FA that a lot of times you use when you hang out at certain friends' houses because their parents aren't there.*

Adolescent: *Yeah, it could happen.*

Clinician: *Thanks for being honest about that. So what do you think would be the triggers in that situation?*

Adolescent: *Someone would have weed or something else and they would ask me if I wanted to use it. Everybody else would be using it.*

Clinician: *Yes, I could see where it would be difficult not to use in that situation. We've talked about plans to avoid triggers in the past. What do you think might be a plan in this situation?*

Adolescent: *I dunno, I can just tell them I don't want to use.*

Clinician: *Sure, that is an option. We can practice some ways to say no assertively—you know, in a way that will make it clear that you really mean it. Let's keep brainstorming. . . . What are some other ways to do deal with this trigger?*

Adolescent: *I suppose I could not go to my friend's house, but I want to.*

Clinician: *Would this be a good time to call Jordan, since he's going to be one of your support people who reminds you not to use?*

Adolescent: *I guess so. That might help. But then what would I do?*

Clinician: *What do you think about suggesting a different thing to do—so that you have something to do and you can continue to spend time with your friends?*

Adolescent: *Maybe.*

Clinician: *What might be some different places to suggest?*

Adolescent:	*We could go to my house and watch a movie or play video games.*
Clinician:	*Would you like doing that?*
Adolescent:	*Yes.*
Clinician:	*What might get in the way of doing that?*
Adolescent:	*They might not want to do that?*
Clinician:	*Yes, that's possible. Then what?*
Adolescent:	*I think I would go with them to my friend's house. Or maybe I'd just see what Jordan was up to.*
Clinician:	*OK, well, it's your decision. Let's talk about the ways to refuse assertively and practice those skills, OK?*

3. Teach, review, and practice assertive refusal skills.

Refusal training is a component of A-CRA behavioral skills training. The training teaches clients to refuse alcohol or drugs assertively. The timing of when to offer this training varies, but it may be provided during any session to prevent relapse when it appears that the client may be in a high-risk situation or following a relapse. It can be revisited often to ensure the skills are generalizable or to improve the client's confidence in refusal skills.

The first part of the procedure is providing an explanation of the six options and giving an example for each one. It can also be helpful to reinforce existing refusal skills by asking clients to demonstrate how they have refused drugs or alcohol in the past. Also ask why they refused in those particular instances. This input can provide additional insight into a possible motivation to refrain from using. Refusal training consists of six basic techniques, any or all of which can be used, depending on the client or situation. Be sure to enlist the help of the client to come up with examples of what to say for each component. The six techniques and examples are listed below. You can hand the client the Resisting Pressure to Use handout (p. 110) as you review the examples.

- **Say, "No, thanks," assertively.** The client must be firm and positive when refusing. If an explanation is needed, then it is acceptable to offer one (e.g., "No thanks—I'm on probation and being screened for drugs."). Casual acquaintances and strangers usually will not ask for an explanation, whereas close friends or family members are likely to ask. A prepared excuse (even a false one) may be helpful at this time but may create complications later that should be discussed. For some clients it might be best to teach them to say "No thanks" without guilt and excuses.
- **Display assertive body language.** It is important for clients to refuse alcohol and drugs by using both words and body language that indicate they are serious and confident. Clients should practice standing up straight, facing the other person, using good eye contact, and stating firmly, "No, thanks." If their physical stance is not assertive, then it may appear to the person who is offering them drugs that the decision not to use alcohol or drugs is not a firm one.
- **Suggest alternatives.** Clients can suggest something other than alcohol or drugs. For example, they could say, "No thanks, but I'd really like a soda" or "No thanks, but I'm starving. Is there anything to eat?" They can also suggest other activities: "No thanks, let's go shoot some hoops." Ask clients to give some examples of what they would suggest.

- **Change the subject.** Changing the subject indicates that the client is not interested in the offer. For example, the client could say, "No, thanks. Hey, what do you think of that new music video?" or "Have you seen that new movie?" Ask clients to give examples of how they would change the subject.
- **Directly address the issue with the aggressor.** If someone persists in offering alcohol or drugs despite receiving a refusal, the client may need to assertively address that person. This type of communication should be a last resort because despite using good communication skills, it still could lead to relationship problems. For example, the client could say, "Hey, I get that you want to get high and I used to get into that, but I'm trying to pass my drug screens now. . . ."
- **Leave the situation.** If all the other techniques fail, then the client can leave the situation (e.g., the party, the place where the others are hanging out).

4. Help the client role play assertive refusal skills with appropriate feedback.

To prepare the client to be ready to use the assertive techniques in real life, conduct a role play. The following are important components of a good role play to teach assertive refusal skills:

- Be sure the role play is two-sided. That is, there is a back and forth exchange between you and the client while you play the part of the person offering drinks or drugs.
- The actual role play is stopped after a relatively brief interchange (less than two minutes), so that you can provide feedback to the client on the brief interchange.
- Ask the client to incorporate at least two of the assertive techniques into the role play.
- At the end of each role play situation, compliment the client for a specific assertive component.
- At the end of each role play situation, work to shape the client's behavior by suggesting the use of at least one (or more) of the options for assertive refusal.
- Ask the client what they did and did not like about the client's performance in the role play.
- Repeat the role play more than once, each time varying your response, so that the client learns how to respond in a more challenging (maybe more realistic) situation. Encourage the client to use additional or new assertive techniques when repeating the role play.

Remember that reverse role plays help the clinician learn the various ways in which an individual is asked to use, and for showing clients how they are perceived by other people. In this situation, *the clinician would play the client* and give nonassertive responses, while the client would play the friend who is asking the client to use with him. The clinician could then give assertive responses (while playing the client) and encourage the client to point out the differences between the two role plays. Reverse role plays should always be followed by regular role plays in order to give the client a chance to practice the refusal skills.

Below is an example of a role play using the components:

Clinician:	*Joe, since we've reviewed all these ways to refuse in an assertive way, let's practice some of them. As you know, it is easier to do this in the real situation when you have practiced them. First let's review them. There are six of them. Can you tell me what they are?*
Adolescent:	*Well, I remember the last one was to leave if they keep bugging you.*
Clinician:	*That's right. What are some of the other ones?*
Adolescent:	*Something about looking like you mean it with your body language.*

Clinician: *Yes, that's good. Can you remember the others? You can go ahead and look at the handout.* [They continue to review until either the adolescent lists all the options or the clinician reviews them again.] *So, when we practice now I'll be one of your friends who wants you to use with him, and you be yourself. Try to use the techniques we talked about. OK, here goes.* [Playing a friend's part.] *Hey Joe, it's good to see you again. Here's some for you.* [Pretends to pass him a blunt.]

Adolescent: *No thanks.* [Adolescent is looking down and speaks in a soft voice.]

Clinician: [As the friend.] *Oh come on. You know you want to smoke it.*

Adolescent: *No, I have to be careful, I really want to get off of probation and they'll make me take a piss test.*

Clinician: *OK. Let's stop here. I like that you said, "No, thanks," and you gave a reason. When you gave a reason, your voice was strong too. What did you notice about this practice? What skills did you do well and what could you have done differently?*

Adolescent: *I feel silly doing this with you, but I know I didn't look you in the eye when I said I didn't want to do it.*

Clinician: *Yeah, I know it's awkward to do role plays, but I'm really glad you are trying. And I agree with your evaluation. Remember how we talked about saying, "No thanks" in a firm voice and facing the person and looking them in the eye? I think I would have felt more like you meant it if you did it that way. Would you be willing to give it a try again?*

Adolescent: *OK.*

Clinician: [As the friend.] *Joe, it's good to see you. I have got the best stuff tonight. Here, have a hit.*

Adolescent: *No thanks, I'm staying clean because I want to get off probation.* [Adolescent has a firmer voice and faces the friend.]

Clinician: *Wow, that was a lot better! It sounded like you really meant it and you were looking at me. Let's practice some more and I'd like you to use at least one other technique. I'm going to be a little more insistent this time. I think I might be even more convinced if you changed the subject. Can you think of something that you could change the subject to?*

Adolescent: *I think so.*

Clinician: *OK. Let's try this again.* [Switches to the friend's role.] *Come on, Joe, you know you want to try it and you're going to be sorry if you don't. I've got this stuff so you'll pass the piss test.*

Adolescent: *Naw. Hey, did I hear you got the new version of War Universe? I was looking forward to playing that.*

Clinician: [As the friend.] *It's over there, but it's so much more fun to play when you're high. Here, have some.*

Adolescent: *You know, I don't get why you are always trying to get me to use. I said no.*

Clinician: *OK, let's stop. You did really good. How did you feel about doing that? What did you like and what didn't you like?*

Adolescent: *It felt pretty good. I thought it was going to be easy to change the subject because I really want to play that new video game, but it was a little harder when you responded by saying it's more fun playing high.*

Clinician: *Yes, I really liked how you suggested playing the video game. And then, when he was still persistent, you did a really good job of being direct with him. That's not always easy, but that would be a good way to do it.*

Resisting Pressure to Use

When you decide to abstain from alcohol or drug use, it can be a big change. People will probably still offer you alcohol or drugs. To help you reach your goal, it is important to know how to refuse alcohol or drugs. Refusing drugs may be easy or more difficult depending on who you are with, where you are, the time of day, and so forth (based on your triggers). Being prepared by practicing refusal skills can help you stay away from drugs and reach your goal. Below are the basic steps to use for refusing alcohol or drugs.

- **Say, "No, thanks"**

- **Display assertive body language**

- **Suggest an alternative**

- **Change the subject**

- **Directly address the issue with the person pressuring you**

- **Leave the situation**

- **Say, "No, thanks."** Of course, if someone offers you alcohol or drugs, saying "No, thanks" is the first thing you would want to do. To make sure the other person knows you are serious, be firm. Often strangers or acquaintances will just accept a "No, thanks" without pressuring you anymore. However, other people such as friends may want to have an explanation. Having a ready-made explanation ("No, thanks, I'm on probation and getting drug tested") can make it easier.

- **Display assertive body language.** Be aware of your posture and body positioning. To get your point across and show you are serious, it is best to look directly at the other person and make eye contact when refusing alcohol or drugs.

- **Suggest an alternative.** For example, if someone offers you a beer, you might suggest something else to drink, like "No, thanks. How about a soda?" You can also suggest something else to do, like "Let's go shoot some hoops."

- **Change the subject.** This shows that you are not really interested in using drugs. For example, say, "No, thanks. What did you think of that new music video?"

- **Directly address the issue with the person pressuring you. Use** this technique as a last resort. It can strain a relationship at times. Use good communication skills, but be direct: "Hey, I get that you want to get high and I used to be into that, but I'm trying to pass my drug screens now. . . ."

- **Leave the situation.** If you've tried everything else and the person still persists, then the best option is to just leave the situation. (e.g., the party, the place where the others are hanging out).

UNIT 2: CHAPTER 9: Relapse Prevention

Rationale

By definition a relapse occurs after a period of abstinence. Many treatment clients may commit to quitting their alcohol or drug use, but they will have a relapse between treatment sessions. These relapses can be learning opportunities, and there are several different techniques that can be used to help clients avoid another relapse.

Learning Objectives

The learning objectives of this procedure are to help clients:

- Identify internal and external triggers that preceded the relapse through the use of a relapse version of the Functional Analysis of Substance Use.
- Identify the chain of events leading to a relapse and learn how to interrupt the chain.
- Outline the components of an individualized Early Warning System to identify high-risk situations.

Timing, Audience, and Delivery Method

This procedure should be completed as needed; namely, after a relapse. When there has not been a recent relapse, it could be used for a client's last alcohol or drug use or for an upcoming high-risk situation.

Materials

Procedure-specific materials include a clipboard, pens, two Functional Analysis of Substance Use—Relapse Version forms (p. 116), a board and markers or paper and pens (for drawing the Behavioral Chain of Events), and a telephone for contacting the person identified as part of the Early Warning System.

General Notes for the Clinician

There are three different Relapse Prevention procedures discussed in this chapter that could be used in a session following a relapse event. In one session, it may be practical to use only two of these procedures. The FA of Substance Use—Relapse Version or the Behavioral Chain both examine the events or triggers that led to the client's relapse. The Behavioral Chain usually shows more detailed information about the small decisions that led to the relapse and can be used to plan for strategies that could be used in future similar situations. The FA of Substance Use—Relapse Version also outlines consequences of the relapse. The Early Warning System is the identification of a monitor who could intervene before the client relapses. Note that while "monitor" was the term used in the original CRA manual, some clinicians and clients are more comfortable with the term "support person," and so this alternate term can be used.

Procedural Steps

1. **Conduct a Functional Analysis of Substance Use focusing on a specific relapse episode.**
2. **Help the client understand the Behavioral Chain of Events that led to the relapse and generate new responses for the future.**
   - **Help the client connect the dots between the events and actions that led to the relapse.**

- Explain to the client that it is easier to make changes early in the chain.
- Help the client develop a strategy for addressing at least two of the problematic decisions.
- Generate and plan for obstacles to carrying out those strategies.
3. Describe and design an individualized Early Warning System.
   - Describe the Early Warning System and encourage the client to set one up.
   - Help the client identify one person (a monitor or support person) to participate in the warning system.
   - Make a specific plan that outlines what the monitor or support person will do when early signs of relapse are noticed.
   - Help the client prepare to discuss expectations with the monitor or support person.
   - Help the client make a plan to contact the monitor or support person, or do so during the session.

Detailed Description

1. **Conduct a Functional Analysis of Substance Use focusing on a specific relapse episode.**

There is a copy of the FA of Substance Use—Relapse Version form at the end of this chapter (p. 116). Basically, it is completed like the standard FA of Substance Use form (refer to Unit 2, Chapter 5 [p. 61]), except that the behavior defined in the central column is the specific relapse event that occurred rather than a typical using episode. All the triggers and consequences that are discussed will be based on the specific relapse event. If preferred, you can instead use the regular FA of Substance Use form as long as the focus is on a specific relapse episode rather than a typical using situation.

2. **Help the client understand the Behavioral Chain of Events that led to the relapse and generate new responses for the future.**
   - Help the client connect the dots between the events and actions that led to the relapse.
   - Explain to the client that it is easier to make changes early in the chain.
   - Help the client develop a strategy for addressing at least two of the problematic decisions.
   - Generate and plan for obstacles to carrying out those strategies.

After a relapse occurs, it is important to help the client examine the chain of events that led to relapse. Possibly it was an abbreviated chain of events; for example, the client attended a party, someone offered him oxycodone, some friends were snorting it, and so he did too. Perhaps the relapse actually started when the client felt bad after receiving a poor report card and being scolded by his dad. To relieve stress, the adolescent went out looking for some using friends so he could get high with them. By going over an actual relapse, the clinician outlines the chain of events that led to the relapse.

The purpose of this exercise is for the client to learn how to interrupt the chain of events as soon as it begins and before it leads to using alcohol or other drugs. These steps can be outlined on a whiteboard or chalkboard.

Table 5 gives an example of the steps in the Behavioral Chain of Events that led to a relapse for an adolescent named Jake. It is followed by a sample dialogue. The steps show how Jake's decisions led him to relapse. The clinician can work with Jake to help him realize alternative actions and at what points he could have taken them to alter the series of events. For example, when he was angry at his dad, he could have called a supportive friend to talk about it or gone outside to play basketball to dissipate his stress.

Table 5. The Behavioral Chain of Events

Jake and his dad had a big fight. They yelled at each other and even got physical. Jake felt really angry about the fight and wondered why his dad had to act that way. Jake went to his room and shut the door. He started thinking about how he would get back at his dad. He also thought that his dad didn't really care about him.

Jake remembered that some of his friends were getting together that night at one of their houses and that they probably would be getting high. Jake snuck out his bedroom window and went over to his friend's house.

He saw some of his old friends crushing Oxy's (oxycodone) and he craved the effects of his favorite drug. His friends welcomed him and were glad to see him. When Jake's friends offered him Oxy, he took it.

Clinician:	*Thanks for telling me about the relapse, Jake. Let's look at what we have here.* [They both look at the drawing of the behavioral chain.] *Do you think it would be easier to make changes earlier or later in this chain of events?*
Adolescent:	*I don't know. It all kind of started when I got in the fight with my dad. I got upset and that started the whole thing.*
Clinician:	*So, it sounds like you are saying that it might have been better to make some different decisions earlier? Is that right?*
Adolescent:	*Yeah.*
Clinician:	*So what ideas do you have about what you could have done differently?*
Adolescent:	*Well, like I kind of knew my dad was in a bad mood and I could have just avoided him.*
Clinician:	*Yes, that's a good idea and that would be making a change really early in the chain, which is good thinking. Can you think of something else you could have done?*
Adolescent:	*Well, I know it helps if I go out and exercise when I get mad like that.*
Clinician:	*Yes, that's a good idea. What kind of exercise could you do?*
Adolescent:	*I usually go out for a bike ride—so I could do that.*
Clinician:	*You know how we always talk about obstacles? So let's discuss what might have gotten in the way if you tried to avoid your dad or if you still got in the fight and needed to make a decision to exercise to address your anger. OK?* [They continue by identifying obstacles and defining strategies to address the obstacles.]

113

Clinician:	[After they have identified obstacles and strategies to address them.] *Jake, you've done a really good job with the Behavioral Chain. I want to be sure that you understand how this can be useful to you in the future. Can you tell me in your own words why we did this and how it might help you avoid relapse in the future?*

3. **Describe and design an individualized Early Warning System.**
    - **Describe the Early Warning System and encourage the individual to set one up.**
    - **Help the client identify one person (a monitor or support person) to participate in the warning system.**
    - **Make a specific plan that outlines what the monitor or support person will do when early signs of relapse are noticed.**
    - **Help the client prepare to discuss expectations with the monitor or support person.**
    - **Help the client make a plan to contact the monitor or support person, or do so during the session.**

The Early Warning System consists of steps that clients can use to identify early warning signs of relapse and contact supportive people who will be available to help in those high-risk situations. The goal is to avert a relapse. As part of this procedure, the client must identify one or more persons who know that the client is trying to abstain from alcohol or drugs and who are willing to help if the client experiences a warning sign of a relapse. A caregiver, peers, boyfriends and girlfriends, a school counselor, an Alcoholics Anonymous sponsor, or others could be part of the support system. An example of a high-risk situation might be when an adolescent male is repeatedly breaking curfew and hanging out with friends with whom he previously used marijuana. As part of the response to this warning sign, a girlfriend whom the adolescent and clinician have previously identified as supportive of his recovery would call the clinician to let her know about this warning sign. The next step in the plan would be for the clinician to see the adolescent as soon as possible to provide direct assistance. A sample dialogue for a clinician working with an adolescent to develop an Early Warning System follows:

Clinician:	*Let's talk about something called the Early Warning System that could help you figure out when you might be doing something that could lead to a relapse. The first thing we need to do is help you become aware of behaviors that may lead to a relapse. The second thing is figure out what you need to do if you see yourself starting to do these things. Another important part of this procedure is to identify someone else who can help you during these times. Are you following me?*
Adolescent:	*Yeah, I think so.*
Clinician:	*OK, good. What are some triggers or high-risk situations we've talked about before?*
Adolescent:	*Well, I used to use when I stayed out late with Jennifer and Bryan.*
Clinician:	*Yes, that's what I'm talking about. That's what we found out when we did the FA of Substance Use. We figured out that is a high-risk situation, and if you started doing that again, what do you think might be a way to stop putting yourself in that situation?*
Adolescent:	*Well, maybe I could talk about it with you.*

Clinician: *Yes, I'd certainly try to help you. But you know, it might be a while before you and I have a session on the schedule. What we find, however, is that it's better if there is someone that can step in and be of help right away when you are facing the high-risk situation or showing some of your early warning signs for relapse. It should be someone who knows you well. For example, it could be a friend or your sister. This would be someone who would notice some of your warning signs, such as staying out with Jennifer and Bryan, and who would be able to participate in the warning system that we come up with today. Is there someone you can think of?*

Adolescent: *Well, I guess it could be Tracy.*

Clinician: *Oh yes, your girlfriend, Tracy. She is certainly supportive of your recovery. What do you think you could ask Tracy to do if she knew that you planned to go out late with Jennifer and Bryan?*

Adolescent: *Well, she probably would know if that was my plan, because I usually tell her what I'm doing. I guess she could talk me out of going with them.*

Clinician: *I think that's a good start, but it might be more helpful if the plan was a little more specific than that. Like maybe if you both agreed that you would do something else at that time. Is there something else you and Tracy really like to do that you might do instead of going out late with those guys?*

Adolescent: *Ummm. Well, we like to watch movies, so maybe she could come over to my house and we could watch a movie together. It would be nice to be able to talk with her.*

Clinician: *That's a good idea. So, the plan will be if Tracy notices, or if you tell her, that you're going to go out with Jennifer and Bryan, she'll instead suggest watching a movie together at your house. Now I've found it really helpful to other people when we actually practice our plan. So let's practice saying what you are going to ask Tracy to do, and then you can call her while we are together. You know, Tracy may have some specific ideas of her own about how to help you in these situations. Are you willing to do this with me?* [Good opportunity to use Systematic Encouragement.]

Adolescent: *Yeah, OK, but I don't think we'll be able to get ahold of Tracy now.*

Clinician: *Well, let's go ahead and practice what you will ask her to do. We can try calling. If we don't get ahold of her, we can make a plan for when you will talk with her. If you'd like, it would be fine to bring her to a session and we can all talk about it together. Since she really wants you to be abstinent, I imagine she'd be willing to help, and that can be really helpful to you.* [They continue to fine-tune the plan and practice how the adolescent will talk to Tracy. They attempt to call her, are not able to reach her, and then make a plan for how the adolescent will contact her.]

A-CRA Functional Analysis of Substance Use— Relapse Version

Relapse is not an event, it is a process.

External Triggers	Internal Triggers	Behavior	Short-Term Positive Consequences: Good Things (rewards)	Long-Term Negative Consequences: Not So Good Things
1. **Who** were you with when you drank/used?	1. What were you **thinking** about right before you drank/used?	1. **What** did you drink/use? (specifically)	1. What did you like about drinking/using with _____ (who)?	1. What were the negative results of your drinking/using in each of these areas: a) Interpersonal b) Physical
2. **Where** did you drink/use?	2. What did you feel **physically** right before you drank/used?	2. **How much** did you drink/use?	2. What did you like about drinking/using at _____ (where)? 3. What did you like about drinking/using _____ (when)? 4. What were some of the good **thoughts and emotions** you had while drinking/using?	c) Emotional d) Legal e) Job
3. **When** did you drink/use? (What time of day)	3. What did you feel **emotionally** right before you drank/used?	3. Over **how long** a period of time did you drink/use?	5. What were some of the good **physical feelings** you had while drinking/using?	f) Financial g) Other

Adapted from *Clinical Guide to Alcohol Treatment: The Community Reinforcement Approach* (Meyers & Smith, 1995)

UNIT 2: CHAPTER 10: Sobriety Sampling

Rationale

It is difficult for most people with substance use problems to commit to lifelong abstinence from alcohol and drugs. It may be even more difficult for adolescents who almost always enter treatment because others pressure them to (e.g., courts, schools, parents) and not because they have made a commitment to change and seek help. The Sobriety Sampling procedure provides an opportunity for clients to commit to a short period of sobriety so they can experience some early success in treatment. The procedure also helps clients build new coping skills or strengthen existing ones and demonstrates to others in their support system that they are serious about making the effort to be substance free.

Learning Objectives

The learning objectives are to help clients:

- Commit to a short period of abstinence from alcohol and drugs.
- Make a specific plan for maintaining sobriety for the agreed-upon period.
- Discuss lessons learned from attempting the period of abstinence.

Timing, Audience, and Delivery Method

This procedure can be initiated at any time during treatment. If the client is actively using, it should be initiated early in treatment once clinical rapport appears established.

Materials

There are no specific materials needed for this procedure.

General Notes for the Clinician

This procedure is intended for clients who are experiencing some level of use. Using the Sobriety Sampling procedure versus requiring total abstinence throughout treatment might raise concerns among some referral sources or clinicians who are more familiar with programs that require total abstinence. Therefore, it is important to educate these people about the rationale for this procedure and that while the goal may be total abstinence, it is necessary to get to that goal in stages. Although less common nowadays, clients used to be discharged from treatment when they tested positive for alcohol or drugs because they were required to stay sober while in treatment. This practice is not recommended because it is basically discharging clients for the *very reason* they are in treatment.

Sobriety is easier to require during residential treatment but much more difficult to enforce during outpatient treatment, and especially so if a client is not involved in court services where there is regular drug testing. Sobriety Sampling might be useful in residential treatment settings when a client is going on a pass home for a given period of time and needs to maintain sobriety.

It is important to note that the Sobriety Sampling components can also be used to address other types of problematic behaviors. For example, A-CRA trained clinicians have used Sobriety Sampling with clients who cut or self-harm and have reported it effective with these problems.

Procedural Steps

1. **Introduce the rationale for the procedure and include some of the common reasons for sampling sobriety while linking it to the client's specific situation. These reasons can include:**
    *   **Committing to short periods of abstinence makes success more likely than committing to a lifetime of abstinence from the start.**
    *   **It will help build new coping skills or strengthen old non-substance-related skills.**
    *   **It will show family and others that the client is committed to the treatment plan, which elicits support.**
    *   **It allows clients to see what life is like, even for short periods, when sober.**
    *   **It allows clients to actively engage in their treatment by setting goals and strategies.**
    *   **It helps clarify triggers or problematic situations that the client had not previously identified.**
2. **Negotiate a reasonable period of sobriety.**
3. **Develop a specific plan for maintaining sobriety for the agreed-upon duration.**
4. **Develop a backup plan.**
5. **Remind the client of reinforcers for sobriety.**

Detailed Description

Begin by tying Sobriety Sampling to a concern or wish that clients have related to their need to stop using. Help them identify a number of advantages to sampling a period of being sober, and be sure to link a period of abstinence to reinforcers that are specific to each client.

1. **Include the rationale for the procedure and include some of the common reasons for sampling sobriety while linking it to the client's specific situation. These reasons can include:**
    *   **Committing to short periods of abstinence makes success more likely than committing to a lifetime of abstinence from the start.**
    *   **It will help build new coping skills or strengthen old non-substance-related skills.**
    *   **It will show family and others that the client is committed to the treatment plan, which elicits support.**
    *   **It allows clients to see what life is like, even for short periods, when sober.**
    *   **It allows clients to actively engage in their treatment by setting goals and strategies.**
    *   **It helps clarify triggers or problematic situations that the client had not previously identified.**

Clinician:	*When we've talked about your using, it has sounded like it is really hard for you not to use.*
Adolescent:	*Yeah, I always seem to end up in the same situations and use. I start feeling anxious, and then I use.*
Clinician:	*Yes, anxiety is one of your main triggers. How about we come up with an agreement about you staying abstinent for a certain length of time? I've found with other young people I work with that it is easier to commit to being sober for a certain period of time, rather than thinking that they have to be sober for the rest of their life. We can also talk about other ways to deal with your anxiety. I know you want to avoid any more problems with probation, right?*

Adolescent:	*Yeah, I can't get in trouble anymore!*
Clinician:	*What would be some of the benefits of staying sober for a period of time?*
Adolescent:	*Well, maybe I could pass my drug test.*
Clinician:	*That would certainly be good and help keep you from getting violated. Can you think of anything else?*
Adolescent:	*Not really. . . .*
Clinician:	*Well, you know you say you always end up using. . . . What if you showed yourself that it was possible for you not to—even if for only a short time? Maybe it would help you learn some ways to avoid using. What do you think?*
Adolescent:	*Yeah, that might be good.*

2. **Negotiate a reasonable period of sobriety.**

The critical part of this procedure is that the identified period of sobriety is a negotiation between you and the client. For example, you could start by suggesting that the client commit to being sober for a month, but that may sound like a really long time to the client. So the client is asked to propose a length of time, and you proceed to negotiate until you settle on a reasonable period of time with which the client is reasonably satisfied. At a minimum, you would like the client to agree to set a goal to maintain sobriety until the next session. However, depending on the client's frequency, duration, and history of use, not all clients can start off sampling sobriety until their next sessions. During the negotiation, you may even need to settle on 2 or 3 days as a start. Also, if you do not already know, find out the client's longest period of sobriety in the past and use this information to help inform a reasonable starting point. Find out what went well in this effort and what problems were encountered. Regardless, the time frame should have a definite start and end point. If possible, link the endpoint to a notable event in the client's life such as a court date, holiday, birthday, or graduation date.

Clinician:	*So, if we had to come up with an agreement about a reasonable period of time for you to be sober, what do you think that would be?*
Adolescent:	*Just for today?*
Clinician:	*Today is a start, but let's try to go for a longer period of time. You've mentioned before that you've gone 5 days without using in the past, so maybe this time we can try . . . say, 2 weeks? What do you think?*
Adolescent:	*Those seem like pretty long times. I dunno.*
Clinician:	*Well, I have always appreciated your honesty. It's best not to commit to something if you're not pretty sure you can do it. What do you think would be more reasonable? And keep in mind all the incentives for staying sober that we just discussed: passing drug tests, staying out of trouble, learning some new skills to help you stay sober. What do you think?*
Adolescent:	*Still don't know. I'd like to, but . . .*

Clinician:	*But you're still not sure. I get that. Tell me what you're comfortable with.*
Adolescent:	*Well, today's Thursday, how about we say I'm not going to use until after the weekend. The weekend is a really hard time not to use.*
Clinician:	*I agree with you the weekend is a challenging time for you. What do you think about maybe extending the time until our next session, next Thursday? You will have already made it through the hardest time, the weekend, and it will be extending it a little more. And don't you have a probation appointment on Wednesday? It'd be nice to have a period of no use before that. How does that sound?*
Adolescent:	*OK. I'll give it a try.*
Clinician:	*Sounds great. Next we need to work together on coming up with a plan about how you are going to maintain your sobriety. I want to help you make this doable.*

3. **Develop a specific plan for maintaining sobriety for the agreed-upon duration.**

It is not enough to secure agreement on the period of sobriety. *It is really important to develop a plan to help the client achieve sobriety during the sampling period.* It can be worthwhile to ask about any upcoming high-risk situations, such as a party on the weekend or a using friend being released from detention. It is also helpful to review the client's FA of Substance Use Behavior to discuss relevant triggers. Use the same five guidelines when developing the strategies that are used when setting goals: (a) state it positively (what the client *will* do), (b) be specific, (c) make it measurable, (d) make it simple and straightforward, and (e) make sure it is under the client's control. It is critical that the client provides input into the plan. And, as is the case with any goal-setting or homework, be sure to identify potential obstacles and discuss ways to overcome them.

Clinician:	*So, we need to talk about what you think will help you maintain your sobriety during this time. Do you have some ideas?*
Adolescent:	*I need to stay away from my using friends.*
Clinician:	*That's a good idea, but from what you've told me before, that is not always easy, is it? I think it is important that we talk more about how to avoid them or what to do if you do run into them.*
Adolescent:	*Yes, I'll probably run into them on the weekend.*
Clinician:	*Where do you usually run in to them?*
Adolescent:	*At parties, at the mall, at fast-food places I usually go to.*
Clinician:	*So what usually happens in these situations? How do you end up using?*
Adolescent:	*They'll give me a signal to meet up and we'll go to a bathroom or outside and get high.*

Clinician:	So what will you do now if one of them gives you the signal to meet you in the bathroom or go outside? Couldn't that happen again?
Adolescent:	I guess. But I think I'll be OK.
Clinician:	What could you do so that you're sure you'll be OK during this week? We don't want to leave anything to chance. For example, is there one of these situations that is more difficult than the others to say no in? Like when you go to parties, is everyone typically using?
Adolescent:	No, there are a couple of my friends that won't bother me. They know I've had to go to rehab.
Clinician:	Sounds like those are some good friends. So, you don't necessarily think parties would be any harder to go to and maintain sobriety?
Adolescent:	Not necessarily.
Clinician:	So what could you do if someone gives you the signal?
Adolescent:	I could use those refusal skills we talked about and go hang out with the friends who I know support me not using.
Clinician:	What if they are not at the party, the mall, or wherever you are?
Adolescent:	I'll have my cell phone with me and I could call my sponsor.

4. Develop a backup plan.

Since unexpected events happen in the real world, and maintaining sobriety even for a week will be difficult for someone who has been using continuously, it is important to have backup plans that follow the guidelines outlined above.

Clinician:	I think we've got the basis of a good plan. Let's talk some about a backup plan.
Adolescent:	Well, I actually have several sponsors, and I have them all programmed into my phone.
Clinician:	That's pretty impressive! You mentioned that your main emotional trigger is getting anxious. What are you most likely to feel anxious about and what's a good plan for dealing with your anxiety?
Adolescent:	I just don't like to say no to my friends, because they're my friends, you know? I guess I'm worried they won't be my friends anymore and I won't have someone to hang out with.
Clinician:	Maybe it will help if you go into the weekend saying to yourself that you're not going to use. Because we've just made this agreement, right? And you know it will help you stay out of trouble. Also, you said you have friends that encourage you not to use, and maybe when you are not using it will be possible to make some other friends that do not use.

Adolescent:	*Yeah, that might help.*
Clinician:	*But that's probably not enough. Let's say you go into the weekend telling yourself that you aren't going to use, but then you have urges to use after all and can't get ahold of your sponsors. Then what? I know this might seem like overkill, but I'm just trying to help you think through all this so you can meet your goal of staying sober until our next session.*
Adolescent:	*Well, my girlfriend is usually with me, and I can suggest we go to the dollar movie.*
Clinician:	*And she would support your desire not to use, and leave the party? That would be great! And if she wasn't with you?*
Adolescent:	*Maybe I could ask one of my supportive friends to go with me to the dollar movie?*
Clinician:	*Why don't we go ahead and call your girlfriend and one of your other supportive friends and tell them about your plan and see if they will do what you need? We can practice the call first.*
Adolescent:	*Sure.*
Clinician:	*After that we can review drug refusal skills.*

5. Remind the client of reinforcers for sobriety.

Review the dialogue above and you will see that there are several instances where the clinician reminded the client of his individualized reinforcers for sobriety. In one instance the clinician tied the agreed-upon period of sobriety to an event in the client's life (the probation appointment). Another technique would be to ask the client to volunteer a reason why the agreed-upon sampling period is a good idea. Since tying desired behavior to reinforcers is so important, be sure to summarize the reinforcers for the proposed period of sobriety at the end of the procedure.

Review What Happens in the Next Session

Essentially, Sobriety Sampling becomes a homework assignment for the next session. As with all homework, it is important to discuss how the plan went. Were clients able to follow the plan as outlined? If so, ask them what they did to be successful and praise them. If they were not able to follow the plan, have them tell you why and discuss a new plan for the next session that addresses the obstacles.

UNIT 2: CHAPTER 11: Communication Skills

Rationale

Clients often have difficulty communicating in a positive manner with parents or others in their lives. Poor communication skills can create additional problems at home, in school, and elsewhere. Helping clients improve these skills can enhance the quality of their relationships with peers, parents, and other adults.

The Communication Skills procedure is taught and practiced in A-CRA client sessions and in Caregiver Only and Family Sessions. This procedure helps both clients and their caregivers understand the need to develop positive communication skills and teach them how to improve their communications skills with practice during and between sessions.

Learning Objectives

The learning objectives are to help clients:

- Understand why positive communication skills are important.
- Learn the three parts of positive communication (making an understanding statement, taking partial responsibility, offering to help).
- Become comfortable using the communication skills through practice during and between sessions.

Timing, Audience, and Delivery Method

Communication skills can be taught in individual sessions or in groups. Group sessions offer a good opportunity to have clients role play with each other. It is important in these situations for participants to receive constructive feedback from the facilitator and other group members. Caregivers are also taught these skills, and in a later family session, clients and caregivers practice these skills together (see Caregiver-Adolescent Relationship Skills Sessions [p. 160]). Communication skills training can be scheduled for a particular session or the topic can be woven into a session based on a client's description of problems exacerbated by poor communication. For example, if a client talks about a situation where an interchange with another person escalated because of poor communication skills, it would be ideal to introduce the training. It is important to revisit this skill frequently because it takes practice to learn to generalize this skill to real-life situations.

Materials

Procedure-specific materials include the Communication Skills handout (p. 140); a clipboard, chalkboard, or whiteboard; pens, markers, or chalk; and an easel for presentation of the material.

General Notes for the Clinician

The skills outlined in this section should be taught in the context of real communication problems clients experience with their parents and other people in their lives. Almost every person has room to improve communication skills, and using actual situations during role plays helps illustrate the relevance and generalizability of positive communication skills. Typical topics for communication skills training are curfew, friends, school, juvenile justice requirements, homework, and housework.

Procedural Steps

1. **Discuss why positive communication is important.**
2. **Teach the three positive communication elements (or an appropriate subset).**
   - **Describe or review each of the three components.**
   - **Provide examples of positive communication and conversation skills.**
3. **Do a reverse role play so that you can model positive communication while role playing as the client, and you can observe how the client portrays the communication style of the person you are going to play in the regular role play.**
   - **Ask the client to point out the communication skills that were modeled during the reverse role play, then point out any that were missed.**
   - **Ask the client what was learned by playing the other person.**
4. **Role play exchanges between the client and another person (e.g., a parent or caregiver).**
   - **Praise the client to reinforce efforts and positive communication skills.**
   - **Ask what the client did and did not like about the role play performance.**
   - **Give specific constructive feedback to help improve skills.**
   - **Repeat the role play at least once so the client can incorporate the feedback.**

Detailed Description

1. **Discuss why positive communication is important.**

Take a few minutes at the beginning to introduce the topic and talk about the importance of communication skills. Find out what reinforcers would motivate clients to improve their communication skills. For example, an adolescent might say, "I'm tired of all the yelling at my house" or "I'm always the one that the teacher punishes." Normalize the importance of improving communication skills by noting that all of us can improve them.

Clinician:	*How was your week?*
Adolescent:	*I think I did really well, but my mom is driving me crazy! I've been doing really good lately, but she still won't let me go hang out with my friends this weekend. I might as well be locked up!*
Clinician:	*You sound frustrated and angry with your mom because it doesn't feel like she recognizes how hard you have been working on your recovery.*
Adolescent:	*Yeah! I just don't know what I have to do to show her that she doesn't have to worry about me all the time? It's like I screwed up once and I'm going to pay for it the rest of my life!*
Clinician:	*That's upsetting, isn't it? Sometimes when you get in these situations, positive communication skills can help. Can you tell me why positive communication might be helpful?* [Asking the client why positive communication is helpful might lead to the identification of a client's reinforcer.]
Adolescent:	*Well, as I said, I really get tired of her yelling at me all the time. If she was more positive, that would be better.*

Clinician:	*I think I can show you some ways that will improve the situation; that is, to help decrease the time your mom sounds upset with you. I'm wondering if we could take a look at how a typical conversation about stuff like this goes between you and your mom. Maybe we can work on it a little so that your mom is more ready to listen to you.*
Adolescent:	*What good does it do for her to listen if she still says no?*
Clinician:	*I can't guarantee that she'll say yes, but there's definitely a better chance that she will at least listen and negotiate with you if she doesn't get defensive right from the start. Do you know what I mean by getting defensive?*
Adolescent:	*Yes. It's like you're ready for a fight.*
Clinician:	*That's right. And if Mom is ready for a fight the moment you open your mouth and ask for something, then what are the chances she's going to agree to anything you want?*
Adolescent:	*None.*
Clinician:	*That's right. So if we work on how you talk to her, I think we can improve your chances. Plus, I'd also bet that if you start talking nicer to your mom, she'll start talking nicer back. Can you see how that might work? Are you willing to give this a try?*

2. **Describe the three positive communication elements (or an appropriate subset).**
   - **Describe or review each of the three components.**
   - **Provide examples of positive communication and conversation skills.**

A-CRA has three basic parts to effective communication:

1. Give an understanding statement.
2. Take partial responsibility.
3. Offer to help.

An *understanding statement* brings feelings of empathy into the conversation. It shows others that the speaker is capable of seeing things from another person's perspective and helps the other person understand the speaker's perspective. The effect on the other person is a feeling of validation, which can decrease defensiveness.

A *partial responsibility statement* indicates that the speaker is willing to accept some of the responsibility in creating, or a role in solving, a problem. It does not mean the speaker is accepting blame or blaming anyone else or that it is up to the other person to solve the problem. It merely acknowledges that the speaker shares responsibility for creating or solving a problem.

An *offer to help* is just that—an offer to help solve the problem. Here, the speaker thinks of ways to facilitate cooperation from the other person. Making an offer to help shows the other person that the speaker is willing to compromise. The speaker also needs to understand that it is important to be willing to listen to possible solutions from the other person.

Used together, these three conversation enhancers communicate that one person wants a change in the other's behavior and is willing to be actively involved and supportive in the process. The outcome is decreased defensiveness and more open lines of communication.

Using an actual situation of poor communication between the client and another person, introduce the three A-CRA communication techniques where they would be helpful. The techniques are generic; they can be used to discuss virtually any situation more effectively.

Clinician:	*OK, Gina, let's begin by looking at this handout on communication. [See the handout on p. 140.] It's helpful because it explains the three parts of positive communication skills and gives examples for each part.*
	Let's use the situation where your mom didn't want you to go out. We can focus on that as we come up with examples of how you could use the different parts of positive communication. Then it would be helpful for you to pretend to be your mother while we practice conversation. I'll pretend to be you so I can see how the conversation goes with her now and so I can demonstrate how you might use these new positive communication skills. Then we'll practice what you might say to her using the communication skills while I pretend to be her. It's always easier to do something for real once you've practiced it.
	So you see on the handout that the first step is to make an understanding statement. The understanding statement is really a big part of improving communication because you are first trying to see where the other person is coming from. When you do that, it increases the possibility that the person will listen to you. First consider the other person's perspective. Why do you think your mom wouldn't want you to go out?
Adolescent:	*She doesn't want me to get in trouble.*
Clinician:	*Why does she think you are going to get in trouble?*
Adolescent:	*Because she thinks I'm going to use again and do something stupid and get in trouble again.*
Clinician:	*Sounds like you know her well. You could say, "I understand that you're afraid I'll use again and get in trouble."*
	What is your perspective? Because you want to tell her where you are coming from so she understands you better. So, from your perspective, what would you say?
Adolescent:	*I need time to be with my friends. I get bored being home all the time.*
Clinician:	*So we answered all these questions. Why do you want to go out? Because you want to spend time with your friends and you get bored at home. That is your perspective and it makes sense. What would you like from her in this situation?*
Adolescent:	*I want her to trust me to go out and do OK. I don't want her always yelling at me about how I messed up.*

Clinician: *OK. I understand how you feel. Next, as you see on the handout, when you make a request, it needs to be brief, positive, and specific. The reason it needs to follow those rules is that if you are brief, it will be easier for someone to get the main message you want to communicate. If you tell a person something long and drawn out, the person may get lost. You want to say it in a* positive, *nice way so the person is more likely to listen to what you are asking for. If you ask for something in a negative way, the person may respond in a negative way. Also, stating your request in a positive way means asking for something you want as opposed to saying what you don't want anymore. It's just easier for the other person to understand it that way. And you need to be* specific *so everyone understands where you are coming from.*

For example, when you ask if you can go out, your mom may not know what you mean by "going out" and could think all kinds of things. And we need to think of how to turn "I don't want you yelling at me" into something stated positively. OK, following the rules of being brief, positive, and specific, what might you say to your mom?

Adolescent: [As himself.] *I want to go over to Keira's Friday night and hang out with her and Michelle. Can we talk about this?*

Clinician: [As mom.] *What would you plan on doing there?*

Adolescent: [As himself.] *I don't know . . . probably just watch some shows.*

Clinician: [As mom.] *Do Keira and Michelle use?*

Adolescent: [As himself.] *Maybe sometimes, but they don't use around me because they know that I've gotten in trouble.*

Clinician: [Out of role play.] *If you feel confident they won't use, then you could mention that too. What do you think?*

Adolescent: *I can see Mom liking that.*

Clinician: *OK. That's really good. So what you might say using the understanding statement is, "Mom, I* understand *you worry about me when I go out. But I would really appreciate it if you would let me go to Keira's Friday night. Michelle's coming too and we could watch some shows and none of us will use." How do you think your mom might respond to asking in that way?*

Adolescent: *It is definitely nicer and it says real clear that we aren't going to use. I guess it would still depend on her mood, though.*

Clinician: *Yes, it might. But a lot of other clients I've worked with have found these skills really helpful. In fact, a lot of parents tell me that they have appreciated how communication has improved in the family.*

Let's move on to the second part, taking partial responsibility. Taking partial responsibility is when you say how something you did might have contributed to the problem. When you do this, it shows you don't blame the other person for the problem. You want to make sure and say something like this in any situation where the person you are talking to sees you as part of the problem. After taking partial responsibility, it's good to restate the request just to keep everyone on track with what you're talking about. So, adding the partial responsibility statement, you might say something like, "Mom, I understand you worry about me when I go out because I have messed up in the past, gotten in trouble, and missed my curfew. But I would really appreciate it if you would let me go to Keira's Friday night. Michelle's coming too and we could watch some shows." Do you understand how I restated the request?

Adolescent: *Yeah, you said something about how you messed up in the past and missed curfew.*

Clinician: *That's right! Now, let's talk about the last part, which is making an offer to help. It isn't too tough. It's just figuring out what you can do to make it more likely you get what you want—to get to go over to your friend's house. What you want to do is make sure your mom is involved in the solution so she is more likely to come to a decision that both of you like. So for this part you want to offer a few suggestions, such as, "If there is anything I can do to help you feel better about this, like setting the alarm on my phone for when I need to leave, or responding right away if you text me. Or if there is anything else you can think of, I'm willing to listen." In that last part, I opened it up to her so she could give a few suggestions for solving the problem to make things easier for her. I also said I would listen or consider it. That way I am not saying I will just do whatever she says as a suggestion, but I will listen to what she says and come to a compromise, something that works out for both of you. So it gives you something closer to what you want. Now let's review the three parts: first an understanding statement, then the partial responsibility statement, then the offer to help. OK?*

Adolescent: *It seems like a lot to remember.*

Clinician: *I know it does at first. I promise it will get easier and that's why we practice.*

3. **Do a reverse role play so that you can model positive communication while role playing as the client, and you can observe how the client portrays the communication style of the person you are going to play in the regular role play.**
   - **Ask the client to point out the communication skills that were modeled during the reverse role play, then point out any that were missed.**
   - **Ask the client what was learned by playing the other person.**

Clinician: *I've found it's helpful, before we practice some more, for me to pretend to be you and you to pretend to be your mom. This is what we call a reverse role play. Just pretend that we're having the beginning of the conversation you had with your mom about going out. Make believe you're your mom. [As adolescent.] Hi, Mom. Can I talk to you a minute?*

Adolescent: [As mom.] *I'm kind of busy. What do you want?*

Clinician: [As adolescent.] *Mom, I understand that you worry about me a lot. But I'd really love to be able to go and hang out with Keira and Michelle Friday night. You know that neither of them will use when I'm with them.*

Adolescent: [As mom.] *But how do I know that you won't use again?*

Clinician: [As adolescent repeating the understanding statement and modeling the addition of partial responsibility and offer to help.] *I can understand why you don't trust me. I know in the past I've smoked when I've gone out, but I'm not doing that anymore. What will help you to trust me when I go out?*

Adolescent: [As mom.] *You need to call or text me every hour.*

Clinician: [As adolescent.] *OK, I guess I can do that. Thanks, Mom.* [Out of role play] *So what did you think about how that conversation went? And can you specifically point out where I used some of the three positive types of communication we just went over?*

Adolescent: *It sounds nicer if you say, "I understand," and that was one of the three parts. And I think my mom would be more willing to listen if I said it like you did.*

Clinician: *That's right. Can you say more about how it made you feel when I said, "I understand"?* [Asks what the adolescent learned about being on the receiving end of an understanding question. Identifies other communication skills used during the reverse role play and asks how they made the client feel.]

Adolescent: *Like I'd probably listen to more of what you had to say.*

Clinician: *Excellent! We're definitely trying to keep the lines of communication open so that you and your mom can talk in a positive way and so that you're more likely to get what you want.*

Adolescent: *This might freak my mom out because she's always saying that I don't care about how she worries about me.*

Clinician: *Well, then you'll definitely get her attention with an understanding statement! But we'll practice it so that you can say it in your own words. You don't even have to say, "I understand" if that sounds too strange.*

Adolescent: *It sounds strange, but it's easy to remember.*

4. **Role play exchanges between the client and another person (e.g., a parent or caregiver).**
   - **Praise the client to reinforce efforts and positive communication skills.**
   - **Ask what the client did and did not like about the role play performance.**
   - **Give specific constructive feedback to help improve skills.**
   - **Repeat the role play at least once so the client can incorporate the feedback.**

   Clinician: *OK. We want you to have the chance to practice using the elements of positive communication. But before we do, let's review how to make a request. It's helpful to make your request in a way that's brief, positive, and specific. Again, the whole point of bothering with these rules is because they help us get something that we want. Let's work on this together with an example. Let's take your request to hang out with your friends on Friday night. It's already brief, so that's* *good. And you're letting your mom know what you'd like to do as opposed to what you don't want to do anymore. In other words, it's great that you're saying that you want to hang out with two of your friends because that's considered a positive statement. A negative statement would be saying that you won't hang out with your using friends. The problem with the negative statement is that it doesn't say who you will be hanging out with—and I'm sure your mom would want to know. Does that sound too confusing?*

Adolescent: *No, I get it. I can do that.*

Clinician: *Great! Let's see now if we can make your request more specific. I bet your mom will be less worried about you if she knows exactly what you want to do with your friends. So how could you make your request to hang out with your friends on Friday night more specific?*

Adolescent: *I'm not sure I understand what you mean.*

Clinician: *We talk to parents about knowing the who, what, when, and where when their kids go out. I think it would help to tell her some of that information. You've already talked about who and where. Wouldn't she have less to worry about if she knew* what *you were doing and* when *you were coming home? And then wouldn't she be more likely to agree to let you go?*

Adolescent: *Maybe.*

Clinician: *You're right; there's no guarantee. But I bet your chances are better. With that in mind, what should we change about your request to hang out with Keira and Michelle on Friday night? What would Mom like to know?*

Adolescent: *I could tell her that I want to go to Michelle's house to listen to music and watch movies.*

Clinician: *Good. Since it's important to you to build back your mom's trust, you know it's important that you follow through with what you're requesting.*

Adolescent: *Of course! I can't afford to get into any more trouble.*

Clinician: *Yes, I know it's really important to you to stay out of trouble, and I think these positive communication skills can really help you with that too. You've been doing a great job of staying out of trouble. . . . All right, the only things you might add to make your request more specific are the times you'll be out and how you plan to get there.*

Adolescent: *Well, she knows I have to take the city bus or the train everywhere.*

Clinician: *I bet it would help if you told your mom these details. Then she'd know exactly what you'd be doing and where . . . and who you'd be with. I'd also suggest that you mention what time you'd be getting home—and how, as well as whether any adults will be there. Can you put that all together and talk to me like I'm your mom?*

Adolescent:	[In role play.] *Mom, I understand that you worry about me a lot, but I haven't gotten into any trouble in over a month now. So, could I please go to Michelle's house Friday night? I'll take the bus both ways and be home by 11:00.*
Clinician:	[As mom.] *That sounds kind of late. And will Michelle's mom be there?*
Adolescent:	[In role play.] *Her mom will be there for sure.*
Clinician:	[As mom.] *Maybe. I need to think about it a little.*
Adolescent:	[In role play.] *OK. Thanks.*
Clinician:	[Outside of role play.] *Good job! What did you like about your conversation?*
Adolescent:	*I didn't get upset. And I knew what I wanted to say, so it wasn't too hard.*
Clinician:	*You made it look easy! And you included a number of the things we talked about adding. Can you tell me some of those things?*
Adolescent:	*I was specific; I told her how I was going to get there, and when I'd get home.*
Clinician:	*Yes. That was excellent. And you were brief and positive. There was just one part that could have been a little more specific. I didn't hear you mention what you'd be doing that night with your friends.*
Adolescent:	*Oh, right.*
Clinician:	*You also started off with an understanding statement. Do you know what you said?*
Adolescent:	*I think I said the same thing I did before, something about her worrying about me.*
Clinician:	*Good. That's right. Now let's try it again. Based on the feedback I've given you, what would you like to add or change this time?*
Adolescent:	*I'm going to tell her what I'll be doing with my friends.*
Clinician:	*Take it away!*
Adolescent:	[In role play.] *Mom, can I talk to you a minute? I understand that you worry about me a lot, but I've been doing really good lately. So is it OK if I go over to Michelle's house Friday night until about 11:00? I'll ride the bus both ways. Oh—and Michelle's mom will be there the whole time. And we're going to just listen to music and watch a movie.*
Clinician:	[As mom.] *Well, I don't know. I guess you have been doing good. I like those two friends. You said Michelle's mom is going to be there?*

Adolescent: [In role play.] *Yes. Do you want to call her?*

Clinician: [Out of role play.] *Wow! You get better and better each time. I like how you even went ahead and suggested that your mom call Michelle's mom. This is getting into another part of positive communication that we talked about briefly: offering to help. I'll get back to that in a minute, though. First—tell me what you liked about your conversation.*

Adolescent: *I remembered to tell her what I was going to be doing at Michelle's. I think I did everything else, too. I was real specific and positive, and I said, "I understand."*

Clinician: *You sure did! Let's move on, then. Remember when we talked about accepting partial responsibility? Do you remember what this means?*

Adolescent: *I'm not sure what you mean. Am I supposed to take partial responsibility for wanting to go out? No, that doesn't sound right. I'm not sure what to say.*

Clinician: *It is a tough one to sort out at first. I'll illustrate with an example in a minute. But as far as what you're supposed to accept partial responsibility for, usually it's for part of the original problem. In this situation, the problem is that your mom won't let you to your friend's house. Can you see what role you played in that? What could you accept responsibility for?*

Adolescent: *She used to let me go over to Michelle's before I got into trouble for smoking weed. Maybe I could accept responsibility for her not trusting me?*

Clinician: *If you're comfortable doing that, it would be perfect. You could say something like, "Mom, I know that one of the reasons you don't want me to go to Michelle's is because I used weed. But I'm not doing that anymore, so. . . ."*

Adolescent: *It's OK to accept some responsibility and then explain why she doesn't need to worry anymore?*

Clinician: *Yes. It's good to reassure her.*

Adolescent: *I can do that.*

Clinician: *As long as you're on a roll, let's review the last part of a positive communication. Do you remember what it is? You actually did something quite similar to this earlier.*

Adolescent: *Was it the offer to help?*

Clinician: *Yes. When you suggested that your mom call Michelle's mother to make sure the mother was going to be there—that was an offer to help. An even better offer might be, "Mom, do you want to call Michelle's mom so you can make sure she's going to be at home Friday night? I can get her phone number from Michelle." Besides being a nice thing to do, an offer to help makes it easier for the other person to give you what you want. But I don't want to put words in your mouth. What other types of offers to help could you make in this situation?*

Adolescent:	*Sometimes my mom likes it when I call her a couple of times while I'm at a friend's house, I guess so that she knows I'm OK.*
Clinician:	*Excellent idea. You could offer to call her from Michelle's a couple of times Friday night. I should also add that sometimes a good offer to help is simply, "How can I help?" The other person might have some clear idea of what they need from you. Let's role play this again. I'll practice using all of the pieces here, but don't worry if you miss some of them when you're having a conversation out in the real world. Before we get started though, can you tell me when would be a good time to have this conversation with your mom? When are the two of you likely to be in good moods?*
Adolescent:	*She's never in a good mood anymore.*
Clinician:	*OK. So what's the best of the bad-mood times for her?*
Adolescent:	*Huh?*
Clinician:	*Even if she's in a bad mood all of the time, there are different degrees of bad.*
Adolescent:	*I get it. And maybe she's not always in a bad mood. Anyway, I have the best luck talking to her after dinner.*
Clinician:	*OK. So when would like to have the talk with your mom?*
Adolescent:	*I think I could do it tonight after dinner.*
Clinician:	*That sounds good! What could get in the way of you doing that?*
Adolescent:	*My mom could be in a bad mood.*
Clinician:	*Yes, that could happen. What would you do in that case?*
Adolescent:	*I could hold off and try tomorrow night.*
Clinician:	*That makes sense. Good. Let's do it! Let's pretend that we've just finished dinner.*
Adolescent:	[In role-play.] *Mom, I've got something to ask you. I understand that you worry about me a lot because of the trouble I've gotten in. But I haven't been in any trouble for a long time now. So is it OK for me to go to Michelle's Friday night? I'll take the bus and be home by 11:00. Here's the phone number for Michelle's mom in case you want to talk to her.*
Clinician:	[As mom.] *Just because you haven't been in trouble for a month doesn't mean that I have nothing to worry about.*
Adolescent:	[In role play.] *I know. It doesn't help that I went behind your back and did those things. But I'm not hanging around with those kids anymore.*

Clinician: [As mom.] *If you were still hanging out with them you'd never get any privileges anymore. Let me think about it.*

Adolescent: [In role play.] *I guess I'll check back with you later then. Thanks for thinking about it.*

Clinician: [Out of role play.] *Good job! Tell me what you liked about your conversation.*

Adolescent: *I used an understanding statement and I offered to help by giving her the phone number. I think I accepted partial responsibility, didn't I?*

Clinician: *Yes. You said you knew it didn't help the situation by going behind your mom's back. That was really good. What about the brief, positive, and specific guidelines?*

Adolescent: *I think I did those when I talked about the time and the transportation, and when I said what I was going to be doing, and . . . oh wait! I didn't say what we were going to be doing that night. I keep forgetting that!*

Clinician: *It might not be necessary. Your mom might agree to let you go anyway. The partial responsibility and the understanding statements themselves are very powerful. And remember that you don't have to use all of these pieces of a positive communication. I also liked how you thanked her for considering your request.*

Adolescent: *But if I can't remember to say it all in here, how am I going to remember to do it with my mom?*

Clinician: *That's why we keep practicing here, so that you're more likely to remember to say what you want to with your mom. Let's do it again, and how about you add that piece this time? Also, I'm going to give you a little bit of a harder time, just in case your mom does. This will be a good test. You've been doing such a good job of not getting upset that I know you'll be able to handle this. [They role play again, and this time the clinician plays the mom as much tougher to convince, since it is important to prepare the client for the most difficult situation. You can also suggest that clients write out what they want to say if they are concerned about forgetting.]*

Additional Notes

- The client does not have to use the exact words "I understand" to convey understanding. Using this statement may not be a fit for the client depending on his or her culture and background. The goal is for the client to use the spirit of an understanding statement. For example, a client might say, "Mom, I get that you think I'm gonna end up in trouble by staying out at night. . . ."
- Recognize the difference between one-sided and two-sided role plays. In a one-sided role-play, clients or clinicians have only a one-sided conversation. For example, the client may state what he or she plans to say and the clinician might give the client feedback, but there is no actual back and forth dialogue between the two parties. It is important that role plays are two-sided, with both the clinician and client participating in the interchange.

- A segment of a role play will typically last under two minutes; then you will stop it and give feedback.
- You need to find something that the client did during the role play that can be praised.
- Also provide specific feedback about how the client could improve use of the communication skills.
- Homework is assigned to try out the new communication skills with a particular person the next week. In the next session, it is important to review how the practice went. Ask the client, "How did it go? What was different about the conversation compared to how it usually feels?"
- As the session is winding down and you are transitioning to the homework assignment, the client may not feel ready to talk to the identified person (e.g., Mom). In this case, you could see whether the client is willing to try out the communication skills with someone else first, like another parent or peer, just to get some practice with the skills. The ultimate goal will still be to talk to the mother, but this is a way of using successive approximations to get to that goal.

Working with a Resistant Adolescent on Communication Skills

In this manual, because we have to illustrate all the components of the skill, we often use examples with clients who appear compliant. Sometimes, clinicians are worried about whether a skill or procedure will work with resistant clients, especially adolescents. We do find that clinicians who are skilled in using A-CRA are able to reduce a client's resistance because they do not use confrontation and they communicate that the client is in control. The following dialogue illustrates how a clinician might approach communication skills training with a resistant adolescent. In this case, the adolescent has already attended a few sessions, and at the last session he rated school and his relationship with his parents low on the Happiness Scale.

Clinician:	*How was your week?*
Adolescent:	*OK, I guess.* [Adolescent responds with short answers, looking down and not wanting to talk.]
Clinician:	*How is school going?*
Adolescent:	*OK.* [Continues to give short answers.]
Clinician:	*Tell me how you and your mom are doing.* [Clinician asks open-ended questions.]
Adolescent:	*She's getting on my nerves.*
Clinician:	*Can you tell me more about that?*
Adolescent:	*She's constantly complaining.*
Clinician:	*What kind of things is she complaining about?*
Adolescent:	*You name it.*
Clinician:	[Clinician sits in silence for a while, giving the client an opportunity to respond without constant questioning. After a short time the clinician tries to elicit details.] *Can you give me an example?*

Adolescent:	*Well, like last night, she was angry with me because I didn't get home by curfew.*
Clinician:	*What was her response when you got home?* [The clinician is trying to find something that the client would invest time in to work on and does not question why the adolescent was not home by curfew.]
Adolescent:	*She started yelling at me.*
Clinician:	*Is that her typical response when she is angry?*
Adolescent:	*Yeah.*
Clinician:	*Then how do you respond?* [Tries to assess the current state of communication between the adolescent and the parent.]
Adolescent:	*I either yell back or ignore her. She is so controlling—always wanting to know my every move.*
Clinician:	*That sounds as if that is difficult for you. Wonder why she does that?*
Adolescent:	*'Cause she doesn't trust me.*
Clinician:	*What do you think is the reason she doesn't trust you?*
Adolescent:	*'Cause I came home drunk about 2 weeks ago. Now she is threatening never to let me drive her car.*
Clinician:	*Were you driving when you were drunk?*
Adolescent:	*Yeah, I had to get home. She wouldn't let me stay at my friends' because she doesn't like them and I needed to get the car back.*
Clinician:	*Why do you think your mom is angry about that?* [Clinician encourages the adolescent to try to verbalize his mom's feelings rather than takes sides with the mother.]
Adolescent:	*'Cause she is concerned and worried about me. I mean I can understand that. She is just weird about how she handles everything.*
Clinician:	*So basically you can understand where your mom is coming from, but you just aren't happy with the way she communicates with you.* [Clinician introduces reflection.]
Adolescent:	*Yeah, she is just always yelling at me.*
Clinician:	*And when she starts yelling, you either start yelling back or walk away?*
Adolescent:	*Yeah.*

Clinician:	*It sounds as if using her car is very important to you and not being able to use it would be a big deal for you.* [Clinician continues to try to motivate the client to work on communication skills.]
Adolescent:	*Yeah! I need it to get to school and work and to go out with my friends.*
Clinician:	*Wow. It wouldn't be good if you couldn't use it. Let's talk about how you can talk to her to get your point across so she will listen.* [Clinician does not mention communication skills per se but still explains how better communication can help improve outcomes for the client.]
Adolescent:	*Yeah, OK, like that's going to happen.*
Clinician:	*We can try. What do we have to lose? I want to be able to help you have a voice and be heard.*
Adolescent:	*Whatever.*
Clinician:	*She will be coming to therapy in a couple of weeks with you, and that would be a good time to try to talk about some issues you have. While both of you are here, I don't want to have you both yelling at each other the whole time and not hearing the other. So let's talk about how we can get your point across. Let's try this out. I'm going to pretend to be your mom. Talk to me, and tell me why you think I should not take your car away.* [Assesses state of communication further.]
Adolescent:	*I think she is being unfair, and it's bull.*
Clinician:	*OK, but talk to me as if I am your mom. I'll be your mom.* [As mom.] *You're not taking my car anymore.*
Adolescent:	[In role play.] *That is bull, Mom, and you know it.*
Clinician:	[As mom.] *You just keep messing up. I need that car too, you know. You're going to have an accident and get in trouble. I can't have that.*
Adolescent:	[In role play.] *How am I supposed to get anywhere? I've got places I need to go. Are you going to take me everywhere?*
Clinician:	[As mom.] *I don't think that's my problem.*
Adolescent:	[Out of role play.] *See what I mean!*
Clinician:	*Good! That gave me an idea of how your conversations might go. Thanks for doing that.* [Clinician offers praise and positive reinforcement even though the response is less than desired.] *OK. There are a couple of things that I want you to try. First thing is to try to stay positive. Sometimes when people feel on the attack, they get defensive and fight back. And our goal is to try to get her to hear you. The other thing is to try to understand where she is coming from and communicate that. You said earlier that you could understand that she worries when you drink and drive. So you can start by saying to her in a calm voice, "Mom, I understand that you worry and are concerned when I drink and drive."*

[Clinician uses modeling and coaching.] *Let me pretend to be you again and you pretend to be your mom, and I'll show you what I mean. I'll start out.* [In reverse role play as adolescent.] *Mom, I understand that you are worried about me, but I don't think you need to take the car away.*

Adolescent: [As mom.] *But you just keep messing up.*

Clinician: [Out of role play.] *Thanks for working with me.* [Continues praising for effort and participation.] *Besides an understanding statement, it helps to get your point across if you take partial responsibility for your half of what is going on. Then make an offer to come to some kind of agreement or resolution about the car. So I'm going to respond to your mom this way.* [In reverse role play as adolescent.] *"Mom, I understand that you are worried when I drink and drive. I made a mistake and drove that night. I know that was bad judgment on my part. I was just worried about not having the car home on time, and I know that I should have probably just called you but I was scared. Is there anything that I can do to reassure you that I won't make that same mistake?"*

Adolescent: *That's not how I talk! That's just not me. Man, please . . . my mom would already be yelling.*

Clinician: *That's a good point. It's kind of weird to talk like that, isn't it? I am going to go over the same stuff with your mom as well, with the goal of having you be able to hear each other's point of view and having you both get what you want. I know you said that it wasn't you, but I'd like for you to give it a try . . . in your words. How about it? I'll be your mom this time around. Talk to me about the issue of the car, starting with the understanding statement, because I think we will have some luck with this and I want to help you get what you want.* [Reinforces rationale for working on communication skills.]

Adolescent: [Beginning the role play as himself.] *Mom, I understand that you're worried when I drink and drive.*

Clinician: [Clinician interrupts to help shape.] *Great! Keep going by talking about how you take some responsibility for the night you drank and drove.*

Adolescent: *And I know that I shouldn't be doing that. It was wrong.*

Clinician: *Tell her what having a car means to you.* [Helps client through communication skills while shaping, coaching, and encouraging.]

Adolescent: *I need to have a car at times to get to school and work and see my friends. I don't want to mess it up by driving drunk, and I really don't want you to take it away from me.*

Clinician: *Fantastic!* [Offers praise and positive reinforcement for any effort no matter how big or small.] *Now offer to help or come to some kind of compromise.*

Adolescent: *Since my car is so important to me, how can I get you to trust me again?*

Clinician: *You did great! How did that feel?*

Adolescent: *Very different.*

Clinician: *But you came up with such good things! And I think if your mom heard you talk like that, she would hear what you had to say about the issue and would be willing to sit down and talk about it. And I will be here to help you. I know it feels weird, and it takes practice. People are more receptive to hearing what you have to say if you aren't yelling and are trying to understand where they are coming from. Now, let's try taking that from the top and I'll respond as your mom.* [They do a two-sided role play with the clinician as mom.]

By the end of the session, the clinician has reviewed the important parts of communication, conducted two-sided role plays with the adolescent, urged him to practice these skills at home so that he will learn to generalize skills outside of sessions, and praised the adolescent for participation and attendance.

Communication Skills

The goal of using communication skills is to be able to get your message across to another person to help you get what you want. Using these communication skills should enable people to compromise or agree on a solution to a problem. When everyone agrees on a solution, compliance by both sides and contentment with the solution are more likely. It is important to stay positive during the communication skills training and avoid blaming.

Understanding statement. The goal of the understanding statement is to open up communication and show that you are aware of another person's thoughts on a problem. That is:

- **Come from the other person's perspective.**
  Example: "Mom, I understand you would like my room cleaned because it is a real mess, and you would like the house to be clean when friends come over."
- **Come from your perspective.**
  Example: "But Jimmy is having a birthday party at his house, and I have not seen Jimmy for a while, so I would really like to go."
- **Make a request (a request should be brief, positive, and specific).**
  Example: "I would really appreciate it if you would let me clean my room later tonight, maybe around 8 p.m. when I get home."

Partial responsibility. The goal of the statement of partial responsibility is to avoid blaming the other person. Remember to state how you or the other person see yourselves fitting into the problem or solution. That is:

- **How do you fit into the problem?**
  Example: "I know I made a real mess by not putting my clothes away, and I have not always followed through with cleaning my room, and I am sorry about that."
- **Repeat the request (optional).**
  Example: "But I would really appreciate if you would let me clean my room around 8 p.m. tonight after I get home from Jimmy's party."

Offer to help. The offer to help is used to show that you are willing to work on a solution that works for everyone and that you would like input from others on possible solutions. That is:

- **Offer several possible solutions.**
  Example: "If there is anything I can do to help make that happen—help out with another chore around the house, help out with dinner, or just do a quick 10-minute cleaning for now and do the rest later—I would really appreciate it."
- **State your openness to listen to and consider the other person's ideas.**
  Example: "Or if there is anything that you can think of, I would be willing to listen."

Following the offer to help, the other person may try to compromise on a solution or do some problem solving. It may be necessary to go through the communication skills again to state your point.

UNIT 2: CHAPTER 12: Problem Solving

Rationale

Problem solving skills are valuable beyond the treatment experience. Training clients in these skills teaches them how to handle the inevitable problems everyone faces in life. These are skills that can improve quality of life and also might reduce the reliance on alcohol or drugs to cope with problems. Learning these skills can also increase clients' sense of self-efficacy and self-esteem. Clients are taught that no matter how large a problem may appear, it can always be broken down into small steps and conquered.

Learning Objectives

The learning objectives are to help clients:

- Understand why improving problem solving skills can help them in recovery and life.
- Learn all seven steps of the Problem Solving procedure.

Timing, Audience, and Delivery Method

Problem solving skills training takes place during an individual client session, during the Caregiver Only Session, and during a Family session. It can be scheduled for a particular session with the client or the topic can be introduced naturally when the client brings up a problem during a session. Thereafter, every time the client brings up a problem situation, the clinician can reintroduce the Problem Solving procedure, and together they can work through the steps to generate solutions and a homework task related to the homework. Note that Problem Solving is another procedure that works well in client groups because members of a group can be very helpful in generating possible solutions during the brainstorming step of the procedure. See the description of the Caregiver Only Sessions and the Family Session for the timing for these sessions.

Materials

Procedure-specific materials include a clipboard; chalkboard; whiteboard; pens, markers, or chalk; an easel (optional); and the How Do I Solve This Problem? form (p. 149).

General Notes for the Clinician

Maintain a positive atmosphere for change throughout the Problem Solving procedure. This positive atmosphere is created by a positive demeanor, an enthusiastic tone of voice, positive expectations for change (a "Yes, you can!" attitude), and praise for the client's efforts. Because problem solving techniques are best learned through practice, listen carefully to the client during sessions for opportunities to use this procedure.

A Problem Solving form, How Do I Solve This Problem?, is at the end of this section. Memorize the steps in the Problem Solving procedure and give copies of the form to the client to complete for reference. While clients do not have to write in the answer to each step as you are teaching the procedure, it will be helpful for them to have a written example of the completed steps. Either you can write it out or have the client do so (if able and willing) once you have finished teaching the steps. The Problem Solving procedure used in this manual is based on the problem solving approach introduced by D'Zurilla and Goldfried (1971) and the CRA work of Meyers and Smith (1995).

Procedural Steps

1. **Introduce (or reintroduce) the technique to the client. Provide the rationale for the procedure.**
2. **Describe each of the seven steps of the Problem Solving procedure (or if a review, ask the client to describe them).**
3. **Conduct the Problem Solving procedure using all seven steps below:**
    *   **Define the problem narrowly.**
    *   **Brainstorm possible solutions.**
    *   **Eliminate undesired suggestions.**
    *   **Select one potential solution that the client can imagine doing in the next week.**
    *   **Generate possible obstacles to that solution.**
    *   **Address each obstacle.**
    *   **Jointly develop a homework task related to the chosen solution.**

Detailed Description

1. **Introduce (or reintroduce) the technique to the client. Provide a rationale for the procedure.**

Below is an example of how the procedure might be introduced prior to a particular problem being raised. Note the rationale for learning the procedure.

> **Clinician:** *Today, Jim, we are going to talk about a technique you can use to solve problems that come up. This technique will be helpful to address not only the problems you encounter during the time you are meeting with me, but problems you will encounter throughout your life, when you're not going through treatment. Often, it seems like the problems we have are overwhelming, but I'm going to show you how to break down solutions to problems into smaller steps that will be easier for you to achieve so that you can make progress toward solving your problems. We'll also talk about the obstacles you encounter as you attempt to solve problems and work on possible solutions for these obstacles.*

The need for problem solving training often emerges naturally; for example:

> **Clinician:** *Tomeka, it sounds as if you have a problem. You're really concerned about bringing your math grade up. You've tried to do it on your own, but it's not working. We can work on this procedure called Problem Solving that can really help you address this problem and other ones that you run in to. All of us encounter problems in our daily lives and this is a technique for breaking problems into smaller steps so that we can make progress toward overcoming them.*

2. **Describe each of the seven steps of the Problem Solving procedure (or if a review, ask the client to describe them).**

The clinician names and explains each of the seven steps of the Problem Solving procedure (see the list below). This explanation can be done before starting to work on a specific problem or while showing the client how to solve a specific problem. You want the client to understand what it takes to complete each step because the goal is to be able to complete the procedure independently. Help the client understand that all seven steps are important when attempting to solve a problem. Be sure to give the client the How Do I Solve This Problem? form as you describe each step of the procedure.

3. **Conduct the Problem Solving procedure using all seven steps below:**
   - **Define the problem narrowly.** This makes the problem manageable.
   - **Brainstorm possible solutions.** Come up with at least five solutions, but even more is better. All possible solutions should be written down. Encourage the client to think outside the box, and if the client gets stuck, feel free to jump in with possible solutions; the client will be able to eliminate unwanted solutions in the next step.
   - **Eliminate undesired suggestions.** Clients can feel free to generate a lot of possible solutions because they will be able to cross out ones they really would not do or ones that are not possible to do in the coming week.
   - **Select one potential solution that the client can imagine doing in the next week.**
   - **Generate possible obstacles to that solution.** Be sure the client is generating obstacles to the chosen solution—not to the original problem.
   - **Address each obstacle.** This is done just as in the Homework procedure—to help plan for challenges that might occur and how they will be addressed.
   - **Jointly develop a homework task related to the chosen solution.** It will be important to select a solution or several small steps that can be completed during the following week.

The first step is to define the problem narrowly.

It takes practice to learn how to narrow the problem, but this is an important step since it increases the chances that progress can be made in a short period of time. The clinician's role is to help guide or shape the client's responses until the problem is defined in a way that short-term solutions can help ameliorate a more complex problem. For example, it is not possible to change a failing grade to a passing grade in one week or to get off probation in even a few weeks—it will take concerted effort over a period of time to completely resolve these problems. Defining the problem narrowly is defining it in terms of behaviors that occur on a day-to-day or week-to-week basis; small pieces of the bigger problem that can be more easily targeted for change. See the example below:

Clinician:	*Joe, tell me more about how you're doing in math. I know you said you were failing, but tell me more about how your grade got where it is.*
Adolescent:	*We have had two math tests so far. I got a 48 on the first one, so I tried to study really hard for the second. I got a 32. If I fail the next two tests, I will have to repeat freshman math.*
Clinician:	*Joe, I'm sorry to hear about this—you sound like you're really worried. I think I can help you with a plan to improve your grade. First of all, we need to narrow down the problem so that it is something you can manage in a short period of time. There are lots of things that go into improving a grade in a class and we need to tackle something that you can see some progress in. What are some of the things that might be contributing to your difficulty in passing the tests? Can you think of any?*
Adolescent:	*Well, when I don't understand something, I don't like to raise my hand in class. I would rather try to figure it out on my own. I also like to watch TV, so when I do*

my homework, the TV is on; and my brother bothers me when I'm trying to study, and I don't always finish my work.

Clinician: *So, I'm hearing you talk about two issues. One is that you do not always understand what the teacher is trying to teach in math class. The second one is that it sounds like you are having trouble doing your homework and may be handing in work that isn't finished? Do these two issues sound like problems that are contributing to your poor test grades?*

Adolescent: *Yes, I think so.*

Clinician: *You know, a lot of schools will find tutors for students who ask for them, and tutors can be really helpful when there is math you do not understand because it is someone who works one on one with you. What do you think about trying to find out whether the school can assign you a tutor? Or is there something else that you would want to try to help with your tests?*

Adolescent: *A tutor might help. But I also think that I need to get better at doing my homework.*

Clinician: *OK. Well, we can make a plan to work on both of these issues this week or just work on one this week and add the other next week. What do you think?*

Adolescent: *I'd like to get better at my homework.*

Clinician: *OK. We can work on that. What does it mean to get better at your homework?*

Adolescent: *Well, it means I need to complete it each day.*

Clinician: *So how about we say the problem we are going to work on next week is "I need to finish my math homework every day." That seems like something manageable that will help with the bigger problem of poor math tests. What do you think?*

Adolescent: *Sounds OK to me.*

The second step is to ask the client to brainstorm possible solutions for solving the problem.

Use brainstorming to generate as many potential solutions to the problem as possible. Follow two important rules for brainstorming:

- Do not criticize any of the potential solutions. It does not matter whether they sound like something the client would never do or whether they are something that has already been tried.
- Go for quantity (at least eight possible solutions).

Write all possible solutions on a whiteboard or a big piece of paper. Do not worry about specificity at this point; you can help the client get more specific once a solution is chosen.

Clinician: *The next thing to do is to think of as many solutions as you can without judging them. Remember, we don't want to eliminate any of the possible solutions yet. What ideas do you have?*

Adolescent:	Maybe studying away from the TV or at the library so my brother doesn't bother me.
Clinician:	Good! What else?
Adolescent:	Maybe I could do my homework with my friend John. He seems to do well on his tests.
Clinician:	That's good. Let's keep going. Remember that you can come up with all kinds of ideas now. We will eliminate ones that you don't think will work in the next step.
Adolescent:	I could do my math homework in study hall.
Clinician:	OK, I'm writing these on the white board. We have four now. Can you think of some other possibilities?
Adolescent:	Sometimes we have a little time toward the end of math class—I could start my homework then.
Clinician:	Good! Maybe then you could also ask your teacher for help if you didn't understand something. What else?
Adolescent:	I could also say I wouldn't watch any TV until I was finished with my homework.
Clinician:	OK. Sounds good. Can you think of a couple more?
Adolescent:	It might help if I didn't have my phone with me. I get distracted really easily.
Clinician:	You've done really well. Let me add a possible solution. What about if you did homework before school?

The third step is to eliminate undesired suggestions.

Help the client narrow down the list of alternatives. First, the client should eliminate any solutions that he or she does not feel comfortable trying. Tell the client that no explanations are necessary for eliminating any alternatives.

Clinician:	OK. You did a really good job of brainstorming. We have eight possible solutions for finishing your homework every day. When I look at these—several have to do with where you would do your homework, but some have to do with other things that are getting in the way, like your phone or the TV. Now is the time when we want to eliminate those things on the list that you know you will not do so that we can arrive at a solution. Are there some of these suggestions that you know you will not do or that just will not work for you? You don't have to explain why you are eliminating suggestions if you don't want to—just feel free to eliminate ones that you don't think will work for you.
Adolescent:	Well, I have enough trouble getting to school on time, so I don't think I'll try to do homework before school.
Clinician:	All right. I'll cross that one out.

Adolescent:	*And I really need to have my phone with me.*
Clinician:	*OK. I'll cross that one out. Are there any other ones that you think you would not do?*
Adolescent:	*Yeah. I don't know, I'm not sure if John can help me. He has a really crazy schedule because he does sports too—and I'm not sure that would work every day.*
Clinician:	*Good thinking. It's important that the solution be one that is under your control, and if he can't schedule with you, then you can't help that. Do you want to cross that one out?*
Adolescent:	*Yeah.*

The fourth step is to help the client select one potential solution that he or she can imagine doing in the next week.

Have the client carefully consider the remaining solutions. Ask, "Do you think you would actually follow through with the solution? Would it work?" It is also important to ask, "Could you see yourself doing this in the next week?" If not, then it will not be possible to move forward with the solution before the next session.

From the pool of remaining solutions, the client should choose one solution and describe exactly how it will be carried out. Again ask, "Which one would be most helpful?" and encourage the client to be as specific as possible (e.g., when? how often? what time of day? with whom?).

The client should now have a specifically defined plan for addressing the problem. The plan should include when the solution will be attempted, how often, and at what times. The client should agree on the number of times to try the solution before the next session. To reinforce this action, ask, "Now, what did you decide you will do?"

Consider whether additional solutions should be attempted before the next session. If the client wishes to try additional solutions, repeat the decision process for each solution. Evaluate with the client the feasibility of the remaining solutions, choose another solution to try, describe exactly how it will be carried out, consider possible obstacles to enacting the solution, and generate a backup plan to overcome the obstacles. A sample dialogue between a clinician and adolescent follows:

Clinician:	*Of the remaining solutions, are there ones that you think would work?*
Adolescent:	*I think they would all be helpful.*
Clinician:	*Which ones do you think might be most helpful—something that you would like to try in the next week? Remember, we want you to succeed and make progress toward solving this problem in a way that you can tell is making a difference.*
Adolescent:	*Well . . . I like the idea of starting my homework at the end of math class—so I can ask the teacher if I need help. Now, I just kind of doodle and daydream.*
Clinician:	*Yes, that sounds good. Would this work? I mean, could you finish during that time?*

Adolescent:	*No, I'd probably just get started. Let's see. . . . I think if I tried to go to the library, I would be away from my brother and the TV, so I could probably get it done.*
Clinician:	*OK. It sounds like you are proposing a two-part solution that sounds doable to me. You could start your homework in your math class and finish it in the library after school. Is that right? Does that sounds like something you could do every day?*
Adolescent:	*Well, maybe most days.*
Clinician:	*Let's get specific so we know if you're able to follow through with the solution. Do you always have time in math class to start your homework? How many days after school would you go to the library?*
Adolescent:	*Most days I have time to start math in math class and I'd probably go to the library at least 3 days during the week.*
Clinician:	*OK. It sounds like we have a solution. Next, like we always do, let's talk about what might get in the way when you try this solution.*

The fifth step is to generate possible obstacles to that solution.

Help the client identify any obstacles to carrying out the solution that could possibly undermine his or her attempts to solve the problem. You might begin by saying, "The next step in problem solving is to identify anything that might get in the way of you being able to do your homework in math class and finish it in the library. Think of as many obstacles as possible, because if we can work through them, then you are more likely to follow through on what you want to do. What might come up during the week that would get in the way?" In the example above, there are several possible obstacles to going to the library three times a week that need to be explored. What if a friend asks Joe to do something fun? How is he going to get to the library? Refer back to the Homework chapter (p. 47) to review how to explore obstacles.

The sixth step is to address each obstacle.

As each obstacle is identified, generate backup plans with the client to circumvent it. For example, if clients think they might forget, ask, "What can you do to make sure you don't forget?" Again, it would be helpful to review the Homework chapter (p. 47) about how to address obstacles. If the obstacles cannot be addressed, then it will be important to pick a new solution.

The seventh and final step is to jointly develop a homework task related to the chosen solution.

Clinician:	*It will be helpful to start on this solution so that we can evaluate how it goes at our next session. What do you think?*
Adolescent:	*Sure, I can start on this tomorrow.*
Clinician:	*Just to make sure we are on the same page, can you remind me what the solution is that you are going to try?*

Adolescent:	*Starting tomorrow, I'm going to start my math homework at the end of math class and start going to the library after school to finish it.*
Clinician:	*You have a good memory! Also, remind me how many days you plan on going to the library after school?*
Adolescent:	*At least 3.*
Clinician:	*That was it. OK. Now let's just review the obstacles we came up with and how you plan to address them.* [They review obstacles and the ways that they discussed to address them.]

Additional Notes

- As part of the homework review at the beginning of the next session, it is important to check whether the client tried the solution and what was the outcome. You might ask, "How did your homework go this week, trying [insert the name of the solution]?" If the client was not able to carry out the solution, ask questions like, "What barriers got in the way?" "What could be done differently next time?" If the solution was carried out, ask whether or not it helped solve the problem. Was the desired outcome attained? For example, in the solution for the sample above, did the adolescent's test grades improve?
- Be sure to praise any efforts by the client to carry out a solution. If solutions did not go well or the client had a difficult time carrying them out, help modify the solution and encourage another try. If an entirely new solution is necessary, repeat the Problem Solving procedure steps.
- If the client did not attempt the assignment, the lack of follow-through could be treated as a problem that needs a solution. The Problem Solving procedure could be applied in this situation. Once clients appear to understand the Problem Solving procedure, they can be asked to demonstrate its use by going through the seven steps when they bring up a new problem during a session.

How Do I Solve This Problem?

1. **Define your problem.** Just one. Keep it real specific. Write it below.

2. **Brainstorm possible solutions.** The more the better! List below.

3. **Eliminate unwanted suggestions.** Cross out any that you can't imagine doing yourself.

4. **Select one potential solution.** Which one can you imagine yourself doing this week? Circle it.

5. **Generate possible obstacles.** What might get in the way of this working? List below.

6. **Address each obstacle.** If you can't solve each obstacle, pick a new solution and go through the steps again.

7. **Make the selected solution for your assignment this week.** List below exactly when and how you'll do it.

8. **Evaluate the outcome.** Did it work? If some changes are needed, list them below and commit to trying it again.

UNIT 2: CHAPTER 13: Caregiver Only Sessions

Rationale

Most adolescents and many transitional age youth (TAY) live with one or more parents. Best practice guidelines recommend that it is important to include parents when working with their children, especially if they live together. Substance use disorders can occur in any family, and it is best to assume that the family has strengths that can be enhanced. Parenting practices are reviewed with parents, since prevention research has revealed that there are several of these practices that can help decrease their children's substance use. We have found that many clinicians do not have much training in working with parents or conducting family sessions, so these sessions are very structured and limited in number. We have always told clinicians that what we outline in the manual is a minimum number of sessions. If clinicians believe more sessions are clinically necessary and they have the skills to do them, then they should feel free to incorporate more sessions as needed. Also, a caregiver does not necessarily have to be a parent, if there is another adult in the client's life who plays a positive and supportive role.

Learning Objectives

The learning objectives are to help caregivers:

- Appreciate the adoption of a positive approach with their adolescent or TAY.
- Understand the importance of their role in the A-CRA approach and treatment.
- Be motivated to participate in the A-CRA treatment episode.
- Improve positive communication skills.
- Improve problem solving Skills.

Timing, Audience, and Delivery Method

A-CRA was designed with a minimum of two Caregiver Only Sessions. These sessions are used to review important information, teach skills, and prime the caregivers for the sessions in which the caregivers and client are brought in together: the Caregiver-Adolescent Relationship Skills Sessions (also known as the Family Sessions). It is important to schedule these sessions early during the client's treatment episode. In fact, it is a good idea to schedule dates and times for the first and second Caregiver Only Sessions when in the process of scheduling the appointment for the first client session, even if the Caregiver Only appointments are several weeks out. These sessions should begin in the third or fourth week of treatment. The caregivers then have the opportunity to practice skills taught before the Caregiver-Adolescent Relationship Skills Sessions. In a two-parent household, it is important to invite both parents to attend but ultimately to work with whoever does attend. Also, in some situations the caregiver may be a grandparent, an older sibling, or another positive adult who is willing to help the client in recovery. It is usually someone who lives with the client.

Materials

Procedure specific materials would include a copy of the Communication Skills handout (p. 140) and the How Do I Solve This Problem? form (p. 182). Also, there is a wallet-sized card for the caregivers that lists the four parenting practices on one side and communication skills on the other. Copies of the card are available at the end of the chapter for duplicating (p. 159).

Procedural Steps

1. **Provide an overview of A-CRA (complete in the first Caregiver Only Session).**
   - **Describe basic objectives of A-CRA (help find healthy, reinforcing lifestyle . . .).**
   - **Outline at least two A-CRA procedures that will be part of treatment.**
   - **Describe the duration of treatment while emphasizing that it is time-limited.**
2. **Set positive expectations for the outcome of treatment by describing the science supporting the approach (complete in the first Caregiver Only Session).**
3. **Review research regarding effective parenting approaches (complete in the first Caregiver Only Session).**
   - **Explain that research has shown these practices to be helpful to keep adolescents sober.**
   - **Give details about each of the four practices.**
   - **Ask what the caregivers are currently doing and how they think they might improve.**
4. **Identify caregivers' reinforcers for continued involvement in their adolescent or TAY's treatment process (begins in the first Caregiver Only Session and continues in the second session).**
5. **Keep discussion about the client positive (expected in both Caregiver Only Sessions).**
6. **Teach the Communication Skills procedure (can be done in the second Caregiver Only Session).**
7. **Teach the Problem Solving Skills procedure (can be done in the second Caregiver Only Session).**

Detailed Description

1. Provide an overview of A-CRA.

Topics that should be reviewed during the overview include ones that are described in the Overview of A-CRA for Clients chapter (p. 22). You can refer back to that section for dialogue examples.

- **Describe basic objectives of A-CRA (help find healthy, reinforcing lifestyle . . .).**

You can describe the objectives of A-CRA treatment succinctly. There are three important parts to the description: (a) noting that the treatment is designed to help the client lead a healthy, reinforcing lifestyle without the use of alcohol and drugs; (b) explaining that learning how to live this healthy lifestyle will involve trying out other enjoyable activities that do not involve substance use; and (c) mentioning the use of reinforcers specific to the client that will be the motivators for a lifestyle change.

- **Outline at least two A-CRA procedures that will be part of treatment.**

When outlining the two or more A-CRA procedures that will be used during treatment, you should (a) explain how these procedures will be used, (b) provide enough detail so the caregivers understand what they are, and (c) relate the use of the procedure to the particular client's situation.

- **Describe the duration of treatment while emphasizing that it is time-limited.**

Durations of treatment may vary somewhat across different treatment organizations, but it is important to provide information about (a) the frequency of sessions (e.g., weekly), (b) the duration (e.g., three months), (c) the length of each session (e.g., an hour), and (d) the format of sessions (e.g., a number of sessions with the client alone, with caregivers alone, and with everyone together).

2. **Set positive expectations for the outcome of treatment by describing the science supporting the approach.**

The most important element for setting positive expectations for the treatment is to emphasize that A-CRA has been found effective in scientific studies. A sample explanation for setting a positive expectation follows:

> **Clinician:** *As you may already know, the treatment that we are using with your son is based on a lot of research, and this research has found that this treatment is effective in helping young people reduce or eliminate their substance use. It is being used in many different treatment programs and in many different states, and we know it is effective for young people with different backgrounds, including ones like your child. So it's not just my opinion that this is a good treatment, we know it works. Do you have any questions?*

3. **Review research regarding effective parenting approaches.**
   - **Explain that research has shown these practices to be helpful to keep adolescents sober.**
   - **Give details about each of the four practices.**
   - **Ask what the caregivers are currently doing and how they think they might improve.**

According to researchers who have studied family factors related to adolescent substance use problems (Bry, 1998; Bry, Catalano, Kumpfer, Lochman, & Szapocznik, 1998; Catalano, 1998; Hops, 1998), the following are four critical practices that parents or caregivers can adopt to help their children or TAY remain abstinent:

- It is important for caregivers to *be good role models* by refraining from using drugs or alcohol in front of their adolescent or TAY. When discussing this with caregivers, tell them that you are not accusing them of having a substance use problem but that it is important for them to understand that being a good role model will help their adolescent or TAY's recovery. Ask them whether they will agree not to use substances in front of their adolescent or TAY. Note that this does not mean that they cannot drink alcohol but that it should not be done in front of the adolescent or TAY.
- A second critical parenting practice is *to increase positive communication* with their adolescent or TAY. Caregivers should strive toward decreasing blame and put-downs and increasing positive

talk with and about their adolescent or TAY. Explain that you will provide them with some tips to improve their communication skills.

- A third important parenting practice is *to monitor their adolescent's whereabouts*, including knowing where he or she is and whom he or she is with.
- A fourth critical parenting practice is *involvement in the adolescent or TAY's life* outside the home.

It is important to maintain a dialogue during the session, so it is helpful to weave a discussion of the four parenting practices into conversation. For example, you may ask, "What are some of your parenting practices that you think you do well?" or "What are some things you do to keep your teenager away from alcohol or drugs?" As you listen to the caregivers' responses, look for opportunities to praise them for positive parenting practices.

During a discussion of the four practices, caregivers may bring up issues or problems. If so, you can begin to talk to the caregivers about their issue of concern while still reviewing all four parenting practices. For example, a parent may say she has a problem showing appreciation to her teen. You may help her practice giving praise or showing appreciation, which could lead to a related homework assignment. As with the individual client sessions, Caregiver Only Sessions also end with a homework assignment. Or the caregiver may reveal that he rarely encourages the teen to attend positive social activities. You may begin helping the caregiver identify positive social activities.

Emphasize that it will be important for the caregivers to support their adolescent or TAY's involvement in non-substance-using activities and that some of this support should come in the form of the caregivers joining their adolescent or TAY in these activities.

Be sure to provide caregivers the opportunity to talk about how they might do some things differently to address these parenting practices.

4. **Identify caregivers' reinforcers for continued involvement in their adolescent or TAY's treatment process.**

- Ask questions to identify caregivers' reinforcers related to their child's sobriety, and use these reinforcers to help motivate the caregiver to try A-CRA.

  Sometimes the caregivers' reinforcers are revealed through conversation, but usually it will take questioning to elicit them. Ask, "What will be better if [the client's name] stops using?" Most caregivers will be able to articulate the benefits for the client. For example, they may want their adolescent to graduate from high school and to avoid incarceration. Other caregivers' motivations may revolve around themselves, such as wanting to make their own lives easier. For example, a caregiver may say, "I want the school system off my back."

  Work with whatever reasons the caregivers offer for wanting their adolescent or TAY to stop using alcohol or drugs, and try to help them see how the clinician, caregiver, and client can work together to achieve their goals.

- Reiterate potential benefits of A-CRA discussed during the overview; emphasize that caregiver involvement in treatment could help improve the relationship between caregivers and their adolescent or TAY and lead to more success in adulthood.

- If caregivers are skeptical because of past treatment failure or because they do not believe that the adolescent or TAY will quit using alcohol or drugs, emphasize that recovery is a process. Tell the caregivers that you believe this program can work. Try to get a commitment to attend at least four A-CRA sessions. You might say something like, "I know you love your son (daughter). Sometimes parents just don't know what to do when there are problems with their children, and sometimes it is helpful to try different things."

5. Keep discussion about the client positive.

If the caregivers begin to emphasize negative aspects of their adolescent or TAY, then it is important to explain why you want the discussion to remain positive by explaining that doing so will "enhance the relationship with [the client's name], which will help him do better in treatment" or that "it will be helpful in identifying the strengths that [the client's name] has, which will be helpful in treatment." Other techniques that can be helpful from *Functional Family Therapy* (Alexander & Parsons, 1982; Waldron & Slesnick, 1998) include:

- **Relabeling behavior.** Change the meaning and value of a negative behavior by describing positive properties of the behavior or by explaining that the adolescent or TAY is not engaging in it to make the caregivers miserable or angry. If possible, suggest positive motives for the behavior, or portray family members as victims rather than perpetrators. For example, the adolescent or TAY may be described as someone who is struggling to become independent and is trying very hard to be accepted by friends. Relabeling behavior gives family members another perspective or new information about behaviors and is most effective if it ascribes benign or benevolent motives. For example, "So when your daughter storms off during an argument, I wonder if she's doing the best she can to avoid losing her temper? It might mean she's actually trying to keep the argument from getting worse."
- **Curtailing blaming.** Communicate to the caregiver that blaming someone for previous problems does not serve any purpose. Emphasize the future, not what happened in the past. For example, "I can really see how all the trouble your son has gotten into has really caused you a lot of grief. We want things to improve for you, so let's see what we can do to get started with that goal in mind."
- **Using a positive focus.** Emphasize family strengths by repeatedly reinforcing aspects of family life that are working well, such as pleasant events and family activities. For example, "Tell me something nice that your son has done during the 15 years he has been a part of your family." Another example: "OK, now let's try to focus on some of his strengths, because then we can find ways to help him succeed. What are some things your son does well?"
- **Using exception statements.** Try exception statements, another technique useful in decreasing family blaming statements (Melidonis & Bry, 1995). To use this technique, ask the caregivers to describe a situation from the past in which the problem behavior was expected to occur but did not. Then probe into what was different about this situation. For example, when a caregiver says that their adolescent is always in a bad mood, in trouble, or some other negative condition, the clinician can say, "It's true he has gotten into trouble a lot lately, but I bet you can think of some times when he was doing what he was supposed to do."

6. Teach the Communication Skills procedure (can be done in the second Caregiver Only Session).

The main advantage to teaching communication skills and problem solving skills during Caregiver Only Sessions is it allows you to spend more time with the caregivers to help them learn and practice the skills, before they are expected to use them during the Caregiver-Adolescent Relationship Skills Session. Refer back to the Communication Skills procedure for specifics (Unit 2, Chapter 11 [p. 123]). Remember that the three components are (a) making an understanding statement, (b) taking partial responsibility, and (c) offering to help.

It is usually easy to find a situation that a caregiver can use to try out their communication skills. Below is an example of how the clinician would teach the skills to the caregiver.

Clinician:	*OK, Mrs. Smith, let's go back to that situation between you and Gina when she comes home late. Let's replay that conversation, break it down into pieces, and try to understand where you are coming from at each point and how you and Gina feel. As we go through the conversation, I'd like to offer three techniques that will help the conversation stay calm and increase the chance that you'll get want you want out of the conversation. The first technique is to try to make an understanding statement. An understanding statement brings empathy into the conversation and helps decrease defensiveness because you're really trying to understand the other's perspective. So what do you think Gina's perspective is on this issue?*
Caregiver:	*I mean, I guess I can understand that she enjoys running around with her friends and is reluctant to come home if they are out having a good time. And we have been fighting a lot lately.*
Clinician:	*That's a great start. Pretend I'm her, and say that understanding statement.*
Caregiver:	*Gina, I understand that it is hard to leave your friends to come home when you are having a good time. I also understand that you may not enjoy being at home because we have been arguing a lot lately.*
Clinician:	*That was really good! You actually had two understanding statements in there and you also took some responsibility with that part about the arguing. We are going to talk about that next because it is one of the components of good communication: taking partial responsibility for the problem or solution.*
Caregiver:	*Well, I don't really think it is my fault we have been arguing so much.*
Clinician:	*I understand. This technique is not to place blame on anyone. It is meant to indicate that you are willing to accept a role in creating or solving the problem.*
Caregiver:	*One thing that I am probably guilty of is not hearing the reasons why she is late, encouraging her to call, or even sitting down to talk to her about solutions to this problem. I just instantly start yelling, and then I get so angry at her response that I say hurtful things to her—like she can move out when she's 18 or can go live with her father and be his problem. That isn't right. That really bothers me.*
Clinician:	*Have you ever shared these feelings with Gina?*
Caregiver:	*No. That's the problem. We can't just sit down and talk without fighting.*
Clinician:	*You have been doing great in here with me. Maybe by going over some of these helpful techniques you will be able to sit down and talk and she will be more willing to do what you ask. So talk to me using the understanding statement and the partial responsibility component.*

Caregiver:	*OK. Gina, I understand that it is hard for you to come home on time when you are having a good time with your friends and to come home to us always arguing. You just get me so angry that I start yelling and . . .*
Clinician:	*You are doing well, but try to use "I" statements. Instead of saying, "You just make me angry," start by saying, "I feel angry when. . . ." Good job on the understanding statement. Start with the partial responsibility again.*
Caregiver:	*I get angry when you are not home when you are supposed to be. I feel like you don't respect me. I get so worried. When I get worried or angry, I start yelling and say things that I don't mean. I would like to change and try to improve our relationship by trying to improve the way we talk to each other.*
Clinician:	*Great. You are doing very well. You explained where you were coming from when you talked about getting worried, and you also talked about saying things that you know bother her. I like that. Now the third component is the offer to help. It is an offer on your part to help solve the problem. Can you think of something you can offer to do to help resolve the issue of Gina's breaking curfew?*
Caregiver:	*I could offer to give her transportation, be open to having her call me if she is going to be late, or discuss the reasons why she has been breaking curfew.*
Clinician:	*That sounds like a good offer to me. Now let's review the three components by having you talk to me as if I'm Gina, using all of them together.*
Caregiver:	*Gina, I understand that it is hard for you to come home on time when you are having a good time with your friends and you come home to us always arguing. I get worried when you are not home when you are supposed to be. When I get worried or angry, I start yelling and say things to you that are hurtful and that I don't mean. I am really sorry. I would like to try to improve our relationship by trying to work on how we talk to each other. I would be open to talking about how you feel about curfew and some of the reasons why you have been breaking it and seeing if we can come up with some ideas together to solve our problem.*
Clinician:	*Fantastic! You put everything together. That is not easy. How did it feel using these techniques?*
Caregiver:	*Weird at first, because I really have to think about what I am saying. I just hope I can do it.*
Clinician:	*We are going to practice more now, so you will feel confident about being able to do it. How do you think Gina will respond if you try talking to her using these techniques?*
Caregiver:	*She will probably wonder what is going on, but I really want our relationship and communication to improve. So I'm willing to give it a shot.*
Clinician:	*Good. I like your openness to trying new things. I will be going over these techniques with Gina as well, so she might be trying these techniques at home too. Later, when we all meet together, we will be using these techniques in our*

family sessions together. We need to continue to practice now by doing some role plays. I'll pretend to be you and you pretend to be Gina. I'll show you how you might use these skills and we can see how Gina might react. [The clinician first guides the caregiver into a two-sided reverse role play, they discuss it, and then the clinician guides the caregiver in a two-sided role play with the caregiver playing herself and the clinician playing the adolescent.]

The two-sided reverse role play helps caregivers understand their adolescent or TAY's point of view, and it gives the clinician a chance to demonstrate or model the techniques. Then it is important for the caregivers to practice their own part of the conversation in a two-sided role play. There would usually be homework related to practicing the skill prior to the next session.

7. **Teach the Problem Solving Skills procedure (can be done in the second Caregiver Only Session).**

Teaching the Caregiver problem solving skills is just like teaching these skills to the client, so refer back to the Problem Solving procedure for details (Unit 2, Chapter 12 [p. 141]). The selected problem can relate to the client, but only if the caregiver actually has control over it. It also could be a problem that is not related to the client but one that concerns the caregiver, such as a problem with work, a car, or a partner.

Additional Notes

Homework. As with the client's sessions, each caregiver session should end with homework. A good homework assignment for the first session would be related to improving one of the four parenting practices. The homework for the second session is often to practice the Communication Skills and to follow through on the solution chosen from the Problem Solving procedure. Just as with the client, it is important to identify obstacles to homework completion and explore solutions.

Need for flexibility. Caregiver sessions are so important that clinicians are encouraged to be quite flexible about where and when they will happen. Experienced A-CRA clinicians have told us that they have done these sessions in caregivers' homes, on caregivers' lunch breaks, at fast-food restaurants (making sure to maintain privacy), driving down the road in a car, and other places. Additionally, it is important to think broadly when identifying a "caregiver." Experience has shown that there are biological parents who for one reason or another are not able to do the caregiver sessions. In these cases, another supportive adult should be identified.

Assess for other needed referrals. One of the steps of the Caregiver Only procedure in the original manual was for the clinician to assess for other needed referrals for the caregiver. This is not an A-CRA–specific procedure, but it is good therapeutic practice and one that we still consider important when working with caregivers. Clinicians have found that many caregivers need mental health or substance use therapy and appreciate referrals for these services. We do not recommend that the A-CRA clinician serve in a dual role as both the client's and the caregivers' therapist. There may also be a need for family work beyond what is available through A-CRA.

Preparing for the Caregiver-Adolescent Relationship Skills Session. During the Caregiver Only Sessions (usually during the second session), it is important to prepare caregivers for the Caregiver-Adolescent Relationship Skills Session by discussing the Three Positive Things exercise: The clinician should explain that caregivers will be asked to say three positive things about their adolescent or TAY at the beginning of the session. If the caregivers have a chance to think about what they will say and practice in advance, they will be less likely to have problems coming up with something positive to say. Caregivers should be told that the purpose for doing this exercise is to start the session on a positive note.

Difficulty scheduling the second Caregiver Only Session. Try to get all the Caregiver Only and Caregiver-Adolescent Relationship Skills Sessions scheduled early in treatment so they are on everyone's calendars. However, if you are having great difficulty scheduling a second session with the caregiver, you may need to proceed with the combined Caregiver-Adolescent Relationship Skills session and teach communication skills and problem solving during that session. If this is the case, then it is important to prepare the caregiver for the Three Positive Things exercise during a telephone call.

Wallet-Sized Card Templates

Proven Ways to Help Your Child Stay Sober

1. *Be a good role model* by not using alcohol or drugs.
2. *Be positive* with your child. Praise appropriate behavior. Decrease blaming and put-downs.
3. *Monitor* your child's behavior and whereabouts. Know what he/she is doing and who he/she is with.
4. *Get involved* in your child's life outside the home. Encourage and promote positive social and recreational activities.

Three Steps to Better Communication

1. Understanding Statement

2. Partial Responsibility Statement
   (Shared role in creating or solving a specific problem)

3. Offer to Help

Proven Ways to Help Your Child Stay Sober

1. *Be a good role model* by not using alcohol or drugs.
2. *Be positive* with your child. Praise appropriate behavior. Decrease blaming and put-downs.
3. *Monitor* your child's behavior and whereabouts. Know what he/she is doing and who he/she is with.
4. *Get involved* in your child's life outside the home. Encourage and promote positive social and recreational activities.

Three Steps to Better Communication

1. Understanding Statement

2. Partial Responsibility Statement
   (Shared role in creating or solving a specific problem)

3. Offer to Help

Proven Ways to Help Your Child Stay Sober

1. *Be a good role model* by not using alcohol or drugs.
2. *Be positive* with your child. Praise appropriate behavior. Decrease blaming and put-downs.
3. *Monitor* your child's behavior and whereabouts. Know what he/she is doing and who he/she is with.
4. *Get involved* in your child's life outside the home. Encourage and promote positive social and recreational activities.

Three Steps to Better Communication

1. Understanding Statement

2. Partial Responsibility Statement
   (Shared role in creating or solving a specific problem)

3. Offer to Help

Proven Ways to Help Your Child Stay Sober

1. *Be a good role model* by not using alcohol or drugs.
2. *Be positive* with your child. Praise appropriate behavior. Decrease blaming and put-downs.
3. *Monitor* your child's behavior and whereabouts. Know what he/she is doing and who he/she is with.
4. *Get involved* in your child's life outside the home. Encourage and promote positive social and recreational activities.

Three Steps to Better Communication

1. Understanding Statement

2. Partial Responsibility Statement
   (Shared role in creating or solving a specific problem)

3. Offer to Help

UNIT 2: CHAPTER 14: Caregiver-Adolescent Relationship Skills (Family Sessions)

Rationale

These sessions bring the client and caregivers together with the goal of practicing skills to improve their relationship. The session begins with the Three Positive Things exercise, where the caregivers and the adolescent or TAY take turns saying three positive things about each other. They complete a tool similar to the Happiness Scale, which is called the Relationship Happiness Scale, and then they talk about what is going well and identify some areas for further practice of communication skills and problem solving. In the ideal situation, both the client and caregivers have learned and practiced positive communication and problem solving skills in prior individual sessions. In this session, they practice these skills with each other with the help of the clinician. The session ends with a CRA tool called the Daily Reminder to Be Nice and homework is assigned to use it in upcoming weeks.

Learning Objectives

The learning objectives are to help caregivers and their adolescents or TAYs:

- Learn how it feels to say positive things about the other person and hear positive things about oneself.
- Learn to identify areas in the relationship that are going well and identify areas to improve.
- Become more comfortable using positive communication with each other.
- Become more comfortable using problem solving skills with each other.
- Learn how to use the Daily Reminder to Be Nice.

Timing, Audience, and Delivery Method

The sessions will occur after the two Caregiver Only Sessions and after the client has learned Communication Skills and Problem Solving Skills and has completed at least one Happiness Scale. Since the goal is to provide the Caregiver Only Sessions in the third or fourth week of treatment, it would be appropriate to start the Caregiver-Adolescent Relationship Skills Sessions around Week 6 of treatment. If the client lives with or sees both parents on a regular basis, then invite both parents to the session. If it is not possible to get both parents, then it is acceptable to have these sessions with one parent or caregiver. Since these sessions build on the Caregiver Only Sessions, it is important that the caregivers be the same as the ones who participated in the Caregiver Only Sessions. Remember that it is very important to prepare both the caregiver and the client for the session so that they are ready to say three positive things about the other person. This is typically done in the individual client and Caregiver Only Sessions that precede the joint session.

Materials

Procedure-specific materials include:

- The Relationship Happiness Scales, adolescent and caregiver versions (p. 178 and 179), clipboards, and pens.
- For the Problem Solving procedure: The How Do I Solve This Problem? form (p. 182), chalkboard or whiteboard, markers or chalk, and possibly an easel.

- For Communication Skills procedure: The Communication Skills handout (p. 181), chalkboard or whiteboard, markers or chalk, and possibly an easel.
- The Daily Reminder to Be Nice form (p. 180).

General Notes for the Clinician

There is a lot of material to cover, which is why we recommend two 60-minute sessions to cover the material. Limiting the session to 60 minutes helps participants stay engaged and focused.

Emphasize to the caregivers and the client that during these sessions the focus is on the positive attributes of the other person. Guide them to face and talk to each other during the Three Positive Things exercise and role plays because the goal is to improve communication between them. They may try to talk through you because they feel awkward in the session or because of their poor communication history, so it may be necessary to redirect them to speak to each other. You can help maintain rapport with both by periodically asking how they are doing.

It is important for you to maintain roughly an equal amount of eye contact with both the caregivers and the adolescent during this session and to avoid siding with one person over the other. Also, emphasize keeping the conversation positive, such as by discouraging any blaming. You can assist by interpreting, coaching, modeling, and shaping as needed.

Shaping is an important principle of operant conditioning (behavior modification). It involves reinforcing (e.g., through praise, tangible rewards) small steps toward achieving a larger goal. It is particularly useful when mastery of a series of small skills, steps, or procedures is necessary to achieve a complex goal. Shaping can be useful for improving any skill. For example, when teaching problem solving skills, the procedure is broken up into several small steps and the clinician shapes competency in each step through teaching, modeling, rehearsal, feedback, and praise.

The session will end with homework, just like during the individual client and Caregiver Only Sessions. A typical homework assignment is to use the Daily Reminder to Be Nice during the week. It is also appropriate for the clinician to help the family set some goals based on the results of the Relationship Happiness Scale.

Procedural Steps

Remember that not all the components are completed in one session. Most clinicians focus on communication skills during one of the family sessions and problem solving skills during the other family session.

1. **Have each person face the other and say three positive things about the other person (required during the first Family Session and often used to begin the second session as well).**
   - **Explain that doing this helps set a positive tone for the session.**
   - **Offer assistance if they have trouble thinking of three things, or praise their efforts.**
   - **Remind the participants to speak directly to each other.**
   - **Ask the recipients to repeat back what they heard.**
2. **Complete the Relationship Happiness Scales (required during the first Family Session).**
3. **Practice communication skills.**
4. **Practice problem solving skills.**
5. **Review the Daily Reminder to Be Nice (recommended for the first Family Session).**
   - **Provide a rationale for its use.**

- **Tell both the caregivers and the client that it is important to complete at least one item every day, even if the other person does not.**
- **Ask the caregivers and the client to find a good place to keep their forms.**
- **Encourage each family member to come up with examples for at least one category and assist as needed.**

Detailed Description

1. **Have each person face the other and say three positive things about the other person (required during the first Family Session and often used to begin the second session as well).**
   - **Explain that doing this helps set a positive tone for the session.**
   - **Offer assistance if they have trouble thinking of three things, or praise their efforts.**
   - **Remind the participants to speak directly to each other.**
   - **Ask the recipients to repeat back what they heard.**

It is helpful to start the session with a brief overview of what is going to happen during the session and a brief check-in on the client's homework assignment. You can acknowledge that you will do a more thorough review of homework in the next individual session. Also, check in with all participants to make sure that there have not been any crises in the family that week that will need to be addressed at some time during the session. If there are crises mentioned, you will need to use your clinical judgment to decide whether they need to be addressed right away or if they can be processed during the course of completing other procedures (e.g., Problem Solving) in the session. Next, you will want to move to the Three Positive Things exercise. Since the main point of this exercise is to set a positive stage for the remainder of the session, it is important for you to keep the exercise positive with praise and constructive feedback; doing so helps prevent the discussion from deteriorating into blaming or an argument. Often, participants may try to talk through the clinician, so make sure that family members are talking to and listening to each other during the exercise and are offering their own feelings in response. There is a lot of material to cover in these sessions, so the exercise should be done in less than 10 minutes. The Three Positive Things exercise is not required for the second session, but clinicians report that they like to start the second session with this exercise as well to set a positive tone. It usually goes quicker because participants are already familiar with the exercise. The example below is with a mother and father as caregivers, but often there will only be one caregiver present, which is acceptable.

Clinician:	*I'm glad everybody made it here today. It shows you all care about each other. You know, we normally start off a session by checking in on your assignment, but since this is a family session, I just want to make sure that everyone is making progress on their homework, and we'll talk more about your assignment, Jack, when we have your individual session. Does that sound OK?*
Adolescent:	*Yes.*
Clinician:	*Mom and Dad, we talked about you preparing for the Three Positive Things exercise. Are you ready for that?*
Mother:	*We are.*
Clinician:	*Great! Be sure to let me know if you don't remember what you were working on for the week.*
Adolescent:	*I've got it covered.*

162

Clinician:	*Good. Then I'll start by giving you an overview of what we're going to do today. Oh—but first, I want to see if anything major happened during the week that we need to make sure we set aside time to address today. Anything?*
Adolescent:	*Nope. Pretty boring week.*
Father:	*Nothing out of the ordinary happened.*
Clinician:	*Fair enough. So I'll go ahead with the agenda, then. As we discussed in our sessions last week, we're going to start by having you each say three positive things about each other. Then we'll do what's called the Relationship Happiness Scale so that we can see how everybody thinks things are going in the home and where you'd like to see some changes. Jack, you've done the regular Happiness Scale already, so this will look pretty familiar to you.*
Adolescent:	*Yeah, I remember that. It's short.*
Clinician:	*Yeah, this one is even shorter. Next, we'll try to negotiate some of the changes you'd like to see—using our best communication skills, of course! If we have time, we'll do some problem solving, too. We'll finish up with an assignment to do, an exercise called the Daily Reminder to Be Nice. Interesting name, isn't it?*
Mother:	*I guess it wouldn't hurt us to be reminded to be nice now and then.*
Clinician:	*I think that's probably true for most people. Let's start with the Three Positive Things exercise. This is a great way for us to start the session on a positive note and also get started with being nice to each other. I know you've all had time to think about this.*
Mother:	*Do you want me to go?*
Clinician:	*Sure, if you're ready. Please tell us three positive things about Jack. And Dad can help with these, too.*
Mother:	*Jack has a lot of friends—people like him. And he's smart.*
Clinician:	*These are terrific! Now, can you look right at Jack and tell him those two positive things?*
Mother:	*Jack, people like you—you are good with people, and I think you're very smart.*
Clinician:	*Excellent. How about another one? Dad?*
Father:	*Jack, for the most part, you have good common sense.*
Clinician:	*OK. Not bad. But maybe you could fix it a little, make it a little more positive? Because when you say "for the most part," it takes some of the compliment away. Do you see what I mean?*
Father:	*Yeah. OK. Then I'll just say, Jack, you have good common sense.*

Clinician:	*Great! Now Jack, can you look at your parents and repeat the three positive things they said about you?*
Adolescent:	*They said I'm smart and have common sense. Oh, and I have a lot of friends.*
Clinician:	*And how does that make you feel to hear your parents say that about you?*
Adolescent:	*It feels good. I wasn't expecting to hear those things.*
Clinician:	*You're surprised?*
Adolescent:	*Well, they don't act like they think those things about me.*
Father:	*Well, sometimes you don't act like you have common sense. So we have to see it first.*
Clinician:	*OK. Let's hold off here. We can get back to that discussion later if you'd like. But we're sticking with the positive things for now. So, Jack, it's your turn. Say three positive things about your mom and your dad. And look right at them when you say it.*
Adolescent:	*Mom and dad, I know you both care about our family.*
Clinician:	*That's a good start. . . .*
Mother:	*It's tough when you're on the spot, isn't it?*
Adolescent:	*Sort of. Mom, you're a very good cook.*
Clinician:	*Very good. One more for your mom and a couple more for your dad*
Adolescent:	*Dad, you get up early and go to work every day—you work hard. Let's see. I like watching football with you. Mom, you work hard too.*
Clinician:	*Well, those are definitely compliments. Mom and Dad, can you repeat back the positive things Jack said about you both?*
Mother:	*It was nice. He said we were caring and that I'm a good cook, a very good cook. He also said I work hard.*
Father:	*And he talked about how I work every day and how hard I work—it's true, but I never thought he noticed. It's true we like to watch football together.*
Clinician:	*And how does it feel to hear Jack say these things about you?*
Mother:	*Like he cares, and he notices some of the things we do for him. It feels good.*
Clinician:	*Dad?*
Father:	*It feels good to hear him recognize my hard work.*

2. Complete the Relationship Happiness Scales (required during the first Family Session).

You will begin by explaining the Relationship Happiness Scale. It is often worthwhile to ask clients to explain it because they have already completed Happiness Scales and it allows them to show off a little (in a positive way) in front of the caregivers. It also helps clients feel more involved in the session. Prior to the session, it is important for clinicians to review the Happiness Scale chapter (p. 28) for a refresher regarding what should be covered for the rationale and instructions. Completing the Relationship Happiness Scale differs somewhat from completing the Happiness Scale because participants complete the Relationship Happiness Scale in reference to how happy they are with the other party in the various categories. Begin the review of their responses to the Relationship Happiness Scale by highlighting several of the categories that received high ratings. Again, this helps foster a positive tone in the session and reminds the family members that there are aspects of each other that they truly like and appreciate. Then help the family select reasonable categories on which to work.

Clinician:	*Nice job, everybody. Let's move on now to the Relationship Happiness Scale [see forms on p. 178 and 179]. Here. I'll give you each your copy. Jack, do you want to start off with the instructions? You've done a slightly different version of this before. But I'll let your parents know what is different with this version in a minute.*
Adolescent:	*See these numbers from 1 to 10 here on this chart? You're supposed to circle how you feel right now in each of these areas. And see how it goes from "completely unhappy" on one end to "completely happy" on the other end. Is that right?*
Clinician:	*Excellent job. Now here's the part that's different. Instead of indicating how happy you are with yourself in each area, you'll be saying how happy you are with somebody else in the family. Mom and Dad, you'll be saying how happy you are with Jack in these areas on the sheet. Work together on it and try to come up with a rating that you both think fits. Jack, you'll be marking off how happy you are with your mom and dad. Try to do just one rating for your parents. If they are really different in a category here and there, though, you can rate them separately and write it in to clarify. What do you think of that?*
Adolescent:	*Sounds OK.*
Clinician:	*It's important to rate the scale as honestly as possible, based on how you feel today. We want to make sure that we're doing this because we're going to use the information to help make changes in the areas that aren't going so well, and it will also give us the chance to look at what's working for you all. So don't let what happened last week or last month influence your ratings. How's that sound?*
Father:	*Good.*
Clinician:	*Good. And when you fill this out, try to rate each category independently. Don't let your feelings about one category influence how you rate another. I know that's hard sometimes, but do the best you can. Like I said, when you're done, we can take a look at the ratings and decide what areas you all want to work on.*
Mother:	*Getting us all to agree on something isn't going to be easy.*

Clinician:	But that's OK, because you can pick different areas to work on. You don't have to agree. So here you are. This should only take a few minutes. Rate how you feel today. Let me know if you have questions. [Five minutes pass.] Let's see what you've got here. Mom and Dad, looks like you gave some nice high ratings for your relationship with Jack in several areas, like "time spent with adolescent" and "affection." You rated those each an 8. Can you tell us how you arrived at those ratings?
Mother:	Jack has always been an affectionate child. And when he's in a good mood he can be a lot of fun.
Clinician:	Jack, how do you feel about hearing these positive things from your parents?
Adolescent:	Good. I like when they tell me I'm fun to hang out with.
Clinician:	Looks like they mean it. What kind of things do you all do together that's fun?
Father:	Sometimes we go fishing together. We used to like going to the movies together. We still like eating out together.
Mother:	I still wish we'd do it more, though.
Clinician:	Right. So a rating of 8 seems pretty accurate, because it allows a little room for improvement. Jack, let's see what areas you rated high for your parents. Your highest was a 7 for "emotional support." Can you tell me a little about that? Why did that get your highest rating?
Adolescent:	Because if I need something, they're there. Like when I got into trouble. They were mad, but they tried to help.
Clinician:	Mom and Dad, what do you make of that?
Mother:	I like hearing it. And I think he's right.
Father:	We do try, but sometimes he makes it hard.
Adolescent:	Well, sometimes it isn't easy talking to you guys about some problems.
Clinician:	It's important for us to steer clear of blaming each other for problems. Instead, let's put it on the list of problems we can address. OK, back to the Relationship Happiness Scale. Let's take a look now at a few categories that you each rated a little lower, like somewhere in the middle of the scale. And these are often the best categories to start working on, so think about which one each of you might like to ask the other person for a change in. Mom and Dad, you rated communication a 5. Can you tell me about why you rated it that way?
Mother:	Because we do talk, but lots of times we're either yelling at Jack or he's yelling at us.
Father:	Yes, there's lots of room for improvement there—for all of us.

Clinician:	*I like how you're using good, positive communication skills as you talk about it. I know we only went over it quickly in an earlier session, but do you remember the three positive parts of a good communication? One of them was to accept partial responsibility. And I think you've done that when you say that everybody in the family could benefit from some communication skills training. Good for you, Dad!*
Father:	*Thanks, I'm trying.*
Clinician:	*I can tell! You also rated "job or school" somewhere in the middle of the scale, a 4. Can you tell me how you settled on that rating?*
Father:	*He's late for school all the time because he won't get up in the morning. We make ourselves nuts trying to get him out of bed. I'm really sick and tired of the battle each morning.*
Adolescent:	*I can't help it! I'm tired.*
Father:	*Well, you wouldn't be so tired if you went to bed at a decent hour.*
Clinician:	*This sounds like an excellent category to make a request in. Would you like this to be an area you make a request in, Mom and Dad?*
Father:	*I'd like to.*
Mother:	*Yes, it would be a good one. We've tried everything.*
Clinician:	*Good. And I think we'll be able to practice our communication skills as we work on it, so you'll get that category partially addressed as well. We might even get to practice problem solving with it, too. OK. Jack, it's your turn. In looking at your Relationship Happiness Scale, I see that you rated "allowance" a 5. Can you explain why you rated it a 5?*
Adolescent:	*Because I don't get enough money. I do a lot of chores and don't get paid much. Most of my friends get more.*
Mother:	*But some of them get less, too.*
Adolescent:	*Who?*
Mother:	*Well, you know Ben's family doesn't have a lot of money . . .*
Adolescent:	*Yeah, but that's different, and besides . . .*
Clinician:	*Let's just hold off on this discussion for a minute, OK? Jack, do you want to select the "allowance" category, then? This would mean that you get to make a request about it this week. It doesn't mean that your parents have to agree, but we'll at least try some negotiation on it. What do you think?*
Adolescent:	*Yeah. I pick "allowance."*

Clinician:	*Good. The next thing we'll do is use our positive communication skills to make requests of each other in these categories.*

3. Practice communication skills.

Refer back to the Communication Skills procedure (p. 123) for more details about using this procedure. If multiple caregivers are present at the session, you want to make sure that each of them has an opportunity to practice. One difference in this procedure in the Family Session is that it is unnecessary to do the reverse role-play because all parties are in the session. Note that since there is a lot of material to cover in the session, it might be difficult to get through communication skills and problem solving. For example, in the dialogue that follows the clinician could have simply continued the negotiation process instead of moving on to the Problem Solving procedure. In that case, the Problem Solving procedure would have been saved for the second Family Session.

Clinician:	*We've already talked today about one of the components of positive communication, accepting partial responsibility. Why do you think it is important to use positive communication?*
Adolescent:	*If we ask something in the right way, we're more likely to get what we want.*
Father:	*Yeah, it just makes me mad if someone yells at me when they want something.*
Clinician:	*You guys are right. It also makes for a more pleasant home environment, if everyone tries to communicate in a positive way. Does anyone remember the other two components of positive communication?*
Adolescent:	*An understanding statement and an offer to help.*
Clinician:	*Perfect! Good for you, Jack. All we have to do now is put these into practice. Not so easy sometimes, though. So before we try to put them all together into a real conversation, let's try to come up with some examples of each of these components. Mom and Dad, let's start with your request for Jack: You said he's late for school because he gets up late in the morning. Tell me what you'd ideally like to see. Remember, you can ask for anything you want, but then usually there will be some negotiation. And it's always best to make your request in a way that's brief, specific, and positive, which means that you ask for what you'd like to see happen. If you ask this way, you will both be more likely to get some of what you want.*
Mother:	*I'd like to have Jack get up after I've asked him once.*
Adolescent:	*But what if I don't hear you because I'm asleep?*
Clinician:	*Thanks, Jack, for identifying an obstacle. That's always important to do. But let's just let your parents work on asking for what they want in a real positive way first. We can sort out the problems later.*
Mother:	*Yeah, like the problem of him having to rush out the door without any breakfast.*
Father:	*And whose fault is it if he doesn't have time for breakfast?*

Adolescent:	*I'm not hungry in the morning anyway!*
Clinician:	*OK. Let's remember that we're going to try to use only positive communication today. I know that it's easy to fall back into old habits. Hey—look at the kind of statement I just used. Did anybody catch it?*
Adolescent:	*Which statement?*
Clinician:	*When I said that I knew it was easy to fall back into old communication habits.*
Adolescent:	*That's easy. It's an understanding statement.*
Clinician:	*You got it, Jack!*
Father:	*How come we never hear that kind of stuff at home?*
Clinician:	*Well, as I said before, this different way of communicating takes a lot of practice. And that's part of what we're here to work on today. So Mom, how about we take your basic request for Jack to get out of bed after you've only called him once, and we add an understanding statement to it. First of all, what's something you could show empathy for when it comes to Jack not wanting to get out of bed? Because an understanding statement is a way of showing empathy.*
Father:	*We shouldn't have to show empathy. He needs to get up. How's he ever going to make it at work someday?*
Clinician:	*But I think the real issue right now is that the two of you wanted to work on the problem of Jack having trouble getting out of bed in the morning. And we're trying something different; we're going the positive communication route. Now, we might have to do some problem solving around the issue too, but that can come later.*
Mother:	*I can say that I realize it's early and the bed feels really good, but he needs to get up and get going so he's not late.*
Clinician:	*Excellent! How about a partial responsibility statement? Can you add that?*
Mother:	*Do I have this right? Am I supposed to accept partial responsibility for Jack not getting up?*
Clinician:	*Yes. And even though you may not feel particularly responsible, a partial responsibility statement sure helps to get the other person to listen.*
Mother:	*I could take responsibility for not sending him to bed earlier, and he could then take responsibility for not going to bed. How about that?*
Father:	*Why don't we do this? Why don't we decide right here and now what time is the proper time to get out of the bed in the morning?*

Clinician: *I think it probably is a good idea to negotiate that. But let's hold off on that for a few minutes and just stick with our communication practice, if that's OK. Mom, the last piece is an offer to help. What do you think?*

Mother: *I could offer to set an earlier bedtime for him, but I'm not sure he'd like it.*

Adolescent: *You're right. I wouldn't.*

Clinician: *An offer to help is usually best when it really feels like something helpful to the other person. You're very wise, Mom, to see that Jack wouldn't experience an earlier bedtime as something welcome. Got anything else?*

Mother: *I could offer to remind him to set his alarm. He forgets to do that a lot.*

Clinician: *Good. Let's go with that for now.*

Father: [Teasing.] *I could offer to say, "Jack, get up. Your legs work fine."*

Clinician: *You certainly could, but again, we're trying to improve the situation, so I'm not sure. . . .*

Father: *I know. I'm just kidding around.*

Clinician: *Fair enough. Mom, can you put it all together and make your request? And make the request directly to Jack. Don't answer yet, Jack. We have to work on your end of the positive communication next.*

Mother: *Jack, I know you don't want to get up in the morning, especially when it's cold out and the bed feels really good. And I probably should have done something to help you get into the habit of going to bed earlier. Your sister used to stay up late too, and she had trouble getting up on time. How about if I remind you to set your alarm each night?*

Clinician: *Wow! You are good at this! You actually used all three components of positive communication. I loved the part about Jack's sister. A great start! All right. Jack, it's your turn. An understanding statement.*

Adolescent: *Same topic?*

Clinician: *Yes. About getting up.*

Adolescent: *Look, Mom and Dad, I understand you want me to get up out of bed on time, but 6:00 is too early. I've got a whole hour and 30 minutes to get up and get ready. Once I'm up, I'm ready.*

Clinician: *All right, Jack, what about partial responsibility? What can you say to show that you're accepting some responsibility for the problem?*

Adolescent: *I don't know. I should go to bed a little bit earlier so I can get up.*

Clinician:	*Excellent. You're accepting responsibility for it, right? OK. The offer to help is just that: offer to help solve the problem. What's that going to be?*
Adolescent:	*I will try.*
Mother:	*No, no, no, no. I will.*
Clinician:	*Don't worry, Mom. We will negotiate the details in a minute. We're just getting started.*
Adolescent:	*I will try to get to bed earlier every night. I'm not saying it will work, but I'll try.*
Clinician:	*Excellent. Very good. Can you put it all together and use all three components?*
Adolescent:	*Mom and Dad, I know it bugs you when I don't get up on time in the morning, and maybe I should go to bed earlier. I'll try harder.*
Father:	*That doesn't sound very convincing. It sounds like what we've heard before.*
Clinician:	*Interesting. Did all of it sound the same? Let's try this again, but this time, Mom, you start it off, and Jack, you respond. Go ahead and say it the way you both just practiced.*
Mother:	*Jack, I'd really appreciate it if you'd get up after I've only called you once. I know it's hard to get out of that warm bed, but I hate to see you late for school. I know your sister had the same problem. I probably should have gotten the two of you into the habit of going to bed earlier. How about if I remind you to set your alarm each night?*
Adolescent:	*Mom, I understand that you get bugged when I don't get up right away. And I know that you worry about me being late for school. I'll try harder to go to bed earlier. The alarm should help. Wait—is that all? I can't remember the rest.*
Clinician:	*Don't worry about it. Let's take a minute to discuss what it feels like to have somebody talk to you this way. Jack, what was it like to have your mom talk to you like this?*
Adolescent:	*It made me want to try to get up on time.*
Clinician:	*That's what I'd guess. And Mom, what was it like to have Jack respond to you like he did?*
Mother:	*I liked it. It felt like he respected me, and that he was really going to try harder.*
Clinician:	*I want to commend both of you. You're both really good at this. Mom, great job with offering to help when you said, "How about I remind you to set your alarm every night." And, Jack, you said two understanding statements to your mom when you told her you know she gets bugged when you don't get up right away and that she worries about you being late for school. Excellent job! And don't worry if you don't include all three components. Lots of time it helps to just add one or two of these statements. The one component that you could also add if you*

wanted to get all three in, Jack, is partial responsibility. You could say something like, "I know that I don't go to bed early enough."

Father: *But is anything going to change?*

Clinician: *That's the key question, isn't it? We've got two people who are listening to each other, which is half the battle, but what has to happen next? Let's start the negotiation, but still use positive communication. What are you all in agreement about so far?*

Father: *Looks like everybody agrees Jack should get up after just being called once. Right, Jack?*

Adolescent: *Yeah, I'm cool with that.*

Clinician: *And your mom offered to remind you about setting your alarm. How's that?*

Adolescent: *That's good, too.*

Clinician: *Your mom also accepted responsibility for not setting an earlier bedtime. How about we have the two of you discuss that?*

Mother: *Jack, instead of having a 10:30 bedtime, how about we make it 10:00? I know it would be hard to adjust to it at first, but maybe we could cut it back gradually, like make it 10:15 for the first week.*

Adolescent: *I really don't want an earlier bedtime. I mean, I understand that you think an earlier bedtime would help me get up earlier, but I'd like to try something else instead.*

Mother: *Like what?*

Adolescent: *Can we just stick with having you remind me about the alarm clock?*

Mother: *Yes, I'm willing to try that, but if it doesn't work, we'll have to figure something else out.*

Clinician: *You've both done a great job making the request and responding. You both used understanding statements. Mom, you said you knew it would be hard for Jack to adjust to an earlier bedtime at first. And Jack, you said you understood that Mom thinks an earlier bedtime is a good idea. Maybe the reminder to set the alarm will make all the difference, but if not, next time we get together we could go ahead and use problem solving skills to come up with another solution as well. What do you think?*

Adolescent: *Sounds good to me.*

Mother: *Sure.*

4. Practice problem solving skills.

Review the Problem Solving procedure (p. 141) because these skills are taught almost the same way in the Family Session. The procedure is modified slightly to accommodate the additional participants. All family members (and sometimes the clinician) offer potential solutions for the brainstorming step. Also, all family members are asked to take turns crossing off things they could not imagine themselves doing, so no one is asked to do something they do not want to do. Since typically all the family members are invested in the problem, they all must agree on the preferred solution. Thus, everyone participates fully in the remaining steps of problem solving. The selected solution, which often involves some type of action from each family member, becomes the assignment.

Clinician:	*So, why do you think it is important to talk about problem solving skills? Why would we want to practice problem solving skills?*
Mother:	*Everyone has problems, and they can be overwhelming.*
Adolescent:	*Yes, but when you learn how to break them down, it becomes easier to try and solve them.*
Clinician:	*So true! And we talk about how to address obstacles that might come up, too. I know we've all done problem solving before, so let's just go right into it. What's the first step?*
Adolescent:	*You've got to say what the problem is.*
Clinician:	*Exactly. That's real important. So, what is the problem we're talking about? Let's be real specific, because then we'll be able to come up with more helpful ideas during brainstorming.*
Father:	*The problem is that Jack doesn't get up when he's called in the morning.*
Clinician:	*Good. Anybody care to modify that slightly, given what we've already agreed upon as part of our communication skills work?*
Mother:	*I'd say that the problem is that Jack needs to get up after being called just once.*
Father:	*Last time we agreed that Mom would remind Jack to set the alarm, but we still had problems.*
Clinician:	*OK, it sounds like it would be helpful to spend a little more time on this problem. Maybe we'll end up changing it a little bit in the process as we discuss the problem more. And speaking of brainstorming . . .* [The procedure continues until they arrive at an agreeable solution.]

Since the first problem was one raised by the caregivers, the clinician would next return to the Relationship Happiness Scale so that the adolescent could have his turn making a specific request. Jack had chosen "allowance" as the category in which he wanted to see some change. His request would be shaped so that it ultimately was brief, specific, and positive. For example, assume that Jack started off saying only that he needed more money. The next iteration could be to request a $10 per week raise in his allowance. The clinician would remind Jack to use his positive communication skills in making his request. With assistance and practice, the final request might be, "Mom and Dad, I understand that you

173

don't think I do much around the house [understanding statement], and maybe I don't right now [partial responsibility], but I am willing to do more. So if I start doing extra chores, like washing dishes [offer to help], can I get another $10 each week in my allowance?" The parents would then negotiate with Jack. For instance, they might agree to an increase in pay only if a specific additional chore is identified and completed each day. Alternatively, they might agree to only a $5 raise. The clinician would remind each family member to use positive communication skills throughout.

5. **Review the Daily Reminder to Be Nice (recommended for the first Family Session).**
   - **Provide a rationale for its use.**
   - **Tell both the caregivers and the client that it is important to complete at least one item every day, even if the other person does not.**
   - **Ask the caregivers and the client to find a good place to keep their forms.**
   - **Encourage each family member to come up with examples for at least one category and assist as needed.**

The Daily Reminder to Be Nice can be introduced in either family session. It is ideal to introduce this procedure during the first session so that the family can have homework related to its use and you can check in with them in their second session about how well they did. See the end of this chapter for a copy of the form (p. 180).

Clinician:	*You guys have been doing a terrific job today!*
Father:	*That's because we're all working together like a team. That's how it should always be.*
Clinician:	*And hopefully it will happen more often, since you can now all use your communication skills. We have one thing yet to do today. I mentioned it earlier. It's called the Daily Reminder to Be Nice. I think you folks are ready for this type of exercise. I'll explain it now and we'll practice a little, but it's something you'll also do as an assignment, if you think it makes sense for you all.*
Mother:	*We need all the help we can get, so I'm sure it will make sense.*
Clinician:	*Good. Basically, we use the Daily Reminder to Be Nice as a way to make sure there are some positive interactions going on in the home every day . . . even when people might not feel like being particularly nice to each other. It's a way to jump-start the pleasant interactions. Although they might feel a little artificial at first, over time they feel very natural. And when one person is saying and doing nice things, it's contagious! The rest of the family tends to automatically join in.*
Father:	*What kinds of things are you talking about? We're all so busy. . . .*
Clinician:	*Good question. They're little things, inexpensive and not very time-consuming. Let's go over a few examples. Take a look at the form. Jack, can you read the first item?*
Adolescent:	*"Did you express appreciation to the other person today?" Appreciation for what?*

Clinician:	*That's the beauty of it. It can be appreciation for anything. Take a moment to think. What's some little thing you can express appreciation to either your mom or dad for?*
Adolescent:	*Mom and Dad, I appreciate you coming to my session today.*
Mother:	*You're welcome, honey.*
Clinician:	*Dad, how did that sound to you?*
Father:	*It sounded good. But if we have to do these, how do I know whether he's just saying these things because he's supposed to?*
Clinician:	*Actually, it might start off that Jack is just saying these things because he's supposed to, but eventually they naturally become sincere because the atmosphere in your home will be getting better. And as all of you start to get along better, you'll all feel like saying and doing nice things for the rest of the family.*
Father:	*I guess so.*
Clinician:	*Well, also remember that you each get to choose which of these items you want to do each day, and how you want to satisfy it. So I would guess that there will be underlying truth to what you choose to say. Anyway, is it worth a try? You can always drop it if it doesn't seem to help.*
Mother:	*I definitely think it's worth a try.*
Father:	*Yeah, you're right.*
Clinician:	*Jack?*
Adolescent:	*Sure. How many are we supposed to do each day?*
Clinician:	*Good question. Just one. Always remember to do at least one thing, even if the other person does not seem to be doing any. You can do more than one if you want to, but one is enough. And Jack, technically you only have to do one of these things for one of your parents each day, but if you're up for a challenge you could try to do one for each of your parents each day. What do you think?*
Adolescent:	*I think it depends on how hard they are to do. And if I remember.*
Clinician:	*Good points. Forgetting to do stuff can always be an obstacle for any kind of assignment, can't it? Let's get to that in a minute. Anyway, you just did the first item. You expressed appreciation to both of your parents for coming today. How would you rate how hard that was to do?*
Adolescent:	*It was pretty easy.*

Clinician:	*Glad to hear that. Let me ask your parents to try that one out before we continue. Hopefully, we'll address your concerns as we go along. Mom and Dad, can you express appreciation to Jack for something?*
Mother:	*Jack, I appreciate the fact that you are coming to therapy every week, even though you didn't want to at first.*
Adolescent:	*Sure, Mom.*
Clinician:	*How did that feel, Jack? Can you tell your mom?*
Adolescent:	*It was nice, Mom.*
Clinician:	*Good job. Dad?*
Father:	*Jack, I appreciate that you're being more honest with us.*
Adolescent:	*Thanks, Dad.*
Clinician:	*Excellent. Let's skip down to the third one: "Did you give the other person a pleasant surprise?" What do you think about that one? Who wants to go first? Just tell us what you could do for that.*
Adolescent:	*I could clean up my room without my mom getting after me for it.*
Mother:	*That would be a great surprise!*
Adolescent:	*But now I can't do it because it wouldn't be a surprise. [Teasing.]*
Mother:	*You can still surprise me because I won't know which day you're going to do it.*
Clinician:	*Good for you, Mom. An excellent idea, Jack. Who's next for the surprise?*
Father:	*And you said we don't have to do each of these every day, right? So maybe I'd be doing the surprise once a week?*
Clinician:	*That would be perfectly fine. Actually, you wouldn't ever have to pick the surprise one if you didn't want to. You could do just the others. But I'd really encourage you to try them all out. Mix it up a bit, you know?*
Father:	*No, that's fine. I was just thinking that I could take everyone out to eat some night for my surprise, but I didn't want to be expected to do something like that all the time.*
Clinician:	*That's totally reasonable to only do a surprise of that size now and then. But who knows? I'm hoping that eventually your family will want to do activities like eating out together on a regular basis. But that's down the road a ways. Jack, what would that be like if your dad took you and your mom out to eat for a surprise?*
Adolescent:	*That would be fun. Oh wait—would I get to pick the restaurant?*

Father:	*We'd all get some say in it. We'd discuss it using our communication skills.* [Teasing.]
Mother:	*Or we'd problem solve how to pick one.* [Teasing.]
Clinician:	*You guys are too much! I've created a monster! Mom, what about your surprise?*
Mother:	*I could make their favorite dessert, chocolate cream pie.*
Adolescent:	*That's a great surprise!*
Father:	*I second that.*
Clinician:	*It's settled then. OK. You all get the idea. And I should also mention that it's important to go ahead and do one of these items each day, even if you're not sure whether the rest of the family is doing them. You might just have missed what they did. And then the whole thing will fall apart if everyone waits for the other person to do something. Agreed?*
Father:	*Agreed.*
Clinician:	*Good. Jack raised an important issue earlier when he said that he might forget to do this. So what's a good way to address this potential obstacle?*
Mother:	*We could use a magnet and put it on the refrigerator.*
Adolescent:	*We could buy a small bulletin board. My friends have those in their kitchens.*
Father:	*I could make us a small bulletin board so we don't have to buy one.*
Clinician:	*Now that's what I call teamwork again!*

Additional Notes

- Although there is sample dialogue for all the procedures in this one chapter, it is important to remember there should be two sessions planned to complete the required items. A-CRA clinicians have found that trying to fit all of the components into one session is too much for the family. Participants are more likely to retain all of the skills taught if they are spread over two sessions.
- If you are new to doing family sessions, we highly recommend that you practice the session ahead of time with a colleague.
- There can be situations in which the family devolves into arguing. Most of the time it will be possible to ask the family to take a time out, take some deep breaths, and then get back to the procedure after everyone is calmed down. On rare occasions, it might be necessary to end the session, modify the procedure, or use other de-escalation techniques. Sessions end with the clinician asking the family to state what the assignments are for the week. As noted, if you think it is clinically necessary and resources are available to do so, more than two family sessions can be scheduled.

Relationship Happiness Scale
(Adolescent Version)

Name:_____ **ID:** _____ **Date:** _____

This scale is intended to estimate your current happiness with your relationship with your parent or caregiver in each of the areas listed below. You are to circle one of the numbers (1 to 10) beside each area. Numbers toward the left end of the 10-unit scale indicate various degrees of unhappiness, whereas numbers toward the right end of the scale reflect increasing levels of happiness. Ask yourself this question as you rate each life area: "How happy am I today with my parent in this area?" In other words, indicate according to the numerical scale (1 to 10) exactly how you feel today. Try to exclude feelings of yesterday and concentrate only on the feelings of today in each of the life areas. Also, try not to allow one category to influence the results of the other categories.

	Completely Unhappy								Completely Happy	
1. Time spent with me	1	2	3	4	5	6	7	8	9	10
2. Allowance	1	2	3	4	5	6	7	8	9	10
3. Communication	1	2	3	4	5	6	7	8	9	10
4. Affection	1	2	3	4	5	6	7	8	9	10
5. Support of school/work	1	2	3	4	5	6	7	8	9	10
6. Emotional support	1	2	3	4	5	6	7	8	9	10
7. General home activities	1	2	3	4	5	6	7	8	9	10
8. General happiness	1	2	3	4	5	6	7	8	9	10

Relationship Happiness Scale
(Caregiver Version)

Name:_____ **ID:** _____ **Date:** _____

This scale is intended to estimate your current happiness with your relationship with your adolescent in each of the eight areas listed below. You are to circle one of the numbers (1 to 10) beside each area. Numbers toward the left end of the 10-unit scale indicate various degrees of unhappiness, whereas numbers toward the right end of the scale reflect increasing levels of happiness. Ask yourself this question as you rate each area: "How happy am I today with my adolescent in this area?" In other words, indicate according to the numerical scale (1 to 10) exactly how you feel today. Try to exclude feelings of yesterday and concentrate only on the feelings of today in each of the life areas. Also, try not to allow one category to influence the results of the other categories.

	Completely Unhappy									Completely Happy
1. Household responsibilities	1	2	3	4	5	6	7	8	9	10
2. Communication	1	2	3	4	5	6	7	8	9	10
3. Affection	1	2	3	4	5	6	7	8	9	10
4. Job or school	1	2	3	4	5	6	7	8	9	10
5. Emotional support	1	2	3	4	5	6	7	8	9	10
6. Time spent with adolescent	1	2	3	4	5	6	7	8	9	10
7. General home atmosphere	1	2	3	4	5	6	7	8	9	10
8. General happiness	1	2	3	4	5	6	7	8	9	10

A-CRA
Daily Reminder to Be Nice

Name: _____

Week Starting: _____

Activity	Day						
	Sun	Mon	Tue	Wed	Thu	Fri	Sat
Did you express appreciation to the other person today?							
Did you compliment the other person on something?							
Did you give the other person a pleasant surprise?							
Did you express affection?							
Did you initiate pleasant conversation?							
Did you offer to help?							

Communication Skills

The goal of using communication skills is to be able to get your message across to another person to help you get what you want. Using these communication skills should enable people to compromise or agree on a solution to a problem. When everyone agrees on a solution, compliance by both sides and contentment with the solution are more likely. It is important to stay positive during the communication skills training and avoid blaming.

Understanding statement. The goal of the understanding statement is to open up communication and show that you are aware of another person's thoughts on a problem. That is:

- **Come from the other person's perspective.**
  Example: "Mom, I understand you would like my room cleaned because it is a real mess, and you would like the house to be clean when friends come over."
- **Come from your perspective.**
  Example: "But Jimmy is having a birthday party at his house, and I have not seen Jimmy for a while, so I would really like to go."
- **Make a request (a request should be brief, positive, and specific).**
  Example: "I would really appreciate it if you would let me clean my room later tonight, maybe around 8 p.m. when I get home."

Partial responsibility. The goal of the statement of partial responsibility is to avoid blaming the other person. Remember to state how you or the other person see yourselves fitting into the problem or solution. That is:

- **How do you fit into the problem?**
  Example: "I know I made a real mess by not putting my clothes away, and I have not always followed through with cleaning my room, and I am sorry about that."
- **Repeat the request (optional).**
  Example: "But I would really appreciate if you would let me clean my room around 8 p.m. tonight after I get home from Jimmy's party."

Offer to help. The offer to help is used to show that you are willing to work on a solution that works for everyone and that you would like input from others on possible solutions. That is:

- **Offer several possible solutions.**
  Example: "If there is anything I can do to help make that happen—help out with another chore around the house, help out with dinner, or just do a quick 10-minute cleaning for now and do the rest later—I would really appreciate it."
- **State your openness to listen to and consider the other person's ideas.**
  Example: "Or if there is anything that you can think of, I would be willing to listen."

Following the offer to help, the other person may try to compromise on a solution or do some problem solving. It may be necessary to go through the communication skills again to state your point.

How Do I Solve This Problem?

1. **Define your problem.** Just one. Keep it real specific. Write it below.

2. **Brainstorm possible solutions.** The more the better! List below.

3. **Eliminate unwanted suggestions.** Cross out any that you can't imagine doing yourself.

4. **Select one potential solution.** Which one can you imagine yourself doing this week? Circle it.

5. **Generate possible obstacles.** What might get in the way of this working? List below.

6. **Address each obstacle.** If you can't solve each obstacle, pick a new solution and go through the steps again.

7. **Make the selected solution for your assignment this week.** List below exactly when and how you'll do it.

8. **Evaluate the outcome.** Did it work? If some changes are needed, list them below and commit to trying it again.

UNIT 2: CHAPTER 15: Couple Relationship Skills

Rationale

Partners or significant others (SOs) can play an important role in clients' recovery process because they are an important part of their social networks and environments. Helping improve these relationships may increase the benefits that clients derive from treatment. TAYs are typically more likely to be involved in relationships with SOs than are younger adolescents. When making the decision to involve SOs in treatment, the clinician should consider the following: the quality of the relationship with the SO, who the client lives with, and whether the SO is supportive of the client's goals. As with the procedures in the Adolescent-Caregiver Relationship Skills sessions, it often takes a fair amount of time to complete all the procedures well. Thus, allowances have been made to complete this procedure over two sessions.

Learning Objectives

The learning objectives are to help clients and their partners:

- Learn how it feels to say positive things about the other person and hear positive things about oneself.
- Learn how to complete the Couple Relationship Happiness Scale.
- Become more comfortable using positive communication with each other.
- Become more comfortable using problem solving skills with each other.
- Learn how to use the Daily Reminder to Be Nice.

Timing, Audience, and Delivery Method

There is no prescribed timing for these sessions, although it is recommended that the client has already learned Communication Skills and Problem Solving Skills and completed at least one Happiness Scale. Review the guidelines below under "General Notes for Clinicians" to help with the decision about when to conduct Couple Relationship Skills or Family Sessions with particular clients.

Materials

Procedure-specific materials include:

- The Couple Relationship Happiness Scale (p. 195; both partners use the same versions), clipboards, and pens.
- For problem solving: The How Do I Solve This Problem form (p. 200), chalkboard or whiteboard, markers or chalk, and possibly an easel.
- For communication skills: The Communication Skills handout (p. 199), chalkboard or whiteboard, markers or chalk, possibly an easel.
- The Daily Reminder to Be Nice form (p. 201).
- The Perfect Relationship form (p. 196).

General Notes for the Clinician

These sessions within CRA are present-oriented, behavioral, and skill-based.

Couple Relationship Skills are generally more likely to be needed with TAYs than with younger adolescents. But you need to evaluate the individual situation to determine whether Couple Relationship Skills, Caregiver-Adolescent Relationship Skills, or both should be conducted with TAYs. A-CRA trainees have reported that many TAYs still live with their parents because they have not yet attained financial independence. It is also possible that a younger person may have a strong enough relationship with an SO to merit a Couple Relationship Skills session. The following guidelines are provided to help make the decision regarding whether to offer a Caregiver-Adolescent Relationship Skills Session, a Couple Relationship session, or both.

A. The TAY is still living with his or her parents (regardless of other circumstances, such as whether there's a boyfriend or girlfriend in the picture, a baby, etc.):
   - Strongly Recommended: Family Sessions and Caregiver Only Sessions (note: normally the client's SO would not attend the family sessions).
   - Circumstances under which you could also do Couple Sessions:
     o The TAY has a partner who is also living with the TAY's family.
     o The TAY is planning to move out relatively soon and live with a partner.
     o The TAY is determined to make a relationship with a partner work even though they are not living together or planning to do so in the near future.
       • In this situation, we recommend first offering Couple Sessions to respect the client as an adult and at the same time starting work on Caregiver Only Sessions. However, if there is difficulty getting either the caregiver or the partner in for a session, schedule whoever you can get in first.

B. The TAY is living with boyfriend or girlfriend:
   - Strongly Recommended: Couple Sessions.
   - Circumstances under which we would also recommend you do a Family Session:
     o The client seems interested in having a caregiver come in (e.g., it might come up when reviewing the "relationship with parents/caregivers" item on the Happiness Scale).
     o The caregivers are still influential in the client's life (e.g., there is a grandchild that the caregivers want to be involved with).
       • If the decision is made to conduct Family Sessions, the clinician should also do the Caregiver Only Sessions. However, in this situation the four positive parenting practices (p. 152) would need to be modified slightly (particularly the one that asks the caregiver to monitor the client's whereabouts closely).
       • There are no standard "partner only" sessions, so normally they would not be conducted. However, if you feel it would improve the success of the Couple Relationship sessions, you could meet with the partner alone and teach Communication or Problem Solving Skills as well as take the opportunity to explain A-CRA and emphasize the positive approach.

C. The TAY is living alone (or with friends):
   - Recommended: Either Family or Couple Sessions (based on clinical judgment), depending on who the client has contact with and who the client would like to involve. For example, there is always an option to have a friend or roommate come to a session when working on Relapse Prevention or Drink/Drug Refusal or to help with practicing Communication and Problem Solving Skills.

Remember that the Couple Relationship Skills session will end with homework, just like client sessions. A typical homework assignment is to use the Daily Reminder to Be Nice form during the week. It is also appropriate for homework to be based on the Perfect Relationship form.

Procedural Steps

1. **Have each person face the other and say three positive things about the other person (required during the first Couple Session).**
    *   **Explain that doing this helps set a positive tone for the session.**
    *   **Offer assistance if they have trouble thinking of three things, or praise their efforts.**
    *   **Remind them to speak directly to each other.**
    *   **Ask the recipient to repeat back what was heard.**
2. **Complete the Couple Relationship Happiness Scales (required during the first Couple Relationship session).**
    *   **Provide rationale.**
    *   **Give instructions.**
    *   **Review some ratings.**
3. **Set goals according to the guidelines and list on the Perfect Relationship form (required during the first Couple Session).**
4. **Teach and practice the Communication Skills procedure.**
5. **Teach and practice the Problem Solving procedure.**
6. **Review the Daily Reminder to Be Nice form (recommended for the first Couple Session).**
    *   **Provide a rationale for its use.**
    *   **Tell the partners that it is important to complete at least one item every day, even if the other person does not.**
    *   **Ask the partners to find a good place to keep their forms.**
    *   **Encourage each partner to come up with examples for at least one category and assist as needed.**

Detailed Description

1. **Have each person face the other and say three positive things about the other person.**
    *   **Explain that doing this helps set a positive tone for the session.**
    *   **Offer assistance if they have trouble thinking of three things, or praise their efforts.**
    *   **Remind them to speak directly to each other.**
    *   **Ask the recipient to repeat back what was heard.**

It is helpful to start the session with a brief overview of what is going to happen during the session and to check in with the client and his or her partner to make sure that there have not been any crises the previous week that will need to be addressed during the session. If there are crises mentioned, you will need to use your clinical judgment to decide whether they need to be addressed right away or can be processed during the course of completing other procedures in the session. Regarding other concerns that do not rise to the level of a true crisis, you can say that you will put them on the agenda and come back to them later in the session. Often they will come up in the context of the Couple Relationship Happiness Scale. Next, you will want to move to the Three Positive Things exercise. Since the main point of this exercise is to set a positive stage for the remainder of the session, it is important for you to keep the exercise positive with praise and constructive feedback; doing so helps prevent the discussion from deteriorating into blaming or an argument. Often, participants may try to talk through the clinician, so make sure the partners are talking to and listening to each other during the exercise. There is a lot of material to cover in these sessions, so the Three Positive Things exercise should be completed in less than 10 minutes. Remember that you have at least two sessions with the couple to get through all the session components. The Three Positive Things exercise is optional but recommended for the second couple session. The example below is with a same-sex couple, although the same example would be relevant for an opposite-sex couple.

Clinician:	*I'm glad you both came here today. It's really nice to meet you, Leslie. Before we get started, I want to check in briefly with Chris about her homework. How did it go this week, Chris?* [They spend a little time reviewing, and the clinician tells the client that they will do a more thorough review in his next individual session.] *Good. Then I'll start by giving you an overview of what we're going to do today. But first, I want to see if anything major happened during the week that we need to make sure we set aside time to address today. Anything?*
Client:	*No, just the usual stuff.*
Clinician:	*OK. Leslie, was there anything that you are really concerned about?*
Partner:	*No, I can't think of anything.*
Clinician:	*OK. So I'll go ahead with the agenda then. We're going to start by having you each say three positive things about each other. I know there are reasons why you want to be together. Sometimes in our day-to-day lives we forget to tell our partners what it is that we like and love about them, and we want to increase the likelihood that you'll take the time to do that. Then we'll do what's called the Couple Relationship Happiness Scale so that we can see how happy you are with each other in different areas of your relationship and where you'd like to see some changes. Chris, you've done the regular Happiness Scale already, so this will look familiar to you.*
Client:	*Oh, OK.*
Clinician:	*It is short and sweet. Next, we'll try to negotiate some of the changes you'd like to see, set some goals, and put them on a form called the Perfect Relationship form. We all want a perfect relationship, right? We might not get perfect, but we'll get closer to perfect! If we have time today, we'll practice communication skills and problem solving skills. If not, we'll do them next time. We'll finish up with an assignment to do an exercise called the Daily Reminder to Be Nice. I know this sound like a lot, but we can accomplish this in two sessions. How does that sound?*
Partner:	*This is all new to me—it sounds like it might help us.*
Clinician:	*Yes, we find that most couples really like these sessions and it is helpful to their relationship. Chris, can you start by telling Leslie the three positive things about her you wanted to share? We had a chance to talk about these in our last session, and you came up with some good ones!*
Client:	*Sure. Leslie wants to help me get sober—and I appreciate that.*
Clinician:	*Let me interrupt for a minute here. That's a good start, but remember you are talking to Leslie, not me, so how would you say this to Leslie?*

Client:	OK. Leslie, I appreciate you want me to get sober. You are also fun to be with and of course, you know I think you are pretty.
Clinician:	*Very good! These are terrific! I like how you looked at Leslie when you were telling her those things.* [As in the Caregiver-Adolescent Relationship Skills Session, the clinician asks the partner to repeat what was said and how she feels about it, and then goes through the exercise with the partner.]

2. **Complete the Couple Relationship Happiness Scales (required during the first Couple Relationship session).**
   - **Provide rationale.**
   - **Give instructions.**
   - **Review some ratings.**

You will begin by explaining the Couple Relationship Happiness Scale. It is often worthwhile to ask clients to explain it to their partners because they have already completed Happiness Scales and it allows them to show off a little (in a positive way) in front of their partners. It also helps clients feel more involved in the session. Prior to the session, it is important for clinicians to review the Happiness Scale chapter (p. 28) for a refresher regarding what should be covered for the rationale and instructions. Completing the Couple Relationship Happiness Scale differs from completing the Happiness Scale in that each participant rates how happy he or she is with the partner in the various categories.

Begin the review of their responses to the Couple Relationship Happiness Scale by highlighting several of the categories that received high ratings. Again, concentrating first on those areas that are rated high helps foster a positive tone in the session and reminds the partners that there are aspects of each other that they truly like and appreciate. You should briefly review high, middle, and low-rated categories (time permitting) before moving on to guiding a goal selection. Then help the couple select one or two areas in which they would like their partner to develop goals. Use of the Couple Relationship Happiness Scale is optional but highly recommended for the second couple session.

Clinician:	*Nice job, you two! Let's move on now to the Couple Relationship Happiness Scale* [p. 195]. *Here. I'll give you each a copy. Chris, do you want to start off with the instructions? You've done a slightly different version of this before. I'll explain what is different with this version in a minute.*
Client:	*See these numbers from 1 to 10 here on this chart? You're supposed to circle how you feel right now in each of these areas. And see how it goes from "completely unhappy" on one end to "completely happy" on the other end. Is that enough?*
Clinician:	*Sure! That's good! Now here's the part that's different. Instead of indicating how happy you are with yourself in each area, you'll be saying how happy you are with your partner in each area. Then we can look at your ratings and talk about areas that are going well in your relationship and areas that you both agree you want to change, then set goals in those areas. We can also use this tool to see if things change over time. Does that make sense?*
Client:	*It does to me.*
Clinician:	*Leslie, I know this is new to you. Is it making sense to you?*

Partner:	*I think I got it.*
Clinician:	*Good. And when you fill this out, try to rate each category independently. Don't let your feelings about one category influence how you rate another. I know that's hard sometimes, but do the best you can. And just so you know, when you're done, we can take a look at the ratings and decide what areas you both want to work on.* [The clinician gives the client and her partner time to complete the Couple Happiness Scales; she reviews some ratings with them following the guidelines for the Happiness Scale procedure then begins to work with them on setting goals.]

3. **Set goals according to the guidelines and list on the Perfect Relationship form (required during the first Couple Session).**

Clinician:	*The next thing we can do with this information is to set some goals for each of you to work on this next week. Each of you can choose an area you'd like your partner to work on. It is good to start with one of the areas that were rated in the middle, say between 4 and 7, because it is easier to improve in an area where you are doing somewhat good already. Also, when we work on goals, we need to be brief, specific, and say it in a positive way. Who would like to go first?*
Partner:	*I will. So, what exactly do I do?*
Clinician:	*Thanks for being willing to go first, Leslie. So look at your Happiness Scale and how you rated Chris in each area. Which one of those areas would you like for Chris to work on? We can work together to set a goal for Chris in that area. Keep in mind that we might need to do some negotiating to get Chris to agree with the strategy for reaching the goal.*
Partner:	*OK. I'd kind of like for Chris to work on something about money management? We have some problems with money.*
Clinician:	*Yes, that is an area that is difficult for a lot of couples. I see you rated it a 5— kind of in the middle. And we talked earlier about how you know she wants to be more careful with money, but you are often surprised when she brings home stuff she's bought. What would you like to ask Chris to do in the area of money management?*
Partner:	*I'd just like her to keep track of our expenses so we can see where the money is going.*
Clinician:	*Let's review how that fits the rules for setting goals. What you said is brief and stated in a positive way. Can you be a little more specific about what you mean by keeping track of expenses?*
Partner:	*Well, I have this notebook that we could use, and she could write what she spends in there every day, and then we could look at it together at the end of the week.*
Clinician:	*OK. We're getting there. Chris, what do you think about this goal? Would you be willing to do this?*

Client:	*Well, I don't know if I want to write it down every time I spend money. That would be a lot.*
Clinician:	*OK. We can negotiate a bit here. This is a good time to learn and practice positive communication skills. These skills will help you guys as you negotiate what you want to do in this area.* [The Communication Skills and Problem Solving Skills procedures are taught so that the couple can use these skills during the process of setting goals on the Perfect Relationship form. In the example above, problem solving also might be used to come up with an agreeable solution to tracking expenses. The clinician helps facilitate negotiation between the two parties until they arrive at a goal both are satisfied with and writes it on the Perfect Relationship form. Using positive communication skills and problem solving skills, each partner will have the opportunity to set goals during the session in one to two areas.]

4. Teach and practice the Communication Skills procedure.

Refer back to the Communication Skills procedure (p. 123) for more details about using this procedure. One difference with this procedure in the Couple Sessions is that it is unnecessary to do the reverse role play because both parties are in the session. Note that since there is a lot of material to cover in the session, it might be difficult to get through communication skills and problem solving in the first Couple Session.

Clinician:	*OK, let's work a little on positive communication skills. Leslie, Chris and I have talked before about how all of us can probably improve how we communicate. This is especially important for couples. Positive communication skills are important because the other person is more likely to listen to us and not get angry. The other person may be more likely to do what we ask. Can either of you think of any other reasons why positive communication is important in your relationship?*
Partner:	*Well, I just think it would be more pleasant around the house and it would feel more like it did when we were first together.*
Clinician:	*Yes. That's a good reason. Chris, can you think of another reason?*
Client:	*I think that covers it pretty well.*
Clinician:	*OK. Now Chris, since you've done this before, can you tell Leslie the three components that we talk about with positive communication skills?*
Client:	*I remember that you start with an understanding statement and you offer to help. And then there is that other part.*
Clinician:	*That's good. You remembered two of them. Why do we use understanding statements?*
Client:	*Saying these things helps the other person know that we get where they are coming from—how they think about things.*

Clinician: *Excellent Chris! And we use the offer to help to show that we are willing to help with whatever solution we need to help make the situation better for both people. So the other part is to take partial responsibility. Here, let me give you this handout on Communication Skills to help you out. Taking partial responsibility is explaining how you might have contributed to creating a problem with the situation you are discussing. OK. Let's decide on an area that you both would want to talk about. Maybe it can be something that came up when we did the Couple Relationship Happiness Scales. Do either of you have an idea? Chris, since you've done this before, would you be willing to go first, so we can show Leslie how it is done?*

Client: *Well, we could talk about Leslie cooking dinner a little more often.*

Clinician: *OK. We can do that. Are you OK with that, Leslie?*

Partner: *I guess so.*

Clinician: *Well, this different way of communicating takes a lot of practice. And that's part of what we're here to work on today. So Chris, how about we take your basic request for Leslie to cook dinner more often and we add an understanding statement to it. First of all, what's something you could show empathy for when it comes to Leslie not cooking dinner as much as you'd like? Because an understanding statement is a way of showing empathy.*

Client: *I can say that I understand she is tired after work and may not feel like cooking dinner.*

Clinician: *Excellent! How about a partial responsibility statement? Can you add that?*

Client: *I could take responsibility for not liking to cook—so it sort of falls on her a lot.*

Clinician: *Yes. That's good. Now, how about an offer to help? This is always important because it shows you're willing to work with Leslie to come to a solution, and I think you can see how it is important with a request like this.*

Client: *I don't know. I don't know how to cook. Maybe I could offer to help order pizza sometime instead of her having to cook.*

Clinician: *That might work; can you put it all together and make your request? And make the request directly to Leslie. Don't answer yet, Leslie. We have to work on your end of the positive communication next.*

Client: *Leslie, I understand that you are tired after work, and it's a lot on you because I hate cooking, but can you cook more often? Some nights I could help by ordering pizza.*

Clinician: *That was good Chris! You actually used all three components of positive communication. A great start! All right. Leslie, it's your turn. Can you say an understanding statement back to Chris?*

Partner: *About me cooking dinner?*

Clinician: *Yes, that's right—in response to his request that you cook dinner more often.*

Partner: *I understand, Chris, that you would like me to cook dinner sometimes.*

Clinician: *All right, Leslie, what about partial responsibility? What can you say to show that you're accepting responsibility for the problem?*

Partner: *Does this work? I don't always have stuff to cook because it is hard to get to the grocery store.*

Clinician: *Excellent. You're accepting responsibility for it, right? OK. The offer to help is just that: offer to help solve the problem. What's that going to be?*

Partner: *I'll try to cook more often.*

Clinician: *OK. It will be helpful to negotiate the details. Could you be a little more specific—like how often you might cook dinner?*

Partner: *I will try to cook dinner at least 4 nights a week.*

Clinician: *Excellent. Very good. Can you put it all together and use all three components? This time I'd like you guys to go back and forth several times and I'm not going to interrupt. Leslie, since we've been through an example, you can try to use those three parts to communication too. [It helps the participants learn these skills to let them have a few exchanges with each other before providing feedback.]*

Partner: *Chris, I understand you would like me to cook dinner more often. It's hard because I am tired after work and I don't always have stuff to cook. I will try to cook dinner at least 4 nights a week.*

Client: *Leslie, I understand you don't have stuff to make sometimes. Maybe I could help with the grocery shopping sometimes.*

Partner: *I know you are busy too, and I appreciate that you are willing to try doing that. Sometimes I don't plan very far ahead, but I could try and I could make a list for you.*

Client: *That would be good—because I'm not sure I'd know what to get.*

Clinician: *Let's take a minute to discuss what it feels like to have somebody talk to you this way. Leslie, what was it like to have Chris talk to you like this?*

Partner: *I definitely liked it better than her saying I never cook, which isn't true! If she would really help more, I think I could cook more meals.*

Clinician: *Chris, what did you think about what Leslie said?*

Client: *I liked her understanding statement. You know, saying she knew I was busy. I also liked how she offered to help by making a list.*

Clinician:	*Yes, she did do those things well. She also took some responsibility by saying that she knew she didn't plan well. You also had a good understanding statement when you acknowledged that she doesn't have groceries all the time. You also offered to help by saying you would go grocery shopping. I didn't hear the partial responsibility part. What might you have said?*
Client:	*Well, I could have said that I don't like to cook and am not much help in that area.*
Clinician:	*Yes, that would have been good. All in all, you guys did a really good job with your communication just then.* [The clinician will help the couple get more specific on how cooking four times a week will happen while encouraging them to continue to use positive communication skills and giving specific feedback about what they do well and what they can improve. The resulting goal should be brief, specific, and measurable, then written on the Perfect Relationship form. Typically, teaching and practicing Problem Solving skills would take place in the second session.]

5. Teach and practice the Problem Solving procedure.

Unlike with the caregivers in most Caregiver-Adolescent Relationship Skill Sessions, the partner in Couple Sessions has not yet learned the Problem Solving procedure in an individual session, so you will need to teach these skills to the partner. It is useful to review the Problem Solving procedure (Unit 2, Chapter 12 [p. 141]) because the procedure is conducted quite similarly to how it is done in the Couple Session. One modification entails accommodating the additional participant by giving both partners the opportunity to raise one or more problems to discuss. Also, for the brainstorming step both partners, and sometimes the clinician, offer potential solutions. Since typically both partners are invested in the problem, they both must agree on the preferred solution, and they each participate fully in the remaining steps of problem solving. Remind the partners to use positive communication skills during the problem solving exercise, and remember to give them the How Do I Solve This Problem? form (p. 200). The selected solution, which often involves some type of action from each partner, becomes the assignment.

6. Review the Daily Reminder to Be Nice form (recommended for the first Couple Session).
   - **Provide a rationale for its use.**
   - **Tell the partners that it is important to complete at least one item every day, even if the other person does not.**
   - **Ask the partners to find a good place to keep their forms.**
   - **Encourage each partner to come up with examples for at least one category and assist as needed.**

It is ideal to introduce the Daily Reminder to Be Nice form in the first couple session so that they can have homework related to its use and you can check in with them in their second couple session about how well they did. See the end of this chapter for a copy of the form (p. 201).

Clinician:	*You guys have been doing a great job today!*
Partner:	*Yeah, I like what we have been talking about.*
Client:	*Yeah, it's helpful to have you come with me.*

Clinician:	*Chris, that's great how you just showed your appreciation to Leslie. We have one thing yet to do today. I mentioned it earlier. It's called the Daily Reminder to Be Nice. I think you two are ready for this type of exercise. I'll explain it now and we'll practice a little, but it's something you'll also do as an assignment, if you think it makes sense for you.*
Client:	*OK.*
Partner:	*OK.*
Clinician:	*Good.* [The clinician hands each partner a Daily Reminder to Be Nice form.] *This form was developed to help couples improve their relationship and it works really well. It is a way to make sure there are some positive interactions going on in the home every day . . . even when one of you might not feel like being particularly nice to the other. It's a way to jump-start the pleasant interactions. Although some of these things might feel a little artificial at first, over time they feel very natural. And when one person is saying and doing nice things, it's contagious! The other person tends to reciprocate.*
Client:	*This is a lot of things to do. . . .*
Clinician:	*Yes, it might look that way at first. But you'll see they're really little things: most of them don't cost anything and they are not very time-consuming. And the goal is to do* one *thing from the list every day. It's important to do that one thing, even if your partner does not seem to be doing one. Let's go over a few examples. Take a look at the form. Chris, can you read the first item?*
Client:	*"Did you express appreciation to the other person today?" Appreciation for what?*
Clinician:	*Well, you just did this a little while ago when you told Leslie it was helpful for her to come to the session. That's the beauty of it. It can be appreciation for anything. Take a moment to think. What's some little thing you can express appreciation to Leslie for?*
Client:	*Hmmm, you mean like how she tells me she loves me?*
Clinician:	*Yes, that's an excellent example. Can you look at Leslie and tell her that?*
Client:	*OK. Leslie, I appreciate that you tell me that you love me.*
Clinician:	*How did that make you feel, Leslie?*
Partner:	*Good. I'm not sure she's ever said that to me before.*
Clinician:	*Good! That's what we are after—to make both of you feel good about yourselves and your relationship because of the little things you say and do for each other.* [The clinician encourages each partner to come up with examples for at least two categories and has each partner practice one of the activities by talking directly to the other. The clinician reminds them that it is important to find a central place to post the form and tells them that it is important to choose at least one activity to

complete every day, even if the other person does not. Remember to thoroughly assess obstacles and discuss ways to overcome them before completing the exercise.]

Additional Notes

Sessions end with the clinician asking the couple to state what the assignments are for the week. Be sure to schedule at least two couple sessions. It is often overwhelming for the partner to attempt to cover all the procedures in one session. In the second session, be sure to check homework completion from the prior session, using procedures from the Homework chapter (p. 47). If you think it is clinically necessary and there are the resources to support them, more than two couple sessions can be scheduled.

For a more detailed description of Couple Relationship Skills, read pages 147–179 in *Clinical Guide to Alcohol Treatment: The Community Reinforcement Approach*, by Robert J. Meyers and Jane Ellen Smith (Guilford, 1995).

Name: _____   Date: _____

Couple Relationship Happiness Scale

This scale is intended to estimate your current happiness with your relationship in each of the ten areas listed below. Ask yourself the following question as you rate each area:

How happy am I today with my partner in this area?

Then circle the number that applies. Numbers toward the left indicate various degrees of unhappiness, while numbers toward the right reflect various levels of happiness.

In other words, by using the proper number you will be indicating just how happy you are with that particular relationship area.

Remember: You are indicating your current happiness, that is, how you feel today. Also, try not to let your feelings in one area influence the ratings in another area.

	Completely Unhappy						Completely Happy			
Household Responsibilities	1	2	3	4	5	6	7	8	9	10
Raising the Children	1	2	3	4	5	6	7	8	9	10
Social Activities	1	2	3	4	5	6	7	8	9	10
Money Management	1	2	3	4	5	6	7	8	9	10
Communication	1	2	3	4	5	6	7	8	9	10
Sex & Affection	1	2	3	4	5	6	7	8	9	10
Job or School	1	2	3	4	5	6	7	8	9	10
Emotional Support	1	2	3	4	5	6	7	8	9	10
Drinking/Drug Use	1	2	3	4	5	6	7	8	9	10
General Happiness	1	2	3	4	5	6	7	8	9	10

Name: _____   Date: _____

Perfect Relationship Form

Under each area listed below, write down the behaviors that would represent an ideal relationship. Be brief, be positive, and state in a specific and measurable way what you would like to see occur.

1.   In Household Responsibilities, I would like my partner to:

    1._____

    2._____

    3._____

    4._____

    5._____

2.   In Raising the Children, I would like my partner to:

    1._____

    2._____

    3._____

    4._____

    5._____

3.   In Social Activities, I would like my partner to:

    1._____

    2._____

    3._____

    4._____

    5._____

4.   In Money Management, I would like my partner to:

     1._____

     2._____

     3._____

     4._____

     5._____

5.   In Communication, I would like my partner to:

     1._____

     2._____

     3._____

     4._____

     5._____

6.   In Sex and Affection, I would like my partner to:

     1._____

     2._____

     3._____

     4._____

     5._____

7.   In Job or School, I would like my partner to:

        1._____

        2._____

        3._____

        4._____

        5._____

8.   In Emotional Support, I would like my partner to:

        1._____

        2._____

        3._____

        4._____

        5._____

9.   In Drinking or Drug Use, I would like my partner to:

        1._____

        2._____

        3._____

        4._____

        5._____

Adapted from *Clinical Guide to Alcohol Treatment: Community Reinforcement Approach* (Meyers & Smith, 1995)

Communication Skills

The goal of using communication skills is to be able to get your message across to another person to help you get what you want. Using these communication skills should enable people to compromise or agree on a solution to a problem. When everyone agrees on a solution, compliance by both sides and contentment with the solution are more likely. It is important to stay positive during the communication skills training and avoid blaming.

Understanding statement. The goal of the understanding statement is to open up communication and show that you are aware of another person's thoughts on a problem. That is:

- **Come from the other person's perspective.**
  Example: "Mom, I understand you would like my room cleaned because it is a real mess, and you would like the house to be clean when friends come over."
- **Come from your perspective.**
  Example: "But Jimmy is having a birthday party at his house, and I have not seen Jimmy for a while, so I would really like to go."
- **Make a request (a request should be brief, positive, and specific).**
  Example: "I would really appreciate it if you would let me clean my room later tonight, maybe around 8 p.m. when I get home."

Partial responsibility. The goal of the statement of partial responsibility is to avoid blaming the other person. Remember to state how you or the other person see yourselves fitting into the problem or solution. That is:

- **How do you fit into the problem?**
  Example: "I know I made a real mess by not putting my clothes away, and I have not always followed through with cleaning my room, and I am sorry about that."
- **Repeat the request (optional).**
  Example: "But I would really appreciate if you would let me clean my room around 8 p.m. tonight after I get home from Jimmy's party."

Offer to help. The offer to help is used to show that you are willing to work on a solution that works for everyone and that you would like input from others on possible solutions. That is:

- **Offer several possible solutions.**
  Example: "If there is anything I can do to help make that happen—help out with another chore around the house, help out with dinner, or just do a quick 10-minute cleaning for now and do the rest later—I would really appreciate it."
- **State your openness to listen to and consider the other person's ideas.**
  Example: "Or if there is anything that you can think of, I would be willing to listen."

Following the offer to help, the other person may try to compromise on a solution or do some problem solving. It may be necessary to go through the communication skills again to state your point.

How Do I Solve This Problem?

1. **Define your problem.** Just one. Keep it real specific. Write it below.

2. **Brainstorm possible solutions.** The more the better! List below.

3. **Eliminate unwanted suggestions.** Cross out any that you can't imagine doing yourself.

4. **Select one potential solution.** Which one can you imagine yourself doing this week? Circle it.

5. **Generate possible obstacles.** What might get in the way of this working? List below.

6. **Address each obstacle.** If you can't solve each obstacle, pick a new solution and go through the steps again.

7. **Make the selected solution for your assignment this week.** List below exactly when and how you'll do it.

8. **Evaluate the outcome.** Did it work? If some changes are needed, list them below and commit to trying it again.

A-CRA
Daily Reminder to Be Nice

Name: _____

Week Starting: _____

Activity	Day						
	Sun	Mon	Tue	Wed	Thu	Fri	Sat
Did you express appreciation to the other person today?							
Did you compliment the other person on something?							
Did you give the other person a pleasant surprise?							
Did you express affection?							
Did you initiate pleasant conversation?							
Did you offer to help?							

UNIT 2: CHAPTER 16: Job Seeking Skills

Rationale

Many adolescents want to find a job because they need or want some income. Employment becomes even more important for TAYs because they need to establish financial independence. Because of the importance of employment across age groups, the job-finding procedure has been an important part of CRA since its inception. We have also learned that it is important to teach clients skills to help them keep a job.

It is important to note that having a job is not necessarily appropriate for all adolescents because balancing schoolwork, treatment requirements, and other positive prosocial activities during the school year may be all that some adolescents can handle. Research has shown that there is a relationship between employment and increased substance use among adolescents. In a small qualitative study, we also learned that some adolescents use work income to support their substance use (S. H. Godley, White, & Passetti, 2006). So when clients say they really want to have a job, it is important to discuss the pros and cons. Jobs make sense if clients have a lot of free time during the school year, are not attending school in the summer, or have dropped out. For many adolescents, working may be a reasonable prosocial activity. However, some work situations have a culture of alcohol or drug use, and it will be important to evaluate this aspect of a potential work environment.

Learning Objectives

The learning objectives are to help clients:

- Learn what is involved in finding a job.
- Learn how to specify or categorize types of jobs of interest.
- Learn how to generate job leads.
- Learn how to make job inquiries.
- Learn how to complete a job application.
- Learn how to prepare for and do well in a job interview.
- Learn skills that are important for job maintenance and satisfaction.

Timing, Audience, and Delivery Method

This procedure can be used at any time after clients make it clear that they want to find a job. The procedure can be completed in individual sessions, but it also works well in group sessions.

Materials

Use the Finding a Job handout (p. 207), which provides guidance for figuring out the type of job a client is interested in, developing a list of contacts for job leads, inquiring about job openings, asking for an application, developing a resume, setting goals related to job finding, and making an interview request. Also attached is a two-page handout for clinicians that lists all the Job Seeking Skills procedure components for reference (p. 208). It may take several sessions with the same client to complete all components. We have also provided a sample employer contact tracking form (p. 210).

General Notes for the Clinician

It will not be possible to review all the topics described here in one session, and often it may take multiple sessions to complete all the session components. Also, discussion of how to keep a job will be best addressed after the client has a job.

Procedural Steps

1. **Provide an overview of the job-finding approach.**
2. **Help clients generate job categories in which they are most interested.**
3. **Generate and follow up on job leads and develop a tracking system.**
4. **Rehearse how to make job inquiries and have the client make inquiries during the session.**
5. **Discuss and practice how to complete applications properly.**
6. **Rehearse interviewing skills.**
7. **Plan for job maintenance and satisfaction.**

Detailed Description

1. **Provide an overview of the job-finding approach.**

The important points to cover in the discussion are:

- Discuss why it is important to have a satisfying job.
  - Start this discussion by asking clients why they think it is important to have a satisfying job and generate additional examples. Reasons include:
    - Money from jobs helps make other rewarding activities and goals more accessible.
    - It may be a good way to meet new nonusing friends.
    - It occupies time, so it competes with using and triggers (e.g., boredom).
- Explain how the job finding process usually goes.
  - It may take a lot of effort to get a job. Successful job seekers make a job out of finding a job (that is, they work at it several hours a day).
  - Being rejected is part of the job finding process, and job seekers should not get discouraged by rejection.
- Explain the recommended steps to finding a job.
  - Generate a list of job areas that are interesting to the job seeker.
  - Understand that the more interviews job seekers have, the better their chances are of finding a job.
  - Make a lot of contacts to generate job leads.
  - Learn how to fill out an application and have needed information for reference.
  - Practice approaching potential employers.
  - Practice interviewing.

2. **Help clients generate job categories in which they are most interested.**

First, give an overview of the job finding process, then help clients identify job areas that interest them, because job leads are more easily generated once possible job categories are identified. Note that job possibilities will depend on age, educational level, and experience. The following questions can help identify interest areas:

- What kind of work have you done (be sure to ask about paid and volunteer experiences)?

- What job training have you had?
- In what type of place would you like to work?
- What would you like to do?
- What is a job you would like to have in the future?

As noted earlier, assess and discuss whether the job category is one that would be risky for continued substance use. For example, working in a bar would be risky for a TAY who has a drinking problem.

Review internet sites that post jobs for teens. For example, Snagajob.com posts Top Teen Industries, Top Teen Employers, and Top Teen Job Titles.

Use other CRA procedures as needed to assist the client in obtaining necessary information. For example, a client may not remember the job title for a particular job he had. Systematic Encouragement and positive communication skills could be used so that he is prepared to call the former employer and get the name of his prior position.

3. Generate and follow up on job leads and develop a tracking system.

Research has shown that the best source of job leads is the people one knows, including friends, acquaintances, and family members. Other important sources of leads are past employers or coworkers. Increasingly, online sites are good sources for job openings. The more traditional sources, like help-wanted ads in the newspaper and job-wanted postings, are still important to use, but they should not be the sole sources for job leads. Provide information about generating a list of leads from each of these sources. We also recommend that clinicians research job-finding resources available in the community and provide this information to the clients. Important steps for this part of job finding are:

- Set up a system to track the job leads generated and actions related to each.
  - o Some of the important information to track for each job lead includes name of company, hiring manager's name, phone number, company address, date application was turned in, date of first contact, date of second contact, and results of each contact. Help the client complete at least part of a real-life example.
- Develop a list of sources to generate job leads. The sources will probably include:
  - o Friends, family, and teachers.
  - o Internet postings (look at these during a session—but also talk about how clients can go to a public library and research these if they do not have a smartphone or computer).
  - o Past employers or coworkers (if applicable).
  - o Newspaper help wanted ads.
  - o Telephone book.
  - o Other community resources for job finding specific to the age of the client.

4. Rehearse how to make job inquiries and have the client make inquiries during the session.

Although the approach may vary somewhat depending on the type of job lead, there are several steps that are important when inquiring about a job over the phone or in person. Be sure to let the client know that it is important not to contact an employer during their busiest times (e.g., a fast food restaurant during the breakfast, lunch, or dinner rush).

Here are some steps to take when talking with an employer about a possible job:

- Introduce yourself.
  - *Hello, my name is _____.*

- Ask for the manager or person in charge (head of department).
  - *I would like to speak to the manager. Can you tell me his or her name, please?*

- If the person is not available, ask to set up an appointment for the same day or the day after.
  - *Is there a time today or in the next few days that would be convenient for us to meet?*

- Once you are able to speak with the manager, explain that you are looking for a job, and ask about openings.
  - *I'm looking for a job in _____. Are there any openings?*

- Give a brief summary of experience or show enthusiasm for working there.
  - *This will be my first job. I really would like to work here and you will find me a dependable worker.*

- Asks about getting an application or an interview.
  - *Can I get an application to complete and set up an interview?*

- If the company is not hiring or willing to provide an interview, the client asks:
  - *Do you anticipate any openings in the near future?* or *Do you know of other businesses that are hiring?*

- Client thanks the employer for his or her time.
  - *I really appreciate you taking the time to talk with me today.*

After explaining the job inquiry steps, conduct a two-sided role play with the client making a job inquiry. Give pertinent feedback. If time permits, have the client use the telephone to do an actual job inquiry of a potential employer (that is, use Systematic Encouragement). Afterwards, provide appropriate praise and constructive feedback for ways to improve.

5. Discuss and practice how to complete applications properly.

Discuss the important steps in completing an application. These include:

- It must be neat and legible (e.g., type or print without cross-outs); for these reasons encourage completing online applications when possible.
- Be sure to include some strengths (these can be personal characteristics).
- Have a plan for handling difficult questions (e.g., leave blank or write "Will discuss in interview").
- Have names and contact information for two people who can be used as references.

Complete one or two applications on paper or online during the session.

6. Rehearse interviewing skills.

Some adolescents have never had a job interview, and others may have had one without having had training in what to do. You can help them develop their skills in this area by explaining how to prepare for interviews and role playing interviews with them.

Cover these points to prepare for an interview:

- Dress appropriately for the job for which you are interviewing.
- Have good hygiene (shower, clean fingernails, comb hair, wear deodorant, etc.).
- Arrive a few minutes early for the interview.
- Plan how to get to the interview on time (e.g., arrange transportation).
- Anticipate and prepare for typical interview topics.
  - o Be ready to describe one's strengths (including personal characteristics).
  - o Be prepared to answer difficult questions (e.g., why one left prior jobs after a short time, any criminal justice involvement that was listed on the application).

After helping the client prepare for an interview, use an actual application that the client has completed and conduct a two-sided job-interview role play with the client. Since the goal of this exercise is to improve the client's interviewing skills, afterwards be sure to:

- Praise the client for using positive communication skills during the interview role play.
- Use shaping to increase the client's use of positive communication skills.

Remember to keep the role-play a reasonable length, about 5 minutes, because it will be important to have time to provide feedback and to repeat the role play multiple times. This will allow the participant the opportunity to incorporate feedback and improve skills in subsequent role plays.

7. Plan for job maintenance and satisfaction.

Once the client is successful at finding a job, it will be important to monitor how the job is going and preemptively help the client understand how to keep the job. During treatment sessions, the clinician can use the Happiness Scale to monitor job satisfaction and weave in appropriate procedures (e.g., communication and problem solving) to aid the client in addressing any problems on the job. If the client has had a job in the past and had job-related problems, it is important to discuss these problems, and if related, tie the problems to substance use. For example, if a client was fired from a previous job for chronic tardiness, it will be important to assess whether the tardiness was attributable to oversleeping after using alcohol or drugs.

If the client has not had a previous job, then you can discuss some possible job-related problems that the client may have in the future and use A-CRA skills to address them, as needed. For example, a situation might arise in which a client is scheduled to work Friday night, but friends want him to come to a party with them. The client can practice using Communication Skills to decline the invitation.

Steps to follow to address job maintenance include:

- Discussing any job-related problems that affected keeping a job in the past.
- Assessing whether the problems were related to substance use and, if so, pointing the link out to the client.
- Identifying triggers that were linked to job-related problems (e.g., taking too much time for breaks, not getting along with coworkers).
- If the client has not had a job, discussing possible job-related problems that the client may have in the future.
- Evaluating current job satisfaction with the Happiness Scale "job" category.
- Practicing CRA Problem Solving and Communication Skills to address job-related problems and communication with coworkers and supervisors.

Finding a Job
(Client Handout)

Make a list of what you're interested in—what you'd like to do.
- D. Think of the kinds of work you've done in the past. ANY experience you've had matters (e.g., volunteer work, community service, helping out at school)
- E. Think about what you're good at or places you'd LIKE to work. Examples: computers, retail (mall), maintenance, waiter (restaurant work), cleaning

Develop a list of contacts for job leads.
- Talk to family members, friends, past bosses
- Look on web sites that have listings of jobs for your age group (e.g., teens or adults)
- Look in phone book yellow pages to locate businesses in the job categories in which you're interested
- Look for help-wanted ads posted in windows of stores or restaurants
- Examine help-wanted ads in the daily newspaper

Inquire about job openings, and ask for an application.
- Introduce yourself
- Ask for the manager or person in charge (head of department)
- If the person is not available, ask to set up an appointment for the same day or the day after
- Once you are able to speak with the manager, explain that you are looking for a job, and ask about openings
- Give a brief summary of experience or show enthusiasm for working there.
- Ask about getting an application or an interview
- If the company is not hiring or is unwilling to provide an interview, ask about other businesses that are hiring
- Thank the employer for his or her time

Set goals when looking for a job.
- Make at least five contacts a day
- Be motivated
- Make a lot of appointments
- Call employers back to check whether a position has opened up
- Turn in applications to as many places as possible

Sample request for an interview:

Hello, my name is _____. I would like to talk to the manager. Can you tell me his or her name, please? I'm looking for a job in _____ (e.g., restaurant work), and I'm wondering whether I could come in to talk about a possible job opening? I have experience in _____, and I'd like to talk to you about any openings you have now or think you will have later. Would you have time this afternoon? (If not) *When is a good time to come back?*

A-CRA's Job Seeking Skills Components
(Clinician Handout)

NOTE: Completing all components may take several sessions with the same client.

Provide Overview

Discuss:

A. Rewards (value) associated with a satisfying job (*at least one example*):
   - The money makes other rewards or goals more accessible
   - Could be a good way to meet new nonusing friends
   - It addresses triggers such as boredom
   - Other _____

B. Difficult aspects of the job-finding process (*at least one example*):
   - It takes a lot of effort to find a job
   - Rejection is often part of the process

C. Job finding's basic premises (*at least two premises*):
   - Need to generate a list of job categories of interest
   - Must make a lot of contacts to generate job leads
   - Need to learn how to complete a job application skillfully
   - Need to practice both contacting potential employers and interviewing
   - Need a lot of interviews (more interviews = better chance of getting a job)

Help Generate Job Categories

Ask standard work experience and interest questions (*at least two questions*):
   - What kind of work has the client done in the past?
   - What type of job training (if any) has the client had?
   - In what type of place or position could the client imagine working?
   - How risky is the desired position in terms of substance use potential?

Generate/Follow-Up Job Leads

A. Develop a list of sources of contacts (*any relevant ones*):
   - Family, friends, acquaintances
   - Past employers or coworkers (if applicable)
   - Internet postings
   - Newspaper job announcements
   - Telephone book
   - Other _____

B. Set up a tracking system (filled in with a real example if possible):
   - First contact date:
   - Company:
   - Contact person's name:
   - Telephone number:
   - Address:
   - Date and result of each call:

Rehearse and Make Phone Calls

A. Explain telephone inquiry steps (*at least four steps*):
- Introduces him or herself
- Asks to speak to the person responsible for hiring
- States that he or she is looking for a job; asks about openings
- Briefly reports his or her qualifications and skills
- Asks about coming in for an application or an interview
- If company is neither hiring nor encouraging an interview:
  - Asks about potential openings in the near future
  - Asks if the employer knows of any other businesses that are hiring
- Thanks employer

B. Role play the call

Complete Applications

Complete an application or discuss considerations when preparing to complete one (*at least three*):
- Explain how application must be neat and legible (e.g., no cross-outs)
- Discuss client's strengths to include (including personal characteristics)
- Develop a strategy for handling difficult questions (e.g., about drug use)
- Discuss having names and numbers for two references

Rehearse Interviews

A. Discuss preparatory points (*at least two*):
- Dressing appropriately
- Having good hygiene
- Being punctual
- Having transportation

B. Cover important interview topics (*at least one*):
- How to highlight one's strengths
- How to handle difficult questions

C. Role play (multiple times)

Plan for Job Maintenance/Satisfaction

A. Job maintenance:
- Discuss reasons for job-related problems in the past (or why the client could potentially have problems)
- Address potential job-related problems (use A-CRA procedures when possible)

B. Current job satisfaction (if applicable):
- Evaluated current job satisfaction with Happiness Scale
- Set new goals or strategies to enhance job satisfaction with Goals of Counseling

Adapted from *Clinical Guide to Alcohol Treatment: The Community Reinforcement Approach* (Meyers & Smith, 1995)

Job Finding Tracking Form

(Note: This is just a sample. Feel free to create any tracking system that works for you and the client.)

Company	
Contact Person	
Telephone Number	
Address	
E-mail	
Website	
First Contact Date	
Result of First Contact	
Second Contact Date	
Result of Second Contact	
Third Contact Date	
Result of Third Contact	

Company	
Contact Person	
Telephone Number	
Address	
E-mail	
Website	
First Contact Date	
Result of First Contact	
Second Contact Date	
Result of Second Contact	
Third Contact Date	
Result of Third Contact	

UNIT 2: CHAPTER 17: Anger Management

The following material is adapted from McKay, Rogers, and McKay (1989).

Rationale

It is important for everyone to learn skills to manage anger, since we all experience it. It may be evident from their histories or assessments that certain clients need to learn skills for managing their anger. Managing anger does not guarantee that negative life situations or events will be resolved, but when clients can manage their anger, they can have healthier lifestyles and minimize the risk of adverse consequences of anger-related behavior.

Learning Objectives

The learning objectives are to help clients:

- Learn to identify reasons to manage anger.
- Learn to recognize early signs of anger.
- Learn how to take time to cool down.
- Learn how to understand another person's position (be empathetic).

Timing, Audience, and Delivery Method

This procedure is useful for all clients. For some clients it may be introduced early in treatment when it is evident from assessment information or comments or behaviors during a session that the client has a problem with anger.

Materials

There is an Anger Management form (p. 217) that can be used by the client during and after the session.

General Notes for the Clinician

This procedure is to help clients who typically express their anger in unhealthy, maladaptive ways, including acting out frequently in a physically or verbally aggressive manner, exploding into rage after initially appearing calm and in control, and getting into altercations at school or into screaming matches with parents or caregivers.

One reason that clients may be angry is that they have been abused, abandoned, or exposed to other life circumstances for which anger is clearly an appropriate response. In these cases, anger may have helped protect them from mental or physical harm or alerted them that something in their environments did not feel right. You can stress to all clients that it is entirely acceptable to feel angry, but it is important to learn how to express anger and negative emotions in ways that do not cause them difficulties.

Another procedure that can be helpful while teaching Anger Management is a Functional Analysis. In this case, an angry event would be identified, and the clinician would help the client identify thoughts, feelings, and behaviors that led up to the angry event and the positive and negative consequences. You also could use a behavioral chain to identify where in the chain of events leading up to the angry episode the client might have interrupted the chain and avoided getting so angry.

Procedural Steps

1. **Identify reasons (i.e., reinforcers) to manage anger.**
   - **Ask for examples of how anger has caused problems for the client.**
   - **Discuss the pros and cons of expressing anger.**
   - **Assist the client in seeing the link between managing anger and achieving goals.**
2. **Discuss why it is important to recognize early warning signs of anger.**
3. **Help the client recognize high-risk situations for anger and starting to feel out of control.**
4. **Teach the client to take time to cool down, and come up with a cool-down phrase.**
5. **Teach the client to foster empathy.**
6. **Provide the client with the Anger Management form.**

Detailed Description

1. **Identify reasons (i.e., reinforcers) to manage anger.**
   - **Ask for examples of how anger has caused problems for the client.**
   - **Discuss the pros and cons of expressing anger.**
   - **Assist the client in seeing the link between managing anger and achieving goals.**

Initially, the clinician should focus on prompting clients to provide examples of how anger episodes have affected their lives and goal achievement. Examples might include physical or verbal fighting that has caused problems with parents and friends. Other consequences of expressing anger in unhealthy ways might include criminal justice involvement or being suspended from school.

Clinician:	*Last week you were telling me about how you got angry with a teacher and you ended up getting a detention. Can you think of any other ways your anger has affected you—like what consequences have you experienced?*
Adolescent:	*Well, I got into an argument with my friend Jeff one night, and we ended up getting into a fight. After that we just didn't spend too much time together.*
Clinician:	*So it sounds like you're saying that in this situation with Jeff, when you got angry it had a negative impact on your friendship. Can you think of other pros or cons to getting angry? Has anything else happened that you have liked or not liked because of your anger?*
Adolescent:	*Sometimes when I get angry at my little brother—he stays out of my stuff for a while, so I like that. But a bad thing that happened was when I got suspended from school for 5 days once after I was in a fight with a kid. My grades ended up being pretty bad because some of the teachers wouldn't let me catch up on the homework.*
Clinician:	*Hmmm. So it sounds like when you get angry with your little brother, it ends up working out for you. He stays out of your stuff. But on the other hand, other times when you got angry you got suspended from school, your grades got worse, and it sounds like you lost a friend because you got angry.*

Adolescent:	*Yeah, that's right.*
Clinician:	*Are you interested in working on getting a better handle on your anger so that you will be more likely to stay in school and keep your friends? Who knows, it may help you have an even better relationship with your brother too. How about it?*
Adolescent:	*Well, it depends on what I have to do.*
Clinician:	*That makes sense. We're going to work together to help you recognize anger early on—when you still have time to get control of yourself, and then we'll talk about some good ways to respond early on that are healthier than getting really angry. How about it?*
Adolescent:	*OK.*

2. Discuss why it is important to recognize early warning signs of anger.

Clinician:	*First, we are going to talk about recognizing early warning signs of anger. Why do you think that would be important?*
Adolescent:	*I'm not sure, what do you mean exactly?*
Clinician:	*Let me see if I can say it another way. Most of us, before we get really angry, have some signs that our anger is starting to build up. We might feel angrier and angrier inside of ourselves even before someone else can tell. Why might it be important to recognize those signs in ourselves?*
Adolescent:	*Oh, I guess so we can stop ourselves from getting really angry?*
Clinician:	*You got it! If you learn to recognize your early warning signs, then you can choose to behave in a healthy manner rather than in a destructive way.*

3. Help clients recognize high-risk situations for anger and starting to feel out of control.

Next, help clients recognize high-risk situations for getting angry and beginning to feel out of control. Some clients may have more skill than others in recognizing their warning signs, but when they can articulate their warning signs, they have a better chance of identifying the need to use anger-management techniques. It is not enough that they know anger-management techniques; they also need to know when to use them.

Ask the client to describe the physical signs of mounting anger, because physiological changes play a part in the body's response to increased arousal. Examples of warning signs include an upset stomach, clenched jaw, sweating, tightened fists, heavy breathing, pacing, cursing, sarcastic remarks, or a fast pulse. These may serve as red flags for the client to step back and cool down. Each client will identify a unique set of physical and behavioral warning signs. Encourage clients to monitor their behavior to learn when they need to intervene to avoid an angry response.

Clinician:	*Let's talk about high-risk situations when you tend to get angry. When I say "high risk," I mean these are situations where you know that you usually get angry. They can be with friends, at school, or at home. Can you think of some?*
Adolescent:	*Well, with my friends I get angry when they don't want to do what I want to do. At school, I get angry if a teacher is always in my face telling me what to do or acting like I'm lazy.*
Clinician:	*These are good examples. I want you to think about some of the early signs you experience when you get angry. Before you get really angry, do you notice any signs that you are getting upset? Some people clench their fists or slam doors or something. Do you notice anything like that? And do you have an idea why it might be helpful to identify these early signs of anger?*
Adolescent:	*So we know when to use these skills?*
Clinician:	*Yes, that's it. Only here it is sort of like so you can tell when you feel triggers in yourself that suggest you are going to get really angry. So what are some?*
Adolescent:	*Well, I notice I feel like my face gets really hot, and I start clenching my fist, and I feel like I want to yell.*
Clinician:	*Good. Remembering those things can be helpful so when you feel some of those signs that show you are getting upset, you can do something else to calm yourself down. That way you don't have to worry about getting really angry and doing something like getting in a fight and getting suspended from school.*

4. Teach the client to take time to cool down, and come up with a cool down phrase.

One technique that has proved useful for anger management is taking the time to calm down. If a client is in an interpersonal situation during which he or she feels physical signs of mounting anger, he or she is encouraged to say, "I need to cool down," or "I need to take a time out" or "I need to take a break." Then the client needs to leave for an agreed amount of time (e.g., 1 hour). Walking out for a specified time does not constitute running away or punishing the other person, but it allows the client time to work through the heat of the moment and to calm down. Since clients are sometimes unable to leave the situation, help them come up with a phrase they can say to themselves that will help them to stay calm, such as "I don't want to get arrested" or "Relax and make it through this."

During the time away, clients are encouraged to engage in a physical activity to reduce tension. They can go for a walk, play some basketball, or participate in a pleasurable activity. It is *not* a time to use substances. If you and the client have already completed it, the Functional Analysis of Prosocial Behavior form can serve as a client-generated guide to the kinds of activities that might be appealing. If not, ask the client to identify some healthy prosocial activities in which to engage. After some time has passed, the client can return to the situation to talk with the other person or can decide to take more time to reduce the tension. Communication Skills training is also important to help clients learn how to express their anger more productively (see Unit 2, Chapter 11 [p. 123]).

When clients find themselves growing angry outside a conversational context, such as thinking about what someone else did or said, they are once again encouraged to engage in tension-reducing activity. Explain that this cooling-down period prevents them from acting impulsively in damaging ways or returning to substance use.

The Problem Solving procedure may be useful in attempting to resolve the situations to which a client is reacting. Once again, in order to manage clients' anger, you will want to revisit the reasons that they have given to remain sober and abstinent.

Clinician:	*Can you think of something positive you have done in the past that has helped calm you down when you have started to get angry?*
Adolescent:	*Sometimes walking around helps calm me down. When I get angry, I just want to leave and try not to think about things.*
Clinician:	*That's great. So you are able to calm down by walking around. What are some of the things you do when you walk around?*
Adolescent:	*I just walk around and think of how much of a jerk the person was.*
Clinician:	*OK. Some people like trying to do different things when they get angry —positive activities like shooting baskets or going to the arcade—to help them calm down and get their minds off things for a little while. What kind of positive thing do you think you would try once you started walking around?*
Adolescent:	*Well, maybe like just going to the park and relaxing to get my mind off things. If I'm really angry, I sometimes like to play video games at home.*
Clinician:	*Those are good ideas that might work when you are hanging out with a friend. So when you start noticing your face getting hot, that you are clenching your fists and feel like yelling, would you be willing to walk around and maybe spend some time relaxing in the park or shooting hoops or head home to play video games? Those activities sound like they might work for you. Would you be willing to try one of these activities the next time you feel yourself getting upset at a friend?*
Adolescent:	*Sure. If I start getting angry, I'll do one of those.*
Clinician:	*OK. Now, we have to think of a healthy alternative for when you have those feelings at school because you just can't walk out of school and go do those things.* [They come up with some healthy activities for school and then spend time exploring obstacles for both situations and come up with solutions that the client can use. They also come up with a cool down phrase that the adolescent can use.]

5. Teach the client to foster empathy.

Many times when people are angry with someone, they do not think about why the other person has acted in a certain way. Fostering empathy is one method of helping a person learn how to examine situations from different viewpoints and defuse anger with understanding. This ability does not mean that anger in a given situation becomes unjustified; simply that anger can be communicated more effectively when the person on the receiving end feels understood and becomes more receptive to the other's position.

One way to foster empathy is to ask clients to imagine themselves in a situation from another person's perspective, then ask them to talk about what it feels like to be in that position. The best way to help them learn to walk in someone else's shoes is through a reverse role play. For example, pick a real-life situation and play the role of the client. The client can play the role of the person with whom he or she is angry and attempt to voice concern from that other point of view.

Following the reverse role play, process the experience with the client. Ask what effect the role play had on his or her understanding of the other person's position and how he or she would handle the same situation if it happens again.

6. Provide the client with the Anger Management form.

Decide based on the client's needs how best to use the Anger Management form. Some clients may find it helpful to complete the form while you go through the procedure, thereby having the completed form as a reference. For others, it could be a homework assignment to complete and bring back to the next session.

Date _____ Client Name _____ Client ID _____ Clinician Name _____

Anger Management

Remember, it's OK to get angry. What is important is how your emotions are expressed. Below are some tips for anger management.

- **How has anger interfered with your life?** What would you like to change?

- **How do you know when you are getting angry?** (Typical signs are an upset stomach, clenched jaw, tightened fist.) If you feel you are beginning to get angry, you can do something before the situation becomes too tense and leads to negative consequences.

  Write your typical signs here:_____

- **Take time to cool down.** Find an activity or spend time away from the situation so you are able to calm down and handle the situation in a way that does not have negative consequences.

- **Remember to use communication skills to help express how you feel, while trying to see how the other person feels.** Try to come to a common solution instead of forcing your decisions on someone else. See the Communications Skills handout.

- **Try to come from the other person's perspective.** Why does the person feel the way he or she does?

UNIT 2: CHAPTER 18: Medication Adherence and Monitoring

Rationale

Medication Adherence and Monitoring is a procedure that was originally developed for adult CRA to be used with clients who were prescribed disulfiram, a medication that acts to deter the use of alcohol by causing the client to become ill if alcohol is consumed. However, we recognized that this procedure was relevant for adolescent and TAY clients who take other kinds of medication, such as antidepressants (for clients with depression and anxiety symptoms), stimulants and nonstimulants (for attention deficit and hyperactive disorder), mood stabilizers (for clients with a bipolar disorder), and antipsychotics (for schizophrenia). Many clients participating in substance use treatment have co-occurring problems that are being treated with medication.

Learning Objectives

The learning objectives are to help clients:

- Learn the pros and cons of taking the prescribed medication.
- Learn about the role of a monitor and choose one.
- Set up a monitoring protocol.
- Learn how to administer their medication.

Timing, Audience, and Delivery Method

This procedure can be used at any time you learn that a client has a prescribed medication to treat a mental health disorder or other problem. Asking about prescribed medications should be a part of a comprehensive intake assessment, and some clients will be prescribed new medications during their substance use treatment episode.

Materials

It is important to have the information about the prescription, including dosage, how best to take the medication, what the medication is prescribed for, side effects, and drug interactions, warnings, and precautions. Depending on your client, where you provide treatment, and the prescribing physician, the information may be gathered via an electronic medical record, by the client bringing in the prescription, through contact with the prescribing physician, during a conversation with the caregiver and client together, or by other means. If you or the client has any questions about the medication, consult with medical staff or the pharmacy with the appropriate release of information or client consent.

General Notes for the Clinician

During this procedure, it is important to help clients choose an appropriate monitor, or person who will assist them in taking medication as prescribed. It is important that the monitor be a supportive person whom the client speaks with daily. For an adolescent, a caregiver is a common monitor. TAYs may want to enlist a significant other as their monitor. If you are not comfortable with the term "monitor," then feel free to use another term.

Procedural Steps

1. Discuss the pros and cons of taking the medication.
2. Help select a monitor and role-play how to approach him or her.
3. Set up the monitoring protocol and what to do if the client refuses to take the medication.
4. Practice administration of the medication.

Detailed Description

1. Discuss the pros and cons of taking the medication.

When asking the client about the disadvantages of taking medication, ask specifically about reasons *not* to take it. Check on other possible reasons that are relevant to the client (e.g., side effects, problems remembering, embarrassment or shame), and if relevant, discuss whether the caregiver or a significant other would support use of the medication. When asking about advantages, talk about positive consequences such as the lessening of family worry, fewer slipups, more productive therapy time, increased self-confidence, more opportunities for positive reinforcement, an increase in available early warning signs, and being better able to attain treatment goals overall.

Clinician:	*I see you brought in your prescription bottle today. That is your Prozac prescription, right?*
Adolescent:	*Right.*
Clinician:	*Thanks for bringing it in so we can talk about taking it. Let's first talk about pros and cons for taking it. The pros are reasons you can see for taking the medication, and the cons are reasons that you might not want to take it. Which one of these would like you like to start with?*
Adolescent:	*How about the cons?*
Clinician:	*Sure, go for it.*
Adolescent:	*I just don't like having to remember to take a pill every day, and I feel like it makes me have trouble going to sleep at night.*
Clinician:	*OK. Well, I'd like to help by setting up a way to help you remember your pill every day. Can I see your bottle, please? [Adolescent hands clinician the bottle.] Yes, I see here that you are supposed to take one 20 mg tablet a day in the morning. I'm just wondering if you actually are taking it in the morning. If you are taking it right before you go to bed, it might cause more problems with going to sleep. I think that's why the prescription says to take it in the morning.*
Adolescent:	*I have such a hard time remembering to take it that most of the time if I take it, it is before bed.*
Clinician:	*OK. Thanks for telling me this detail. Again, it's why we are talking about the medication, so we can set up a system that will make it more likely that you will remember to take it and at the right time. How about telling me some pros or reasons why you think it is good to take this medication.*

Adolescent: *I just don't want to feel so sad all the time, and I can tell it helps me with that.*

Clinician: *Yes, this medication has been shown to help with depression symptoms. I'm really glad to hear that you can tell it is helping you feel better. Can you think of anything else?*

Adolescent: *Well, as we've talked about, sometimes when I'm feeling down I want to use alcohol or drugs to make me feel better. And if I do go ahead and use, it only works for a short period of time, and then I crash again.*

Clinician: *Yes, that's exactly right—you and I talked about how feeling sad is a trigger for you to use. Remember, you wanted to have a goal on your treatment plan to take your antidepressant medication to avoid feeling sad and help you stay sober. Can you think of any other reasons that you want to take it?*

Adolescent: *My mom was really worried about how down I was getting, so I want to get better so she doesn't worry so much.*

Clinician: *That's certainly a good reason. Let me just summarize here. You said you didn't like how you had to remember to take a pill every day and that it seems like it makes it harder for you to get to sleep at night. On the pro side, you said that you want to take it so you feel better—not sad, and that you would be less likely to use if you were feeling better, and you don't want your mom to worry about you being depressed. Do I have this right?*

Adolescent: *Yeah.*

Clinician: *Can you think of any other pros and cons?*

Adolescent: *Not really. That pretty much covers it.*

Clinician: *OK. Good job! If you're on board with this, we'll set up a system for you to take the Prozac in the morning, and hopefully that will help with going to sleep at night. But if it doesn't, be sure to talk about that with your doctor next time you see her. OK?*

Adolescent: *OK.*

2. Help select a monitor and role-play how to approach him or her.

Discuss why a monitor is important (e.g., support system, help with accountability, Early Warning System) and what this person's role would be (supportive and not punitive, part of the medication-taking ritual, etc.). Determine who might be an appropriate monitor while considering that person's availability and reliability and any other obstacles. Discuss inviting the selected person to be a monitor, including when and how to ask him or her. Conduct a role play in which the client asks the person to be a monitor. After the role play, provide specific feedback to the client about what was done well and what could be improved, and repeat the role-play.

Clinician: *So, let's talk more about this system I keep referring to. Basically, we want to think of someone that can help you remember to take your medication at the right time. Many of us can benefit from someone helping us remember to take our* *medication. We want to make sure this person does the reminding in a positive way—that they are supportive—and not a nagger in a negative way. So they help make sure you take your medication, and they do so in a way that makes you know they want what is best for you. Does that make sense?*

Adolescent: *I think so. Who would it be?*

Clinician: *Yes, let's talk about that. So I already told you some things that are important about the person we call a monitor. It's also important that you see or talk to this person when you need to take your medication. In your case, that would be every morning. Do you have some ideas?*

Adolescent: *Well, it's most likely gonna have to be my mom.*

Clinician: *Yes, I was kind of thinking that, too. Do you feel like your mom supports you and would be good about remembering to remind you to help take your medication?*

Adolescent: *She already does, but we don't have a regular time or anything like that. And, like I said, she wants me to get better.*

Clinician: *OK. Are you guys usually around each other in the morning?*

Adolescent: *Well, she usually leaves the house before I do. I walk to school a little later.*

Clinician: *Are you up and about when she leaves or are you still in bed?*

Adolescent: *I'm usually just about to get up—she comes and tells me to get up and says goodbye.*

Clinician: *How do you think your mom might help with you taking your medication in the morning? Do you have any ideas?*

Adolescent: *Hmmm. Maybe she could bring me some water and the pill when she comes in to wake me up in the morning. I think that might work.*

Clinician: *That sounds like a really good plan to me. Well, the next thing we need to do is ask her. So we would need to explain to her that we would like her to help out as a monitor to help you take your Prozac and ask her if she would be willing to. But we'd practice asking her first. Sometimes we ask the monitors to come to a session—or you could ask her yourself. So we've talked about some of this. Basically, you want to ask her if she would help you take your medication, bring you water in the morning, and remind you to take it before she goes to work. It's helpful if she watches you take your pill, just so you don't forget and hop in the shower or something. Also, it's best if you start out by explaining why it is important for her to help. Are you ready to try and role play this request?*

Adolescent: *OK. You want me to go first?*

Clinician: *Yes, I'll pretend to be your mom.*

Adolescent:	[Starts role play.] *Hey Mom, I want to talk to you about something that my therapist and I talked about. OK?*
Clinician:	[As mom.] *Sure, what's up?*
Adolescent:	*My therapist said it would be a good idea to have someone help me to remember to take my medication every day and I thought you would be the best person to do this.*
Clinician:	[As mom.] *Don't I already do that?*
Adolescent:	*You do, and I appreciate it. But she reminded me that the label says I'm supposed to take the medication in the morning. So she suggested that when you come in to wake me up that you bring my water and I have my pill bottle right there and you remind me to take my medication. I always like how you say goodbye to me before you leave for work, so I think this would be a good time. What do you think?*
Clinician:	[As mom.] *Yes, I think I could do that.*
Adolescent:	*Great, Mom! Thanks a lot!*
Clinician:	[Out of role play.] *You did a really good job with that role play! I liked how you explained what you wanted her to do, when you wanted her to do it, and where. Those were very good details—so she knew what you expected. It might have helped if you said something in the beginning about how you know that she wants you to feel better and that helping you take your medication like she has been doing has helped with this and this new idea would help even more. You also could tell her the part about how it would be helpful if she watches you take it after she brings the water—just to make sure you don't forget. How about we do another role play and include these extra pieces?* [The clinician asks the client what he did and did not like about the role play.]

3. **Set up the monitoring protocol and what to do if the client refuses to take the medication.**

Setting up the protocol means to decide on the details about (a) *when* the medication would be given, (b) *where* the medication would be given, (c) *how* the medication would be given (by the client or the monitor), and (d) *what* the client wants the monitor to do if the client refuses to take the medication. If the monitor is going to attend a session, the protocol should be set up then, with his or her direct input. Emphasize that giving and taking the medication should be a pleasurable experience and both the client and the monitor should use positive reinforcement before and after taking the medication.

Clinician:	*Let's be sure we covered everything we need to about setting up the protocol. We need to be sure we've talked about four things: when to take your medication, where you will take it, how you will take—that is, if you will take it or your mom will give it to you—and what your mom will do if you don't want to take it when you are supposed to. Can you summarize what we talked about and how you feel about it?*
Adolescent:	*Sure. We talked about my mom giving me the Prozac when she comes to say goodbye to me in the morning. I think that will work.*

Clinician:	*I know this sounds pretty detailed, but it is helpful to figure out the details. Do you want to give it to yourself while your mom watches or actually have your mom hand you the water and the pill?*
Adolescent:	*I don't think she needs to hand it to me. She can just watch me take it.*
Clinician:	*OK. That's good. So we have the when, where, and how. I don't know that this will happen—maybe if you wake up late and don't want to take it—but we usually also talk about what your monitor, in this case your mom, should do if you refuse to take the medication, OK? What should your mom do if you say you don't want to take it some morning?*
Adolescent:	*I dunno. Why do we have to figure this out?*
Clinician:	*We're just trying to cover all the bases. Like I said, it may never happen, but it will be helpful for your mom to know what the plan is in case it does happen. We always do this as part of the monitoring plan.*
Adolescent:	*OK. Well, she could remind me that we talked about this as part of the plan and offer to give it to me.*
Clinician:	*That's a good suggestion. It will be important to talk about that with your mom if she comes in to talk about this or for you to talk about it with her.*

To complete the procedure in the example above, the clinician could ask the client how she might make the event pleasurable for her mom (e.g., thank her, tell her that she loves her).

4. Practice administration of the medication.

Ideally, the monitor should attend a session to practice administering the medication. If this is not possible, the clinician and the client should do a role play to practice the medication administration. Remind the client (and monitor) in advance of the positive communication that should take place during the administration and how taking the medication should be a pleasant event in general. After the role play, provide specific feedback to the client (and monitor) and repeat the role play. Emphasize that the client is ultimately responsible for taking the medication.

UNIT 3: Addressing Client Needs, Discharge, Training, and Research Support

We intentionally saved the next four chapters for the end of the manual. We thought it was important for readers to understand the A-CRA procedures in order to appreciate how different procedures are useful in addressing individual needs. Recommendations for discharge and sample dialogue during a discharge session are provided in Chapter 2. We also felt that readers would have a better understanding of our recommendations for training, certification, and supervision once they learned more about the intervention. Finally, we know that not everyone wants to dig into the research that supports the intervention. Still, many readers will want to know about the research and where to go to read published work in more depth, so we end the body of the manual with a chapter on A-CRA research findings.

UNIT 3: CHAPTER 1: Addressing Individual Needs with A-CRA

Almost every time we conduct a new A-CRA training workshop, a few clinicians tell the trainers that the population they work with is *really* difficult or different. What they seem to be saying is that their clients are challenging to engage in treatment, are involved in the juvenile justice system, have co-occurring mental health problems, are in gangs, have learning problems, or live in an environment or family that will not be conducive to recovery. In other words, the youth they see for substance use treatment have multiple problems. Some clinicians are concerned that their clients are culturally different from the clients for whom A-CRA has been found to be effective and they are worried that A-CRA will not fit their clients' cultures. These are legitimate concerns, and we appreciate that clinicians raise these very important clinical issues.

In response to these concerns, we reiterate that A-CRA is a flexible, client-driven treatment, so it lends itself to work with each person who presents to treatment. Each will bring different strengths, experiences, learning styles, and issues into therapy, and the A-CRA clinician is trained to adjust the session and choose procedures based on those individual characteristics. For example, the Happiness Scale allows clients to tell the clinician what is most important to them and to set goals in those areas, which is likely to increase their engagement in treatment. We also encourage clinicians to implement other appropriate treatments concurrently (e.g., psychiatric medications, trauma-focused approaches) as needed. Treatment leaders and researchers have consistently said that integrated treatment approaches should be the gold standard when treating those with co-occurring mental health problems, and we endorse this approach (S. H. Godley, Smith et al., 2014).

Our assertion that A-CRA is effective at addressing individual needs is not based on theory or beliefs alone. Since A-CRA has now been implemented with over 11,000 clients in over 270 organizations, we have experience with and data on a large number of clients. Both we and others have conducted a number of analyses to assess A-CRA effectiveness with different types of clients. Below we detail the research that supports A-CRA's use with various subpopulations, and we offer recommendations for individualizing the approach based on presenting client characteristics.

Gender and Culture

Background

Gender. National statistics indicate that the rate of illicit drug use is about the same (9.1% and 9.5%) for adolescent girls and boys; however, a much smaller percentage of admissions (30%) are adolescent females (United States Department of Health and Human Services, SAMHSA, & OAS, 2008). Researchers who have studied gender differences of adolescents admitted to treatment have found that females were more likely to have more substance use problems, psychological difficulties, family-related problems, and sexual abuse experiences, while males had more school and legal problems (S. H. Godley, Hedges, & Hunter, 2011).

Race. The need for behavioral treatments to be culturally competent began to be widely discussed in the 1980s. D. W. Sue and colleagues (1982) provided a set of multicultural counseling competencies. The federal government also recognized the importance of placing greater emphasis on the importance of providing effective mental health care to all populations (President's New Freedom Commission on Mental Health, 2003; S. Sue, 2006; United States Department of Health and Human Services, 2001). Some experts suggest that the best method of ensuring culturally competent treatment is by teaching clinicians cultural knowledge and skills and how to show respect for different cultural groups (Campbell & Alexander, 2002; Hwang, Wood, Lin, & Cheung, 2006; S. Sue, 2006). Others have suggested that cultural competence must also be evaluated at the level of the treatment model and thus have called for studies to examine whether particular EBTs are effective across cultural groups (Bernal, Jimenez-Chafey, & Rodriguez, 2009).

Research Findings

To assess whether there were gender or ethnic group differences in A-CRA engagement or outcomes, we examined data from over 1,100 adolescents who received A-CRA in 15 states. We compared data on four measures to assess the "acceptability" of treatment for the different groups. These variables were initiation, engagement, total session attendance, and treatment satisfaction scores. Using the Washington Circle definitions for initiation and engagement, clients were counted as having *initiated* treatment if they received a second treatment session within 14 days of their first session. They were counted as having been *engaged* in treatment if they received two additional treatment sessions within 30 days of meeting the criteria for initiation. *Total session attendance* was a count of the total number of A-CRA sessions they attended. Finally, *treatment satisfaction* was based on a standardized treatment-satisfaction measure that clients completed after 3 months in treatment.

Overall, the client initiation and engagement rates were high and equivalent for gender and race. About 96% of males were highly satisfied with the treatment, as were 94% of the females—so both groups had high rates of treatment satisfaction, but females did have statistically significant lower rates of satisfaction. We investigated further to see whether we could determine why there were differences in satisfaction rates. We found that males were more likely to agree that staff helped them with their substance use (92%) as compared with females (86%), and overall, those least likely to be satisfied with treatment were younger, female, and less abstinent at the 3-month follow-up. It is possible that females who did not attain abstinence accounted for the difference in satisfaction rates, but it is difficult to know whether they would have been more satisfied with a different substance use treatment approach without further analyses. African American adolescents had significantly higher rates of treatment satisfaction than Caucasian adolescents, but all groups had satisfaction rates of 94% or higher, suggesting high A-CRA satisfaction across ethnic groups.

We also examined whether there were gender or ethnic differences in A-CRA treatment effectiveness outcomes. We compared days abstinent from alcohol or other drugs in the past 90 days at 3 and 6 months after clients began their treatment. We also compared the number of people in each group who were in recovery. Being in recovery meant that a person was living in the community (not in residential or detention settings), was abstinent from any substance in the preceding month, and reported no substance-related problems. We found that females reported more days of abstinence (92% of the days) than males (85% of the days), but both groups had about the same rate of change. Therefore, females started and ended with more days of abstinence than males. The rate of being in recovery 6 months after treatment entry was not significantly different for males or females. All ethnic groups had significant increases in days abstinent from alcohol and other drugs and in the percentages of clients who were in recovery across the measurement period. Importantly, these improvements did not differ across ethnic groups at the 6-month follow-up. Males had equivalent gains in abstinence and recovery compared with females despite the fact that males had greater intake severity and different outcomes at 6 months. Overall, this research shows that A-CRA can be well implemented across gender and ethnic groups and is equally effective across ethnic groups (S. H. Godley et al., 2011). Additional information is available in the Research chapter (p. 243) for program evaluation findings from sites that served predominately Hispanic populations.

Recommendations for Addressing Gender and Culture with A-CRA

Broadly, gender and cultural differences are addressed in A-CRA because clinicians are trained to identify and increase access to each client's individualized goals and to draw upon each client's social, recreational, familial, school, or vocational reinforcers (Meyers & Smith, 1995). These goals and reinforcers may be similar across gender and different cultures, but they also may be gender or culture specific.

Gender. While some female clients may set goals similar to some male clients (e.g., improve grades or relationship with parents), they also may set goals that are specific to their gender. For example, if a female identifies birth control as a need, then Problem Solving Skills could be used to identify a solution. If a female has a problem with a male coworker making inappropriate comments to her, Communication Skills (or Problem Solving) could be used to address the issue. If a female is in a domestic violence situation, Problem Solving Skills could again be implemented, and the clinician may also use Systematic Encouragement to identify and access community agencies that could help. The bottom line: The standard A-CRA procedures would still be used for these gender-specific issues, but they would target the problem at hand.

Culture and Ethnicity. We believe that a starting point for culturally competent delivery of A-CRA is for clinical staff to have an understanding of the different cultures served. We define culture very broadly, and clients may belong to several cultures. For example, a culture could be a specific Native American tribe, a specific urban culture, a rural southern United States setting, a favela culture in Brazil, or even the broad youth culture. We convened a committee of staff from different provider organizations across the US to make recommendations for how to enhance the cultural competence of A-CRA. The following are recommendations they made.

- **Staff background.** It is helpful to recruit clinicians to be trained in A-CRA who have similar cultural backgrounds and language as the clients served. It is not always possible to do so, and in that situation it is important for clinicians to learn as much as they can about the culture and customs of the groups with which they are working. Many organizations have annual training sessions on cultural competence.
- **Clinical supervision.** When reviewing recorded clinical sessions, it is important for the clinical supervisor to help clinicians understand cultural values and nuances that affect the delivery of the treatment.
- **Language.** The first A-CRA manual and all the client forms have been translated into Dutch, French, Portuguese, and Spanish. We also know that clinicians will often need to adapt language based on different cultural groups. For example, both the clinician and client may speak English, but it may be important to incorporate some of the slang popular in a given geographical area when serving clients from that area. Youth may be more comfortable speaking a language besides English (e.g., Spanish), but their written skills may not be as good in that language. Parents may be more comfortable in a different language than their children.
- **Nonverbal communication.** Cultures can be different with regard to nonverbal communication (eye contact, sense of personal space, touching), and it is important for the clinician to learn and respect these differences. For example, clinicians who were Asian and Native American told us that these cultures were less likely to be comfortable with direct eye contact.
- **Age differences and age of immigration.** The age at which youth or parents immigrate to another country will affect their level of acculturation to their new country and may affect their comfort with certain components of A-CRA procedures. For example, some parents may not be comfortable role playing communication skills with their adolescents, so clinicians will either

need to spend more time preparing these parents for the role playing exercises or modify the procedures accordingly.

- **Learning style.** Some clients will respond better to primarily verbal interaction and others may learn from writing on forms as they learn the procedures. Still others may need a much slower pace to go through A-CRA procedures. It is acceptable to adapt to the learning style of the client.
- **Additions.** There may be additional activities added based on culture. For example, in a site serving primarily Mexican Americans along the border, the celebration of cultural festivals was added. These events provided a reinforcing activity for both parents and their adolescent children.

Co-Occurring Mental Health Problems

Background

Estimates are that between 55% and 88% of adolescents who enter substance use treatment have co-occurring psychiatric problems. The most common of the co-occurring problems are in the category of externalizing disorders (e.g., conduct disorder and ADHD.) Also common are depression, anxiety, and traumatic stress (internalizing disorders). Since there is such a high rate of co-occurring mental health problems, many experts have suggested that integrated treatments addressing both substance use and other mental health problems at the same time are preferable to sequential treatment of the different problems. In addition, research suggests that there are two treatment approaches in particular that have been shown to be effective with substance use disorders and different mental health problems that commonly co-occur with substance use: cognitive behavioral therapy (CBT) and family therapy. Components of these two approaches have been found effective in the treatment of substance use and the most commonly co-occurring disorders (e.g., depression, posttraumatic stress, conduct disorder and behavior problems, ADHD.) A-CRA includes many of these same components and so may have common mechanisms of change that will help clients with co-occurring disorders (S. H. Godley, Smith et al., 2014).

Research Findings

Given the prevalence of adolescents presenting to treatment with co-occurring substance use and mental health disorders, we thought it was important to examine how well participants who had these co-occurring problems responded to A-CRA. We conducted a study (S. H. Godley, Hunter et al., 2014) to examine the relationship between A-CRA participation for groups of adolescents with different co-occurring problems with regard to treatment engagement, retention, and satisfaction, and with substance use and emotional problem outcomes. There were four comparison groups: The non-comorbid group included participants who did not report symptoms that met criteria for any psychiatric problem. The internalizing group included participants reporting *DSM-IV* symptoms indicating generalized anxiety, major depression, or traumatic stress. The externalizing group included those reporting symptoms indicating conduct disorder or attention deficit hyperactivity disorder (ADHD). The mixed group included participants reporting symptoms that related to criteria for at least one externalizing and one internalizing problem. Replicating other findings that people with co-occurring problems have more severe problems overall, we found that participants with co-occurring problems reported more days of substance use and emotional problems at intake to treatment than participants with substance use disorders only. All groups received equivalent exposure to A-CRA during treatment implementation as measured by treatment engagement and retention. All groups had high and equivalent treatment satisfaction scores 3 months after beginning treatment. At the 12-month follow-up, adolescents classified as externalizers (n = 468) or with both externalizing and internalizing problems (n = 674) had significantly greater improvement in their days of abstinence and substance problems relative to adolescents with substance use disorders only (n = 666). We also found that adolescents reporting symptoms of internalizing (n = 154), externalizing, or both externalizing and internalizing disorders had significantly greater improvements in days of emotional problems relative to adolescents with substance use disorders only.

Recommendations for Implementing A-CRA for Clients with Co-Occurring Problems

Many A-CRA training participants have raised questions about how best to treat adolescents who have co-occurring psychiatric problems. To address their questions, our training team developed a supplemental training session that provided additional information about adapting A-CRA for these purposes. This session was co-taught by clinical psychologist and co-developer Dr. Jane Ellen Smith and by psychiatrists specializing in the treatment of adolescents with addictive disorders, Dr. Geetha Subramaniam and Dr. Diana Chu. Below is a summary of recommendations that were provided in the course. We would also recommend reading "The Adolescent Community Reinforcement Approach (A-CRA) as a Model Paradigm for the Management of Adolescents with Substance Use Disorders and Co-Occurring Psychiatric Disorders" (S. H. Godley, Smith et al., 2014), in which we have a table of A-CRA components that have been found effective for specific co-occurring problems.

It is necessary for clinicians working in substance use treatment to be familiar with the *DSM-5* symptoms of each psychiatric disorder and to familiarize themselves with the psychiatric medications that are commonly prescribed for those disorders and their side effects. It is very important for clinicians to teach clients to communicate medication problems to their physicians (by using Communication Skills components). Clinicians may also need to alert clients' physicians if there appear to be problems with medication compliance or side effects. For all situations in which clients are prescribed a psychiatric medication, it is important for clinicians to use the Medication Adherence and Monitoring Procedure (described in Unit 2, Chapter 18 [p. 218]). Below we provide recommendations for specific co-occurring disorders.

Depression. The treatment focus for depressed adolescents is to increase rates of positive reinforcement in their lives and to improve their social skills. To address low rates of positive reinforcement, we recommend using the following A-CRA procedures: (a) FA of Prosocial Behavior, (b) Increasing Prosocial Activity, (c) Problem Solving, (d) Happiness Scale paired with (e) Goal Setting, and (f) Systematic Encouragement. To help ameliorate social skills deficits, the following procedures can be helpful: (a) Communication Skills, (b) Goal Setting, and (c) Problem Solving. It is also important to work with caregivers of depressed adolescents to increase the support they provide. The skills that can be helpful with the caregivers include (a) the Daily Reminder to Be Nice, (b) the Relationship Happiness Scale, (c) Goal Setting, (d) Problem Solving, and (e) Communication Skills.

Generalized Anxiety Disorder (GAD). The treatment focus for adolescents with GAD is to identify triggers for anxious feelings and thoughts and to develop a coping plan to address those triggers before they become debilitating. A Functional Analysis can be used to learn more about the most anxious times or situations and to help identify the triggers. The following types of homework assignments can be useful as well: (a) practice labeling feelings, (b) track catastrophic thoughts, and (c) monitor daily fluctuations in thoughts and feelings. The coping plan would involve (a) Problem Solving and (b) homework to gradually increase exposure to the feared cues (internal and external) with rewards built in for doing so. Caregivers of adolescents with GAD can learn to support their child with (a) Communication Skills so they can ask about coping plans and praise homework compliance, (b) Problem Solving so they can help their child develop a coping plan, and (c) training in how to model nonanxious behavior.

Trauma-Related Problems. The treatment focus for adolescents with trauma-related problems is to ameliorate skills deficits and to provide psychoeducation and exposure therapy. Clinicians are not trained in trauma-related psychoeducation or exposure therapy as part of their A-CRA training, but certain A-CRA procedures can help facilitate linkage to additional services. The following A-CRA procedures will address skill deficits: (a) Communication Skills to help express feelings and get assistance when needed, (b) Problem Solving to identify coping strategies and relax, and (c) Homework to have the client practice labeling feelings experienced between sessions and challenging negative thoughts. A-CRA clinicians may also have had training in addressing trauma, but if clients need to seek additional treatment with a clinician who has had specialized training in psychoeducation and exposure therapy, then the A-CRA clinician can provide (a) Systematic Encouragement to help the client make an appointment to see a trauma-focused trained clinician, (b) Communication Skills so the client can more easily talk to the other clinician, and (c) goal setting. A-CRA procedures that will assist parents of these adolescents to support their child include (a) Systematic Encouragement to help their adolescent get to a trauma-trained clinician, (b) Communication Skills to encourage conversations, (c) Problem Solving to help their adolescent with coping strategies, and (d) Caregiver Only and Family Sessions to create a positive home environment.

Conduct Disorder and Behavior Problems. The treatment focus for adolescents with conduct disorder is to address skill deficits, increase caregiver involvement, and improve the clients' involvement in other systems (e.g., school and community). A-CRA procedures that can enhance the relevant skills are (a) Increasing Prosocial Activity, (b) Communication Skills, (c) Drink/Drug Refusal, (d) Problem Solving, and (e) Anger Management. Behavioral contracts may also be helpful in changing behavior by making it clear how clients can earn rewards for positive behavior change. To enhance the caregiver-adolescent relationship and caregiver involvement, the following A-CRA procedures are helpful: (a) the standard Caregiver Only Sessions and (b) the standard Family Sessions.

ADHD. The treatment focus for adolescents with ADHD is to improve their performance in everyday tasks and interactions. It is also important to focus on failures or problems that are secondary to ADHD. A-CRA procedures that could be helpful in improving performance are (a) Medication Adherence and Monitoring by training adolescents to monitor ADHD medication compliance, (b) Communication Skills to discuss medication side effects, and (c) Goal Setting to promote participation in treatment. Addressing the problems that are secondary to ADHD, the clinician can use (a) Anger Management, (b) Relapse Prevention to help clients learn the cues that require preventative behaviors, and (c) Goal Setting. The following A-CRA procedures can be helpful with caregivers to support their child who has ADHD: (a) Medication Adherence and Monitoring, (b) Goal Setting with contingent rewards, (c) Communication Skills, and (d) Problem Solving.

Juvenile Justice Involved Youth

Background

Estimates are that between 49% and 70% of adolescents referred to substance use treatment are also involved in the juvenile justice system. A large majority of adolescents are arrested for drug-related offenses, and there is additional research that links adolescents who use alcohol and illicit drugs to other illicit activities including burglary, vandalism, and other crimes (Hunter, Godley, Hesson-McInnis, & Roozen, 2014). It is clear that juvenile justice authorities want adolescents under their supervision to participate in substance use treatment so that those adolescents reduce their illicit alcohol and drug use and their involvement in other illegal activities.

Research Findings

Our review of the literature revealed that the relationship between substance use and illegal activity was not clear. We also wanted to find out whether participating in A-CRA (a) reduced juvenile justice system involvement by reducing substance use, (b) directly reduced illegal activity, or (c) directly reduced both juvenile justice involvement and illegal activity. We had a large sample of adolescents who participated in A-CRA and were involved in the juvenile justice system. We chose to analyze follow-up data from those who reported that they had been involved in illegal activity at their treatment intake (N = 1,467). The statistical analyses we conducted provided support that participation in A-CRA had a significant, direct relationship with reduced substance use; a significant, indirect relationship with reduced illegal activity through reductions in substance use; and a significant indirect relationship with reduced juvenile justice system involvement through reductions in both substance use and illegal activity (Hunter, Godley, Hesson-McInnis, & Roozen, 2014)

Recommendations for Implementing A-CRA with Juvenile Justice Involved Youth

We have found that it is important for treatment providers that are implementing A-CRA to educate juvenile justice authorities (including judges and court officials) about the intervention, including that A-CRA has a research base and that clinicians undergo substantial training to learn how to deliver it. It is also important to talk about some A-CRA procedures and how they are used. For example, the court may require abstinence. Abstinence would always be a goal of A-CRA, but sometimes with certain clients it is important to approach the goal in small pieces, so the Sobriety Sampling procedure (Unit 2, Chapter 10 [p. 117]) may be used. We also think it is beneficial to treatment clients when the roles between court officials and treatment professionals are differentiated appropriately. For example, juvenile justice authorities would use urine test results and other data to decide on the delivery or lifting of sanctions, while treatment professionals would use urine test results in a therapeutic way (e.g., do an FA of Substance Use—Relapse Version). Toward this end, we recommend that juvenile justice professionals conduct urine tests and inform the A-CRA provider rather than the other way around. Adolescent drug courts have also become more prevalent, and A-CRA has been implemented successfully in drug court settings (see Corvalan-Wood, Rajaee, & Godley, 2011).

We often hear from clinicians that clients are more compliant with treatment attendance when they are under sanctions from their juvenile justice system. To the extent that this is true, it is important to use this source of motivation as a reinforcer for participating in treatment and for trying out new skills and prosocial activities.

Transitional Age Youth

Background

Since transitional age youth (ages 18–24) may be living with their parents, peers, or romantic partners, they present with a much greater range of relationship concerns and other problems. In 2010, we began looking into the issue of TAYs and could find relatively little in the published literature that targeted this group, despite the fact that it has the highest proportion of individuals meeting criteria for a substance use disorder. As a result of their adult status, TAYs have more freedom and fewer parental and legal limitations and therefore are likely to experience greater alcohol and drug use and related problems. While many will age out of their problematic use, others will not. Indeed, 20% of all publicly funded treatment admissions are for TAYs (SAMHSA, 2007). These are important reasons to better understand and improve treatment for TAYs, but unfortunately, few randomized clinical trials have focused solely on TAYs using evidence-based treatment, and what evidence does exist is equivocal (Carroll et al., 2012).

Research Findings

D. C. Smith, Godley, Godley, and Dennis (2011) studied A-CRA effectiveness for adolescents versus TAYs over a 6-month follow-up period and found mixed results. In most cases, both groups improved equally, but at 6 months after the start of A-CRA treatment, adolescents had less heavy alcohol use and were more likely to be abstinent. Both adolescents and TAYs reduced the degree of substance problems experienced at follow-up, and there was no difference in problems experienced between the groups.

In another study comparing adolescents to TAYs receiving A-CRA, Garner, Hunter, Smith, Smith, and Godley (2014) examined several outcomes including the relationship between child maltreatment and substance use, substance-related problems, emotional problems, and HIV risk. The researchers found no difference in the number and type of A-CRA sessions attended by age group. Both TAY and adolescent groups with pre-existing child abuse or neglect issues experienced significantly greater reductions in substance use, substance-related problems, emotional problems, and HIV risk than their counterparts without prior histories of child maltreatment. These findings are important because of the lack of research showing the effects of evidence-based treatments for young people who have experienced both child maltreatment and substance use disorders. Although replications are needed, A-CRA holds promise for application within the child welfare system as well as for young adults presenting for substance treatment who may have experienced abuse or neglect from family members.

Recommendations for Implementing A-CRA with TAYs

Because many TAYs are in transition between living with parents and living with friends, romantic partners, or on their own, we increased the required procedures for a TAY certification to include the relationship procedure from adult CRA. Medication Adherence and Monitoring and Job Finding procedures were also deemed important to include when treating TAYs.

A-CRA for Opioid Problem Use

Background

Adolescent opioid use has doubled over the last decade, and during this period there has been a tenfold increase in admissions to substance treatment programs for adolescents with primary opioid use disorders specific to prescription opioids (SAMHSA, 2012; SAMHSA & OAS, 2008). As of this writing, some states have declared opioid use a statewide emergency. Funds have been earmarked to increase the availability of treatment, and the U.S. Congress is considering legislation to further expand the availability of treatment for opioid disorders.

Research Findings

As this manual goes to press, A-CRA researchers are completing a study that compared A-CRA outpatient treatment response of adolescents with either opioid problem use (OPU) or marijuana and alcohol problem use (MAPU). This study focused on (a) intake differences and similarities between the two groups, (b) clinicians' ability to engage and retain youth in A-CRA treatment, and (c) clinical outcomes for the two distinct groups. Consistent with prior reports in the literature, the OPU group was overrepresented by females and white adolescents. The MAPU group reported very little use of drugs other than marijuana and alcohol. Conversely, the OPU group not only reported high use of opiates but also high use of marijuana, alcohol, and other illegal drugs. Compounding matters, the OPU group demonstrated significantly greater severity in the areas of homelessness, family problems, school attendance, mental health problems, risky sex, and violence toward others. In short, the OPU clients presented a much more complicated clinical picture than the MAPU clients. In terms of A-CRA treatment implementation, there was no evidence of differences between groups with regard to engagement, retention, family sessions, or treatment satisfaction. Clinical outcome data collected at intake and at 3, 6, and 12 months postintake revealed that the OPU and MAPU groups decreased substance use significantly over time and that the OPU group decreased alcohol and opioid use at a greater rate. The OPU group also reported greater decreases in their emotional problems than the MAPU group. However, at the end of 12 months the OPU group still showed greater emotional problem severity and spent more time in residential treatment than their MAPU counterparts. These findings suggest that youth presenting with OPU can be engaged and retained in A-CRA, but they will be among the most complex cases to treat in outpatient settings. Nevertheless, A-CRA treatment was effective in reducing a great deal of drug using behavior and harm as well as improving emotional functioning.

Recommendations for Implementing A-CRA for Adolescents with OPU

A-CRA appears to be a reasonable treatment for adolescents with OPU. However, additional research is needed to test A-CRA as an accompaniment to medication-assisted treatment for opioid use disorders, since prior research has shown some effectiveness for medication-assisted treatment (Subramaniam et al., 2011). It is also necessary to place a greater emphasis on co-occurring mental health problems that may require more focused use of A-CRA procedures, including Medication Adherence and Monitoring for medication-assisted treatment, to target specific mental health symptoms (see the section on Co-Occurring Problems on p. 229). If available, it may be necessary to step these adolescents up to residential treatment or intensive outpatient treatment or to keep them in outpatient treatment for a longer period of time. They may also require more in-home therapy and crisis intervention services over an extended period of time. When these clients are working on sobriety or in an inpatient program, it is also important to work with them to develop a withdrawal plan.

UNIT 3: CHAPTER 2: Discharge Recommendations

Talking with clients about discharge should begin in the first session and be revisited periodically throughout treatment so they know what to expect. If you are able to meet with the client for a discharge session, it is important to accomplish certain tasks in this session. Optimally, the client will feel positive about the treatment and the progress that has been made. When you acknowledge the client's hard work during treatment and reinforce the skills learned, it can help provide motivation to access additional services in the future, if they are needed.

Tasks during the discharge session are to review progress made during treatment by briefly reexamining the Functional Analyses that have been completed and the Happiness Scale and Goals of Counseling forms. You should (a) reinforce progress made toward goals, (b) discuss with clients whether they would like to set additional goals in areas in which goals were completed, and (c) discuss progress made toward achieving unmet goals as well as continuing care or recovery management goals. Be sure to provide positive expectations for success with statements like, "You have done a really good job while in treatment, and I think you will have great success reaching your goals outside of treatment, too." Ask clients how they feel about ending treatment and discuss any concerns.

The remainder of this section contains a step-by-step description for conducting the closing session.

1. Check in with the client and provide an overview of the session.

Take a few minutes at the beginning of the session to check how the client is doing and provide a framework for what will be covered during the closing session.

Clinician:	*Last time we met, you were going to try using the Daily Reminder to Be Nice technique. How has that been going?*
Adolescent:	*It's going pretty well. I've been telling my mom that I love her, and she has been making more pasta for me.*
Clinician:	*Remember how we always talk about obstacles to achieving your assignment for the week? Let's talk about anything that made it difficult for you to complete the Daily Reminder to Be Nice.* [Clinician and adolescent spend more time talking about obstacles and problem solving.]
Clinician:	*OK, since this is your last session, I would like for us to talk again about the progress you've made in treatment and some of the things that could happen now. I'm also going to give you some information that can help you remember some of the things we did.*

2. Review the client's progress.

A good way to review a client's progress is to look at previous Goals of Counseling forms and talk about what goals have been accomplished. Another helpful review is to compare Happiness Scales that were completed over the course of treatment. Often these will reflect a pattern of improvement. It would also be important to discuss any unmet goals from prior Goals of Counseling forms and help clarify plans for achieving these goals.

Clinician: *First of all, let's discuss your first goal, which was to get at least a C in all of your classes. How is this going?*

Adolescent: *I've been doing pretty well. I'm not doing as well as I want to do yet.*

Clinician: *How about algebra?*

Adolescent: *I had a make-up test. But I don't know what my grade is in there.*

Clinician: *You probably want to check on that. Remember that you can also use those problem solving skills to think of other ways to get help for your difficult subjects. That can help you out. You've done really well with that—figuring out different solutions. That is something I really appreciate about you. Another goal was to stay sober and drug-free for 90 to 180 days. Making it to 50 days was a first milestone. You have almost made it this long, and you've done really well. You had one time that you had a problem, and you said that you were going to bring in your cousin for the Early Warning System. Have you talked to her about that?*

Adolescent: *I've talked to her about that, and she is supposed to remind me about my goal if she notices me hanging out with Mike and Mark.*

Clinician: *Can you review for me some of the obstacles you had in trying to improve your grades and in staying sober and clean and how you overcame them?* [Clinician and adolescent have a discussion about these obstacles, and clinician reinforces solutions and helps problem solve remaining obstacles, if needed.]

Clinician: *One of the other things you did was look at different activities you could have fun at while staying away from drugs and alcohol when you were doing them. What are some of the things you really enjoyed?*

Adolescent: *I went and played pool at the university's bowling and billiard center, and I thought that was pretty cool.*

Clinician: *What are some other things that you've done?*

Adolescent: *I went bowling with a couple of friends.*

Clinician: *And you also mentioned that you wanted to play laser tag. The good thing is that you were having fun and you got to do something and got your mind off things. Did you have any obstacles or roadblocks to doing these things? How did you overcome them?* [They have more discussion about obstacles.]

Let's review your Functional Analysis of Substance Use a little. You know, when we talked about your outside and inside triggers, one of the things that is a little different is that you said if you were bored, you would get restless and smoke pot. We talked about how a positive thing you got out of using marijuana was that it kept you from getting bored. But we also talked about the bad things that happened when you used, including that your mom and sister would get upset about it and you were spending your money, which was bad because you were spending too much money and you had some legal problems. Now when you smoked with Mike, it was really different—you were kind of anxious. That was kind of a different situation. What could you have said to yourself?

Adolescent: *Well, I could have thought about some of the bad things that happen when I use.*

Clinician: *Good. And this was one of the things you did a really good job of when you were meeting with me . . . talking about ways to keep things from happening. And most of the time you were successful. One of the other things is to find another activity you enjoy doing instead. We went through a Functional Analysis of Prosocial Behavior about taking care of your iguana, and that activity was good because when you did it, you didn't have to worry about getting in trouble as you did when smoking marijuana.*

3. Talk with clients about what they have gained from the treatment experience.

When clients verbalize treatment benefits, it helps reinforce new behaviors.

Clinician: *We've worked on a lot of things, and you've done really well with things including problem solving and relapse prevention. What are some things you think you gained from being in treatment?*

Adolescent: *I actually want to go out and do stuff instead of going out and getting high.*

Clinician: *And what is something that you like about that?*

Adolescent: *It gets me out of the house and people don't think I'm ignoring them.*

Clinician: *So it has improved your relationship with your friends. That's not something we really have talked about. Has it improved your relationship with your friend Susan? And how about your friends who were attending AA meetings?*

Adolescent: *Yeah, Susan used to smoke pot and I would do it with her. And even when she started going out with Mike, he would call to do stuff and we would just sit around at my house and do nothing. And then I got arrested and I quit smoking pot and stuff and quit hanging out with Susan, and the next thing I know she started coming around again and she was quitting, too.*

Clinician: *So she's been supportive of what you wanted and that's helped out, too—even though she was not the first person you thought of. Now all these people are really good supports for you. Sounds as if you got some really positive things coming here . . . problem solving and figuring out some other things you could do besides use marijuana. Is there anything else you gained from coming here?*

Adolescent: *Knowing how to prevent myself from going out and doing drugs. Like before I never thought, oh this would happen if I smoked pot. Now I think about things that could happen if I start smoking again.*

Clinician: *It sounds as if you are looking at the big picture. There were some things that you liked about smoking pot and before you tended to concentrate on those, but now you are seeing the whole picture. This doesn't surprise me, because you did*

236

really well in our sessions talking about these things. One thing I'd like to do now is have you fill out a Happiness Scale. Let's finish that up and look at some of the changes in your life.

[Clinician shows the client earlier Happiness Scales and points out the differences between earlier ones and the current one.]

Clinician: *Here is a difference with relationship with caregivers—from a 6 to a 9.*

Adolescent: *Now it is just easier to talk with my mom. Like yesterday, she started going off on me, and instead of blowing up I just said, "Do you want me to tell you what I did with my money?" And then we just talked about things calmly.*

Clinician: *That's really great. I bet you are both happier when you can do that. I see another difference with education—from a 6 to a 9.*

Adolescent: *Yeah, I was failing my classes. Now my grades have improved.*

Clinician: *It's good because you set some goals and you've worked at them. Communication went from an 8 to a 10. Can you tell me what happened there?*

Adolescent: *Well, communication with my friends hasn't changed. But now with my mom and dad, it is better. She listens now, and it is easier to talk with her. She listens to what I have to say. Before she'd just say, "You're wrong."*

Clinician: *Sounds really good. Things are working well for you. I'm wondering whether you have any goals from here on out?*

Adolescent: *I'd like to graduate with my class. I'm thinking of taking a correspondence course to help do this. I could do that.*

4. **Provide the client with reference information on procedures that have been covered during treatment.**

Consider providing a discharge packet to each client for reference. The contents of the packet can vary based on the client's needs and can include the following:

- Information on positive social activities.
- A list of tasks that are a part of each procedure (e.g., Goals of Counseling, Communication Skills, Problem Solving, and Relapse Prevention, including use refusal).
- Completed forms including the Functional Analysis of Substance Use Behavior, Functional Analysis of Prosocial Behavior, and Goals of Counseling.

You can individualize the forms and packet by using the client's information and input.

5. **Reinforce the client's efforts and hard work.**

This verbal reinforcement is woven throughout the session as illustrated in the sample dialogue above.

6. **Review the status of other referrals made during treatment (include continuing care or other recovery activities) and the options for future treatment.**

If the client demonstrated the need for additional services during treatment (e.g., residential treatment, psychiatric treatment, family counseling), appropriate referrals should have been made. However, discharge is an appropriate time to review the client's progress with these other services and reinforce continued involvement with them, if needed. Talk with the client about how to access additional services in the future. The discharge packet can include contact information for treatment resources (e.g., mental health treatment, continuing care, self-help groups). Include contact information for addressing substance use problems as well.

Other options include an open invitation for clients to call the clinician if they feel the need to in the future or to schedule a monthly call for a limited time. Consider scheduling a follow-up appointment within 2 to 3 months as well.

7. Consider other optional activities appropriate for a closing session, such as joint completion of a discharge form and giving the client a completion certificate.

Optional activities during this session depend on each treatment organization's guidelines. For example, if your treatment organization has a standard discharge form that needs to be completed for the clinical record, then you can complete it with clients so that they are fully aware of what their discharge recommendations are. It is recommended that clinicians give clients a completion certificate (see Appendix 2 [p. 263]) or some other symbol to commemorate their completion of the treatment program.

UNIT 3: CHAPTER 3: Selection, Training, and Supervision of A-CRA Clinicians and Supervisors

States and organizations have different requirements for credentialing clinicians as substance use treatment counselors, and the Association for Addiction Professionals (NAADAC) offers three levels of addiction counselor certification. The selection characteristics discussed in this chapter are mostly independent of state licensing or certification requirements. Certification as an A-CRA clinician requires demonstrating competence in the use of A-CRA procedures during clinical sessions with treatment clients. It takes several months to complete the certification process, and we know from comments by those who have done so successfully that it can be challenging. Still, a large majority of those who have completed the process have reported that it helps them learn new skills that are worthwhile in working with their substance use treatment clients. There is also an A-CRA clinical supervisor certification process that allows each provider organization to sustain A-CRA after their initial implementation period. As of January 2016, we have certified over 1,000 clinicians and supervisors in A-CRA.

Some clinicians may be new to using a treatment manual and may be concerned that using one would restrict their ability to address client needs. This manual is constructed with a menu of procedures and skills that the clinician will introduce in treatment as clinically necessary. It provides structure and consistency while allowing clinicians to use their clinical skills to determine which procedures to introduce (and when) on the basis of clients' challenges, goals, and reinforcers. We conducted a qualitative study on the use of manual-based therapies and found that clinicians liked the structure and consistency that a manual provided for their work. For those using the A-CRA manual, they also said that it was flexible enough to allow them to address individual needs. As one clinician said:

> I think the manual allows you to be able to go with what [the client] brings in. What the manual offers can work toward anything, so you can go wherever the client is, because the skills that you're offering aren't for specific types [of problems]. (S. H. Godley, White et al., 2001).

Recommended Educational and Experiential Qualifications

Generally, we recommend that an A-CRA clinician have a bachelor's degree in a counseling-related field plus 2 years' experience or a master's degree in a counseling-related field. We have also trained and certified individuals who do not have a bachelor's degree but who are in recovery and certified as addiction counselors. The majority of clinicians who have been trained and certified in A-CRA have completed their master's degrees. Those who have completed a graduate degree have often studied evidence-based treatments and understand what is involved in implementing behavioral or cognitive behavioral approaches. Although not required, this background is helpful. Prior experience with counseling adolescents or working with substance use treatment is also preferred.

Skills and Knowledge

During the training and certification process, a clinician will learn and demonstrate mastery in delivering the A-CRA procedures. We believe that the following skills and knowledge are also essential to good delivery of A-CRA:

- Education and experience in interpreting clinical assessments.
- Good general clinical skills.
- Knowledge and understanding of the developmental issues of adolescence.

We assume that a comprehensive biopsychosocial assessment is a prerequisite before an adolescent or TAY begins treatment. A clinician needs skills in interpreting clinical assessment information to understand the client's background and broad clinical needs (e.g., co-occurring mental health problems, family situation, justice system involvement, educational issues).

As we discussed in the General Clinical Skills chapter in Unit 1 (p. 19), these skills are important when implementing any therapy model. Good clinical skills promote client engagement, and research suggests they play an important role in improving client outcomes. Evaluating these skills in an interview situation can be difficult. Possible ways to assess whether a clinician has these skills is to review a sample therapy tape or to obtain references from previous supervisors who observed the clinician's therapeutic skills.

Adolescent developmental stages and accompanying behaviors are extremely important for the clinician to know or learn during training because working with adolescents or TAYs is very different than working with older adults. For example, while we do not recommend using confrontation with clients of any age, it is especially ineffective with adolescents given that one of the development hallmarks of this age group is to assert independence from adults. As a consequence, they may become argumentative or reject lecturing, advice, and anything remotely confrontational in nature.

Personal Qualities

We cannot say enough about the importance of positive personal qualities for an A-CRA clinician. Warm and enthusiastic interpersonal skills are highly desired for A-CRA clinicians. They also need to approach therapy with a nonjudgmental attitude. Clinicians who prefer analytic, didactic or lecturing, or confrontational approaches would not be good candidates for A-CRA training. Perseverance, tenacity, and the willingness to keep working with clients even when they are making little progress in treatment are other personal characteristics of successful A-CRA clinicians. Additionally, it is important that an A-CRA clinician candidate be open to learning and receiving feedback on a manual-based behavioral or cognitive behavioral approach, which includes a review of their audio-recorded treatment sessions by A-CRA expert raters.

Requirements to Promote Client Engagement

A-CRA has several features designed to increase client engagement in treatment. Many of these features have been reviewed already and include (a) remaining nonjudgmental, (b) learning what the client's reinforcers are, (c) using these reinforcers along with the Happiness Scale to develop goals that are important to the client, and (d) conducting sessions in an upbeat, positive way. Despite these engagement strategies, adolescents and caregivers may experience one or more barriers to attending sessions. An A-CRA-trained clinician can first use problem solving strategies to identify ways to engage and retain clients and caregivers in treatment. Travel to a client's home, school, or other locations may also be necessary if a client has problems attending clinic sessions (e.g., because of transportation problems) or is in a controlled environment (e.g., a juvenile detention center) and the treatment organization employing the clinician allows community visits.

Clinician Training

Attendance at an A-CRA training workshop is the official start of the training process. Prior to attending training, clinicians are asked to become familiar with the intervention by reading the A-CRA treatment manual and taking a quiz. The initial training workshop includes lectures, an opportunity for questions and answers, demonstrations of procedures, participant practice with trainer feedback, and an exercise that involves practice rating of a sample clinical session. After training, clinicians return to their treatment organizations and begin to provide A-CRA sessions to clients at their agencies, which is when they truly become skilled in the delivery of the procedures. During these sessions, they implement the A-CRA procedures as needed by individual clients and upload sessions to a secure web-based system. The sessions are rated by expert raters who also give the trainees narrative feedback about what they did well or what they need to improve for specific procedures and overall. Clinicians also participate in periodic telephone coaching calls with trainees from other organizations led by an expert coach or trainer. These coaching calls include reviews of specific procedures that trainees request, assistance with any problems that trainees are having with particular procedures, and a case presentation for discussion and feedback.

Clinician Certification

Certification is a multistep process, and these steps are reviewed in detail with trainees at the end of the training workshop. Since A-CRA session ratings are such an important part of the certification process, it is important to provide more information about the rating process and the coding manual used by A-CRA session raters. All trainees begin recording and uploading digital session recordings (DSRs) to a secure website after completing the training. DSRs are rated by individuals who are certified A-CRA clinicians or supervisors, and who have gone through an intensive rater training process. Their ratings are based on a standardized coding manual (J. E. Smith et al., 2007). The manual is more than 150 pages and contains operational definitions for numeric ratings of each component of 19 A-CRA procedures. Clinicians also are given overall scores every session with regard to whether they exhibited the appropriate A-CRA therapeutic style and goals, and introduced procedures at clinically relevant times. Four categories of General Clinical Skills (warmth/understanding, nonjudgmental, maintenance of session focus, and appropriate activity level) are rated each session as well. A total of 77 components are listed on the A-CRA checklist. Raters decide which procedures are appropriate to rate on the basis of what they hear the clinician doing during the session. The numeric ratings range from 1 (poor) to 5 (excellent). A 3 or higher is required to "pass" a component, and all components for a procedure must be at least a 3 for the clinician to "pass" the procedure. Typically, an A-CRA rater codes multiple components for an identified A-CRA procedure, including the "Overall" and "General Clinical Skills" components. A study evaluated A-CRA raters' ability to reliably rate clinicians delivering A-CRA and found that raters could be trained to provide consistent ratings (J. E. Smith et al., 2014).

Complete and current descriptions of training, certification, and coaching can be found at
http://ebtx.chestnut.org/Training-and-Certification

Supervisor Selection

We differentiate between a supervisor who is primarily administrative and one who is clinical, in that the latter has a role in training new clinicians and ongoing mentoring and supervision of clinicians in their practice. We have designed the A-CRA training and certification process so that a site can continue to implement A-CRA and train new clinicians in the model through a certified supervisor. We recommend that supervisors have an advanced practice degree and are already in a supervisory role and have or are able to pick up a small treatment caseload so they can work toward clinician certification. Supervisors are expected to attain at least the first level of A-CRA clinical certification so that they understand the treatment and have experienced the certification process themselves. This helps supervisors be more effective mentors for clinicians as they go through the training and certification process. If a site does not have a clinical supervisor available to work with A-CRA clinicians, then we recommend choosing a clinician with excellent clinical skills to go through the supervisor training and certification process. Then it would be important to give this new senior clinician or supervisor a reduced caseload to allow time for A-CRA clinical supervision duties (e.g., conducting supervision session, listening to and reviewing clinicians' clinical sessions, and training new clinicians).

Supervisor Training

The first goal of supervisor training and certification is to help supervisors learn the skills needed to assist their clinicians in improving their A-CRA clinical skills and attain certification. The second goal is to prepare supervisors to provide training and certification to new clinicians hired by their agency. The supervisors begin the process by attending the same workshop as the clinicians and working on their clinical certification at the same time that they complete other parts of supervisor training. Like clinician certification, supervisor training and certification is competency based. The competencies specific to supervisors include (a) learning how to rate clinical sessions and (b) learning how to conduct A-CRA supervision sessions.

Supervisor Certification

Besides attaining the first level of clinician certification, there are other requirements for supervisor certification. One of these is demonstrating competent supervision of an A-CRA clinician during an actual supervisor session. As with clinical certification, supervisors record supervision sessions, and they are reviewed by expert raters. The supervisor is expected to review the clinicians' caseloads with them. If available, the case review report may be used. This is a tracking log used to monitor specific client-treatment process indicators (e.g., number of sessions, procedures received), which can be used to focus discussion of specific cases on the clinician's caseload. Supervisors are also expected to provide feedback on clinical sessions after listening to DSRs and completing coding of the session. During supervision meetings, supervisors may also listen to a recorded session and give feedback or role play specific procedures for improvement. There is a coding manual that is used by expert raters to evaluate whether the supervisors meet the competency requirements for a supervision session (Hupp, Mertig, Malek, Godley, & Godley, 2009). We recommend that each clinician receive an individual A-CRA supervision session on a weekly or biweekly basis.

Complete and current descriptions of training, certification, and coaching can be found at http://ebtx.chestnut.org/Training-and-Certification.

Fidelity Monitoring after Certification

Research suggests that it is common for clinicians to "drift" after training in evidence-based treatments. Ideally, a supervisor would continue to conduct weekly supervision sessions and ongoing fidelity monitoring of certified clinicians via reviews and ratings of randomly selected sessions. At a minimum, we recommend rating at least one of each certified clinician's sessions every other month. These reviews provide important guidance for the feedback that the supervisor will supply or the role plays that will be conducted during a supervision session to help clinicians improve their skills.

Certified Clinical Supervisors and A-CRA Sustainability

The certified clinical supervisor is the key to sustaining A-CRA within a provider organization because this supervisor can train and certify new clinicians as needed. The process requires time and effort from the supervisor, given that A-CRA trainings will need to be conducted and clinician trainees' audio-recorded sessions will need to be reviewed. Many organizations have opted to have more than one supervisor complete the supervisor certification process so that they have redundancy in the event that one supervisor leaves the organization.

UNIT 3: CHAPTER 4: Research Supporting A-CRA Effectiveness

Since the earliest days of CRA we have been asked why the model was named the "Community Reinforcement Approach." It is a fair question and one that goes to the core of what CRA and A-CRA are about. The name Community Reinforcement Approach recognizes that everyone lives within a community context and each of us wants to be involved in reinforcing activities and relationships in our communities. Most of us are reinforced for our constructive relationships and activities that protect us from harm including involvement with drugs. People who develop a substance use disorder often have people, places, and things that positively reinforce (increase the likelihood of) their continued use of alcohol and other drugs. The goal of CRA treatment is to help people reshape their relationship to their community by trying new healthy and pleasant activities and to redefine or develop new relationships that are based on mutually enjoyable prosocial activities and improved communication. In short, CRA clinicians help clients find specific sources of reinforcement in their communities that are incompatible with and replace reinforcement derived from alcohol and other drugs. CRA clinicians do this by (a) teaching new life and social skills and reviewing clients' practice of these skills in their community (b) assisting clients to sample drug-free recreational and leisure activities, and (c) working in therapy to increase positive communication and problem solving with family, friends, and romantic relationships.

The Community Reinforcement Approach (CRA) existed long before the advent of the Adolescent Community Reinforcement Approach (A-CRA). Dating back to 1973, CRA was designed for adults and was found to be an effective behavioral intervention for alcohol use disorders (Azrin, 1976; Azrin et al., 1982; Hunt & Azrin, 1973). Since these early days, there have been multiple randomized clinical trials of CRA (J. E. Smith et al., 1998) and CRA enhanced with contingency management for cocaine use (Higgins et al., 1993, 1994, 2003; Secades-Villa, Garcia-Rodriguez, Higgins, Fernandez-Hermida, & Carballo, 2008), opioid use (Abbott et al., 1998; DeJong, Roozen, van Rossum, Krabbe, & Kerkhof, 2007; Roozen et al., 2006) and various drug combinations such as cocaine and marijuana use (Budney, Higgins, Delaney, Kent, & Bickel, 1991) and opioid and cocaine use (Schottenfeld, Pantalon, Chaarski, & Pakes, 2000). CRA has also been found to be cost-effective (Wolfe & Meyers, 1999). CRA was among the first behavioral interventions to achieve endorsements as an effective treatment in multiple literature reviews and meta-analyses (Finney & Monahan, 1996; Holder, Longabaugh, Miller, & Rubonis, 1991; W. R. Miller, Wilbourne, & Hettema, 2003; W. R. Miller, Brown et al., 1995; W. R. Miller, Zweben, & Johnson, 2005).

CRA Adaptation for Adolescents: The Development of A-CRA

In 1996, national survey data indicated that marijuana use among adolescents had surged to its highest level in 12 years. Despite these data, there were no tested interventions for adolescents presenting to treatment with cannabis use disorders. In response, the U.S. Center for Substance Abuse Treatment funded four organizations to develop and test several specific treatment interventions for adolescents with cannabis use disorders. Mark D. Godley at Chestnut Health Systems and its partner, Robert J. Meyers, PhD, and Associates, were both active in the early development and testing of CRA, so when Chestnut won one of the CYT site grants, this team began the work of making CRA an adolescent-specific intervention to be tested in the CYT trial. This work resulted in the first A-CRA manual (S. H. Godley et al., 2001), which was tested in the CYT study (described below). Although many of the CRA procedures were appropriate for use with adolescents, a significant amount of adaptation was required and was guided by the following:

1. All procedures needed to have illustrative dialogue specific to adolescents in treatment to show how A-CRA was developmentally appropriate for use with adolescents. Such dialogue included

attention to adolescent-specific details such as communication issues with parents or problems related to school conduct or academic performance.

2. Specific parent or caregiver procedures were necessary to help caregivers better understand what clinicians were working on with their adolescents, provide research-based parenting advice, and teach communication and problem solving skills to be used in family sessions.

3. Specific sessions and procedures were designed to increase appreciation and helpfulness within the family. These procedures were augmented by practicing communication and problem solving skills in sessions with the clinician so that both caregivers and adolescents could learn constructive ways of dealing with sources of conflict in the relationship.

4. Some procedures, such as the Happiness Scale, were revised to include adolescent-specific issues to assess current life satisfaction. For example, the CRA Happiness Scale was expanded to include categories such as "allowance" and "school." We also developed Relationship Happiness Scales to be used by clients and caregivers to assess satisfaction with these relationships and to form the foundation for goal setting to improve the relationships.

Randomized Controlled Trials

The Cannabis Youth Treatment Study Background and Design

In response to the lack of evidence-based outpatient therapies for adolescent cannabis use disorders, the U.S. Center for Substance Abuse Treatment funded a multisite randomized trial of outpatient therapy in 1997. This study took place in four locations: the University of Connecticut, the Children's Hospital of Philadelphia, Chestnut Health Systems in Illinois, and Operation Parental Awareness and Responsibility in Florida. In all, 600 adolescents were enrolled and randomly allocated to one of five manual guided treatments:

MET/CBT5. This was a five-session treatment composed of two individual sessions of Motivational Enhancement Therapy (MET) and three weekly group sessions of Cognitive Behavioral Therapy (CBT). The MET sessions focused on factors that might motivate substance-abusing adolescents to change. In the CBT sessions, adolescents learned skills to cope with problems and meet needs in ways that did not involve turning to marijuana or alcohol. This treatment was one of three interventions conducted at all four sites. MET/CBT5 was designed to be inexpensive and in line with what many parents and insurers seek as a basic intervention.

MET/CBT12. This treatment was composed of two sessions of MET and 10 weekly group sessions of CBT. It was designed to be a longer version of MET/CBT5 so that it could test for dosage effects. MET/CBT12 was more in line with the type of treatment usually provided for adolescents.

FSN. The Family Support Network (FSN) treatment included the MET/CBT12 therapy plus engagement-type case management, family support groups, and aftercare. This treatment was designed to wrap several additional low-cost services around MET/CBT12 and to address family issues and services in line with CSAT Treatment Improvement Protocol (TIP) series recommendations.

A-CRA. The Adolescent Community Reinforcement Approach was composed of 10 individual sessions with the adolescent, two individual sessions with one or more caregivers (e.g., a single parent or both parents), and two sessions with the adolescent and caregivers together. The intervention focused on helping the adolescent improve relationships and access rewarding activities and services in order to effectively compete with and discontinue marijuana and other drug use. A-CRA clinicians taught adolescents how to find new reinforcers or enhance existing reinforcers for staying substance free, how to use existing community resources that were believed to support positive change, and how to develop a positive support system within family and friends.

MDFT. Multidimensional Family Therapy (MDFT) was a 12-week treatment composed of 12 to 15 individual or family-focused sessions depending on need. Additionally, it included telephone and case management contacts. Sessions addressed roles, problem areas, and interactions among family members. This treatment used an integrated approach to family issues and focused on helping adolescents build more effective and age-appropriate interpersonal and conflict-resolution skills. It also helped parents establish a more effective and supportive parenting style. Finally, treatment stressed the importance of building appropriate social supports with peers, schools, and other involved service providers.

CYT Study Findings

As of 2016, the CYT study is still the single largest and one of the best implemented and controlled studies of outpatient treatment for adolescents with substance disorders. The findings from the CYT study confirmed that each of these well-thought-out treatments were effective in reducing substance use and problems for youth. *However, A-CRA emerged at the top of the rankings for cost-effectiveness.* More specifically, A-CRA cost less per day of obtained abstinence and less per adolescent in recovery than MDFT, FSN, and MET/CBT12. It ranked very similar in cost-effectiveness to the brief version of MET/CBT5. Specifically, in one arm of the study it was less expensive per unit of outcome while in the other arm it was more costly than MET/CBT5 per unit of outcome (Dennis et al., 2004). Because of the strong cost-effectiveness findings, combined with its versatility (sessions designed for youth and families and flexible timing for use of A-CRA procedures in clinical work), the U.S. Center for Substance Abuse Treatment launched the Assertive Adolescent and Family Treatment (AAFT) grant initiative in 2006. The AAFT initiative became one of the largest replications of a behavioral treatment in the U.S. Over the course of four funded cohorts, from 2006 to 2011, A-CRA was implemented in more than 80 provider organizations in the U.S. Additional sections of this chapter and Chapter 1 in this unit (p. 225) summarize important research findings from this replication.

A-CRA for Adolescents and Transitional Age Youth (TAY)

Slesnick and her colleagues (2007) conducted one of the earlier randomized trials of A-CRA. This study was important because of its design, which was random assignment to either A-CRA or treatment as usual. In addition, the study included both adolescents and TAY, most of who were homeless and attended a drop-in center during the course of the intervention. Of the 155 youth enrolled, a high percentage was Hispanic (30%) and mixed-ethnicity youth (22%). A-CRA treatment was designed to last 3 months, and outcome data were reported at 6 months after intake. The authors stated that adolescents and TAY in the A-CRA condition had significantly greater improvements in substance use, social stability, and depression compared to those in the treatment as usual condition. The investigators concluded that the "Community Reinforcement Approach therapy has the potential to impact homeless youth over the long term" (p. 1249). This study was noteworthy for its effects on treating homeless youth with substance use disorders and for its inclusion of a broad age range, encompassing youth and TAY. Homeless youth are likely to have less social support and more significant problems than those residing with family, relatives, or friends, suggesting that A-CRA is beneficial for a broad range of problem severity that youth may experience.

A-CRA Delivered through Assertive Continuing Care for Adolescents Discharged from Residential Treatment

Background

Although residential treatment for adolescents is much less prevalent than outpatient treatment, it remains an essential service in the continuum of treatment modalities. Admission to residential treatment is often justified on the basis of client placement criteria developed by the American Society for Addiction Medicine (ASAM). Thus, referrals to residential treatment are typically for those adolescents experiencing severe problems related to their substance disorder resulting in tenuous functioning within their families, schools, and communities. Although aftercare or continuing care has always been an important concept for clients leaving residential treatment, payers have exerted considerable pressure over the years on residential providers to shorten lengths of stay. As a result, the significance of having solid continuing care programs to provide ongoing outpatient treatment and support for these adolescents has increased considerably. Importantly, these programs provide assistance with overall adjustment to family, school, and community life as well.

Assertive Continuing Care (ACC) is a combination of A-CRA, case management, and community visits. The major goals of ACC are to rapidly engage the client and family into A-CRA services postdischarge and to continue to provide A-CRA services to further support the recovery process. Those who want additional information on case management, community visits, and rapid engagement can download the ACC manual from Chestnut Health Systems' website (see Appendix 3 on p. 264 for online resources).

Study Findings

The remainder of this section is devoted to describing the implementation of A-CRA in the context of postresidential community-based delivery of A-CRA and summarizing its effects as evaluated through randomized clinical trials research.

In the first study, a total of 183 adolescents were enrolled to examine linkage rates of youth linked into A-CRA services and retention in services and clinical outcomes (M. D. Godley et al., 2002, 2007). Findings from this study demonstrated that adolescents randomized to receive ACC (which included A-CRA treatment) were significantly more likely to receive treatment following residential discharge than adolescents randomized to Aftercare Services as Usual (94% vs. 54% linked to treatment). Adolescents in the ACC condition were also significantly more likely to abstain from marijuana use throughout the 9 months of data collection. Moreover, adolescents in the ACC condition who achieved 12 or more weeks of abstinence immediately following residential discharge were significantly more likely to maintain abstinence through the 9-month follow-up interval.

A second postresidential discharge ACC study (M. D. Godley, Godley et al., 2014) expanded its scope to evaluate four conditions: ACC Only, Contingency Management Only, ACC plus Contingency Management, and Continuing Care Services as Usual. In this study ACC remained unchanged. Its main component continued to be A-CRA supplemented by rapid engagement (first A-CRA service within 2 weeks of residential discharge) and case management services as needed. A total of 337 adolescents were randomly allocated to one of the four conditions. Within the first 2 weeks following discharge from residential treatment, 75% of the adolescents in ACC were engaged in A-CRA services compared to 49% in the Continuing Care Services as Usual condition. Adolescents in the ACC Only and the Contingency Management Only conditions responded comparably, with both conditions having significantly less alcohol and marijuana use over a 12-month postresidential follow-up period than the Continuing Care Services as Usual group. In addition, both of these groups resulted in nearly twice the rate of remission at

Month 12 than the Continuing Care Services as Usual Group. The combined ACC plus Contingency Management condition was not as effective as either of the two conditions alone.

These two studies provide strong evidence that within the context of continuing care, the rapid engagement and delivery of A-CRA services helps increase early and ongoing abstinence and leads to significantly better recovery outcomes than typical outpatient services following discharge from residential treatment.

Extending A-CRA Outpatient Treatment Duration with ACC: Findings from the AAFT Initiative

As described above in the CYT section of this chapter (p. 245), the U.S. Center for Substance Abuse Treatment launched the AAFT grant initiative because of the cost-effectiveness of A-CRA. With the advent of studies that showed the promise of A-CRA embedded within ACC to further improve or extend clinical outcomes, the CSAT initiative required that treatment providers combine at least 3 months of A-CRA (typically clinic-based) with an additional 3 months of ACC (typically home or school-based sessions). This became known as A-CRA/ACC and was implemented in more than 80 grantee organizations throughout the U.S. One of those grantees conducted a clinical trial of 112 adolescents randomly assigned to either A-CRA/ACC or to a treatment as usual condition (Henderson et al., 2016). All adolescents were involved in the juvenile justice system, and nearly 90% met criteria for a *DSM-IV* substance abuse or dependence diagnosis. The majority of adolescents in each condition also had one or more co-occurring mental health problems. The authors reported good implementation of the model. At the 3 and 6-month follow-up interviews after treatment intake, the findings from this well-controlled study revealed that the adolescents treated by A-CRA/ACC experienced significantly fewer substance related problems than adolescents in the treatment as usual condition, and this reduction in problems remained significant through the 12-month follow-up period (Henderson et al., 2016).

Cross-Site Evaluation of the AAFT Grant Initiative

A contract was awarded to Advocates for Human Potential, Inc. to conduct both a quantitative and qualitative cross-site evaluation of the third cohort of AAFT (14 grantees). Completed in September 2012, the evaluation reported findings related to agency, staff, and client characteristics and their relationship with A-CRA/ACC implementation, implementation progress, and overall effect on grantees and clients (Tobin et al., 2012). Below are some of the main findings from the report:

- 54% of the clinical staff had an advanced degree and 69% were certified addiction counselors.
- About 75% of the clients served were male, but racial diversity was high.
- About 40% of the clients served were age 12 to 17 and 60% age 18 to 24.
- Grantees reported high use of several material supports from A-CRA/ACC (e.g., manual, treatment forms, and the clinician certification process).
- A-CRA fidelity checks were rated high by the grantees.
- Some difficulties with audio-recording in community locations were noted.
- Grantees were "overwhelmingly pleased" with the support service provided by A-CRA/ACC staff at Chestnut Health Systems.
- All grantees achieved A-CRA/ACC clinician and supervisor certification.
- Family engagement was considered the biggest problem, and across grantees there was a wide range of success, with A-CRA parent/caregiver engagement ranging from a low of 18% to a high of 88%.

- Clinicians greatly appreciated the flexibility of the A-CRA model because it allowed them to match the appropriate procedure to clients' current needs as well as to repeat procedures as needed.
- The average client retention rate in A-CRA was 78% across all the grantees.
- The clients appreciated the home and community visits as well as the assistance that A-CRA/ACC clinicians provided in other areas such as mental health problems and educational and vocational goals.
- Grantees with stronger A-CRA/ACC implementation were reported to have better client outcomes than grantees with weaker implementation; in other words, better implementation of A-CRA/ACC predicted better clinical outcomes for the clients.

Published Program Evaluation Studies from AAFT Grantees

Prospective, randomized clinical trials (RCTs) are the gold standard for inferring causality of treatment effects. However, RCTs are not always possible for a number of reasons. The CSAT A-CRA/ACC grantees have produced several published program evaluations using sophisticated analytic techniques that control for many alternative interpretations to the outcome, but not all. Below we report on the four A-CRA/ACC evaluation studies from AAFT of which we are aware.

Ruiz, Korchmaros, Greene, and Hedges (2011) reported results from 144 adolescents enrolled at an AAFT site in a southwestern state. Adolescents were primarily male and Hispanic. A path analytic model was used to study effects of A-CRA/ACC treatment at 6 months and 12 months after intake. This study revealed that engagement in treatment (more A-CRA sessions) predicted improved outcomes, even when controlling for other measured variables such as gender. The authors concluded that assertive strategies to engage and retain clients over several months of outpatient treatment (e.g., community visits) were key to improving alcohol and other substance use outcomes.

McGarvey and colleagues (2014) evaluated an A-CRA/ACC extended outpatient program in Virginia and compared 147 adolescents from urban and rural areas. They concluded that the model was effective regardless of location. Overall, they found significant decreases in cannabis use (the drug of choice for these participants) and increasing rates of abstinence out to the 12-month follow-up. Adolescents also reported significant improvements in school attendance and conduct at school from the intake assessment measurement to the 12-month follow-up measurement. The authors attribute the similarity of effective findings for rural and urban participants to the A-CRA/ACC certification, monitoring, and supervision process.

Strunz, Jungerman, Kinyua, and Frew (2015) reported another evaluation of an A-CRA/ACC extended outpatient study conducted in a southeastern state serving predominantly Hispanic adolescents (90%). The authors examined substance use outcomes over a 12-month time period in relation to dose or time in treatment. Care was taken to control for confounding variables, including intake level of substance use. Results indicated a significant reduction in substance use over time, although not complete abstinence for most adolescents. The authors employed sophisticated analytic techniques to predict average amounts of substance use at each follow-up interval and concluded that the average substance use reductions were substantially the same as those achieved for comparable follow-up intervals in the homeless adolescents randomized trial by Slesnick and colleagues (2007) reported above. These findings are important because they show a convergence of expected levels of reduced harm to self and others in two distinctly different adolescent subpopulations. The authors concluded that their study supports the use of A-CRA/ACC with adolescents across multiple cultural boundaries.

Curtis and Wodarski (2015) evaluated the effect of A-CRA/ACC in eastern Tennessee with 107 adolescents and young adults age 12 to 24. Most of the participants met *DSM-IV-TR* criteria for substance abuse or substance dependence and reported symptoms of co-occurring mental health disorders. The authors reported several significant findings at 6 months, including a decrease in illegal drug use, a decrease in alcohol consumption, a decrease in criminal activity, a decrease in violent behaviors, and an increase in cognitive ability. Additional findings at 6 months included decreased risky sexual behaviors and increased participant interaction with supportive friends and family. The authors noted that because of the success of A-CRA/ACC, officials at the Helen Ross McNabb Center in Knoxville, TN were able to sustain A-CRA/ACC because they received permission to invoice TennCare (Medicaid) for A-CRA/ACC services after the CSAT grant ended.

References

Abbott, P. J., Weller, S. B., Delaney, H. D., & Moore, B. A. (1998). Community Reinforcement Approach in the treatment of opiate addicts. *American Journal of Drug and Alcohol Abuse, 24*(1), 17–30. doi:10.3109/00952999809001696

Alexander, J. F., & Parsons, B. V. (Eds.). (1982). *Functional family therapy.* Monterey, CA: Brooks/Cole.

American Psychiatric Association. (2000). *Diagnostic and statistical manual of mental disorders* (4th ed., text rev.). Washington, DC: Author.

American Psychiatric Association. (2013). *Diagnostic and statistical manual of mental disorders* (5th ed.). Washington, DC: Author.

American Society of Addiction Medicine. (1996). *Patient placement criteria for the treatment of psychoactive substance use disorders* (2nd ed.). Chevy Chase, MD: Author.

Ammerman, S. (2015). The impact of marijuana polices on youth. *Pediatrics, 135*(3), 1825. doi:10.1542/peds.2014-4146

Azrin, N. H. (1976). Improvements in the community reinforcement approach to alcoholism. *Behavior Research and Therapy, 14,* 339–348. doi:10.1016/0005-7967(76)90021-8

Azrin, N. H., Donohue, B., Besalel, V. A., Kogan, E. S., & Acierno, R. (1994). Youth drug treatment: A controlled outcome study. *Journal of Child and Adolescent Substance Abuse, 3,* 1–16. doi:10.1300/J029v03n03_01

Azrin, N. H., McMahon, P. T., Donohue, B., Besalel, V. A., Lapinski, K. J., Kogan, E. S., Acierno, R. E., & Galloway, E. (1994). Behavior therapy for drug abuse: A controlled treatment outcome study. *Behavior Research and Therapy, 32,* 857–866. doi:10.1016/0005-7967(94)90166-X

Azrin, N. H., Sisson, R. W., Meyers, R., & Godley, M. (1982). Alcoholism treatment by disulfiram and community reinforcement therapy. *Behavioral Therapy and Experimental Psychiatry, 13*(2), 105–122. doi:10.1016/0005-7916(82)90050-7

Bergen, H. A., Martin, G., Roeger, L., & Allison, S. (2005). Perceived academic performance and alcohol, tobacco and marijuana use: longitudinal relationships in young community adolescents. *Addictive Behaviors, 30*(8), 1563–1573. doi:10.1016/j.addbeh.2005.02.012

Bernal, G., Jimenez-Chafey, M. I., & Rodriguez, M. M. D. (2009). Cultural adaptation of treatments: A resource for considering culture in evidence-based practice. *Professional Psychology: Research & Practice, 40*(4), 361–368. doi: 10.1037/a0016401

Brown, S. A., & Tapert, S. F. (2004). Adolescence and the trajectory of alcohol use: Basic to clinical studies. *Annals of the New York Academy of Sciences, 1021,* 234–244. doi:10.1196/annals.1308.028

Brown, S. A., Tapert, S. F., Granholm, E., & Delis, D. C. (2000). Neurocognitive functioning of adolescents: Effects of protracted alcohol use. *Alcoholism: Clinical and Experimental Research, 24,* 164–171. doi:10.1111/j.1530-0277.2000.tb04586.x

Bry, B. H. (1998, January). The targeted adolescent family and multisystems intervention (TAFMI): Prevention intervention with youths at risk for substance abuse. Workshop presented at the Eighth International Conference on Treatment of Addictive Behaviors, Santa Fe, NM.

Bry, B. H., Catalano, R. F., Kumpfer, K. L., Lochman, J. E., & Szapocznik, J. (1998). Scientific findings from family prevention intervention research in drug abuse prevention through family intervention. In R. S. Ashery, E. B. Robertson, & K. L. Kumpher (eds.), *Drug Abuse Prevention Through Family Interventions* (NIDA Research Monograph 177; pp. 103–129). Rockville, MD: NIDA. Retrieved from https://archives.drugabuse.gov/pdf/monographs/monograph177/monograph177.pdf

Budney, A. J., Higgins, S. T., Delaney, D. D., Kent, L., & Bickel, W. K. (1991). Contingent reinforcement of abstinence with individuals abusing cocaine and marijuana. *Journal of Applied Behavior Analysis*, *24*, 657–665. doi:10.1901/jaba.1991.24-657

Campbell, C. I., & Alexander, J. A. (2002). Culturally competent treatment practices and ancillary service use in outpatient substance abuse treatment. *Journal of Substance Abuse Treatment*, *22*, 109–119. doi: 10.1016/S0740-5472(02)00221-0

Carroll, K. M., Nich, C., LaPaglia, D. M., Peters, E. N., Easton, C. J., & Petry, N. M. (2012). Combining cognitive behavioral therapy and contingency management to enhance their effects in treating cannabis dependence: Less can be more, more or less. *Addiction*, *107*, 1650–1659.

Catalano, R. F. (1998, January). The importance of the family to the prevention and treatment of substance abuse. Keynote address presented at the Eighth International Conference on Treatment of Addictive Behaviors, Santa Fe, NM.

Cerdá, M., Wall, M., Keyes, K. M., Galea, S., & Hasin, D. (2012). Medical marijuana laws in 50 states: Investigating the relationship between state legalization of medical marijuana and marijuana use, abuse and dependence. *Drug and Alcohol Dependence*, *120*(1), 22–27. doi:10.1016/j.drugalcdep.2011.06.011

Cermak, T. (2015). Cognitive harms associated with regular adolescent marijuana use: A briefing paper submitted to the California Blue Ribbon Commission on Marijuana Policy. Retrieved from https://www.safeandsmartpolicy.org/wp-content/uploads/2015/05/Cognitive-Harms-of-Heavy-MJ-authored-and-submitted-by-T-Cermak-MD-in-hi....pdf

Chan, Y.-F., Dennis, M. L., & Funk, R. R. (2008). Prevalence and comorbidity of major internalizing and externalizing problems among adolescents and adults presenting to substance abuse treatment. *Journal of Substance Abuse Treatment*, *34*(1), 14–24. doi:10.1016/j.jsat.2006.12.031

Chan, Y.-F., Passetti, L. L., Garner, B. R., Lloyd, J. J., & Dennis, M. L. (2011). HIV risk behaviors: Risky sexual activities and needle use among adolescents in substance abuse treatment. *AIDS and Behavior*, *15*, 114–124. doi:10.1007/s10461-010-9702-3

Choo, E. K., Benz, M., Zaller, N., Warren, O., Rising, K. L., & McConnell, K. J. (2014). The impact of state medical marijuana legislation on adolescent marijuana use. *Journal of Adolescent Health*, *55*, 160–166. doi:10.1016/j.jadohealth.2014.02.018

Corvalan-Wood, J., Rajaee, L., & Godley, S. H. (2011). Implementing evidence-based treatment in a TASC drug court system. *Counselor*, *12*, 10–15.

Crews, F., He, J., & Hodge, C. (2007) Adolescent cortical development: a critical period of vulnerability for addiction. *Pharmacology Biochemistry and Behavior, 86*, 189–199. doi:10.1016/j.pbb.2006.12.001

Curtis, S. V., & Wodarski, J. S. (2015). The East Tennessee assertive adolescent family treatment program: A three-year evaluation. *Social Work in Public Health, 30*(3), 225–235. doi: 10.1080/19371918.2014.992713

De Bellis, M. D., Narasimhan, A., Thatcher, D. L., Keshavan, M. S., Soloff, P., & Clark, D. B. (2005). Prefrontal cortex, thalamus and cerebellar volumes in adolescents and young adults with adolescent onset alcohol use disorders and co-morbid mental disorders. *Alcoholism: Clinical and Experimental Research, 29*(9), 1590–1600. doi:10.1097/01.alc.0000179368.87886.76

De Jong, C. A. J., Roozen, H. G., van Rossum, L. G. M., Krabbe, P. F. M., & Kerkhof, A. J. F. M. (2007). High abstinence rates in heroin addicts by a new comprehensive treatment approach. *American Journal on Addictions, 16*, 124–130. doi:10.1080/10550490601184472

Dennis, M. L., Godley, S.H., Diamond, G., Tims, F.M., Babor, T., Donaldson, J., . . . Funk, R. (2004). The Cannabis Youth Treatment (CYT) study: Main findings from two randomized trials. *Journal of Substance Abuse Treatment, 27*, 193–213. doi:10.1016/j.jsat.2003.09.005

Dennis, M. L., Titus, J. C., White, M. K., Unsicker, J., & Hodgkins, D. (2003). *Global Appraisal of Individual Needs (GAIN): Administration guide for the GAIN and related measures*. Bloomington, IL: Chestnut Health Systems.

Diamond, G. S., Godley, S. H., Liddle, H., Webb, C., Sampl, S., Tims, F., & Meyers, R. (2002). Five outpatient models for adolescent marijuana use: A description of the Cannabis Youth Treatment interventions. *Addiction, 97*, 69–82. doi:10.1046/j.1360-0443.97.s01.3.x

Diamond, G. S., Leckrone, J., Dennis, M. L., & Godley, S. H. (2006). The Cannabis Youth Treatment study: The treatment models and preliminary findings. In R. Roffman, & R. Stephens (eds.), *Cannabis dependence: Its nature, consequences, and treatment* (pp. 247–274). Cambridge, UK: Cambridge University Press.

D'Zurilla, T., & Goldfried, M. R. (1971). Problem solving and behavior motivation. *Journal of Abnormal Psychology, 78*, 107–126. doi:10.1037/h0031360

Edlund, M. J., Forman-Hoffman, V. L., Winder, C. R., Heller, D. C., Kroutil, L. A., Lipari, R. N., & Colpe, L. (2015). Opioid abuse and depression in adolescents: Results from the National Survey on Drug Use and Health. *Drug and Alcohol Dependence, 152*, 131–138. doi:10.1016/j.drugalcdep.2015.04.010

Finney, J. W., & Monahan, S. C. (1996). The cost-effectiveness of treatment for alcoholism: A second approximation. *Journal of Studies on Alcohol, 57*, 229–243. doi:10.15288/jsa.1996.57.229

Friese, B., & Grube, J. W. (2013). Legalization of medical marijuana and marijuana use among youths. *Drugs: Education, Prevention and Policy, 20*(1), 33–39. doi:10.3109/09687637.2012.713408

Garner, B. R., Godley, S. H., Funk, R. R., Dennis, M. L., Smith, J. E., & Godley, M. D. (2009). Exposure to Adolescent Community Reinforcement Approach treatment procedures as a mediator of the relationship between adolescent substance abuse treatment retention and outcome. *Journal of Substance Abuse Treatment, 36*, 252–264. doi:10.1016/j.jsat.2008.06.007

Garner, B. R., Hunter, B. D., Smith, D. C., Smith, J. E., & Godley, M. D. (2014). The relationship between child maltreatment and substance abuse treatment outcomes among emerging adults and adolescents. *Child Maltreatment, 19*(3–4), 261–269. doi:10.1177/1077559514547264

Godley, M. D., Godley, S. H., Dennis, M. L., Funk, R. R., & Passetti, L. L. (2002). Preliminary outcomes from the assertive continuing care experiment for adolescents discharged from residential treatment. *Journal of Substance Abuse Treatment, 23*(1), 21–32. doi:10.1016/S0740-5472(02)00230-1

Godley, M. D., Godley, S. H., Dennis, M. L., Funk, R. R., & Passetti, L. L. (2007). The effectiveness of assertive continuing care on continuing care linkage, adherence, and abstinence following residential treatment for substance use disorders in adolescents. *Addiction, 102*, 81–93. doi:10.1111/j.1360-0443.2006.01648.x

Godley, M. D., Godley, S. H., Dennis, M. L., Funk, R. R., Passetti, L. L., & Petry, N. (2014). A randomized trial of Assertive Continuing Care and contingency management for adolescents with substance use disorders. *Journal of Consulting and Clinical Psychology, 82*, 40–51. doi:10.1037/a0035264

Godley, S. H., Hedges, K., & Hunter, B. (2011). Gender and racial differences in treatment process and outcome among participants in the Adolescent Community Reinforcement Approach. *Psychology of Addictive Behaviors, 25*, 143–154. doi:10.1037/a0022179

Godley, S. H., Hunter, B. D., Fernández-Artamendi, S., Smith, J. E., Meyers, R. J., & Godley, M. D. (2014). A comparison of treatment outcomes for Adolescent Community Reinforcement Approach participants with and without co-occurring disorders. *Journal of Substance Abuse Treatment, 46*, 463–471. doi:10.1016/j.jsat.2013.10.013

Godley, S. H., Meyers, R. J., Smith, J. E., Godley, M. D., Titus, J. C., Karvinen, T., . . . Kelberg, P. (2001). *The Adolescent Community Reinforcement Approach (ACRA) for adolescent cannabis users* (DHHS Publication No. (SMA) 01-3489, Cannabis Youth Treatment (CYT) Manual Series, Volume 4). Rockville, MD: Center for Substance Abuse Treatment, Substance Abuse and Mental Health Services Administration. Retrieved from http://ebtx.chestnut.org/Portals/0/Documents/ACRA_CYT_v4.pdf

Godley, S. H., Meyers, R. J., Smith, J. E., Godley, M. D., Titus, J. C., Karvinen, T., . . . Kelberg, P. (2001). *The Adolescent Community Reinforcement Approach (ACRA) for adolescent cannabis users* (DHHS Publication No. (SMA) 01-3489, Cannabis Youth Treatment (CYT) Manual Series, Volume 4) (Novadic-Kentron, Dutch Trans.). Rockville, MD: Center for Substance Abuse Treatment, Substance Abuse and Mental Health Services Administration. Retrieved from http://ebtx.chestnut.org/ LinkClick.aspx?fileticket=K2fVr_wkp-s%3d&portalid=0

Godley, S. H., Meyers, R. J., Smith, J. E., Godley, M. D., Titus, J. C., Karvinen, T., . . . Kelberg, P. (2001). *The Adolescent Community Reinforcement Approach (ACRA) for adolescent cannabis users* (DHHS Publication No. (SMA) 01-3489, Cannabis Youth Treatment (CYT) Manual Series, Volume 4) (Dave Smith Youth Treatment Centre, French Trans.). Rockville, MD: Center for Substance Abuse Treatment, Substance Abuse and Mental Health Services Administration. Retrieved from http://ebtx.chestnut.org/Portals/0/Documents/ACRA_FR%20-%20vol%204.pdf

Godley, S. H., Meyers, R. J., Smith, J. E., Godley, M. D., Titus, J. C., Karvinen, T., . . . Kelberg, P. (2001). *The Adolescent Community Reinforcement Approach (ACRA) for adolescent cannabis users* (DHHS Publication No. (SMA) 01-3489, Cannabis Youth Treatment (CYT) Manual Series, Volume 4) (M. C. S. Dias, L. Anderson, Portuguese Trans.). Rockville, MD: Center for Substance Abuse Treatment, Substance Abuse and Mental Health Services Administration. Retrieved from http://ebtx.chestnut.org/Portals/0/Documents/ACRA_Tradução_procedimentos_FULL_MANUAL.pdf

Godley, S. H., Meyers, R. J., Smith, J. E., Godley, M. D., Titus, J. C., Karvinen, T., . . . Kelberg, P. (2001). *The Adolescent Community Reinforcement Approach (ACRA) for adolescent cannabis users* (DHHS Publication No. (SMA) 01-3489, Cannabis Youth Treatment (CYT) Manual Series, Volume 4) (S. Fernández-Artamendi, J. R., Fernández-Hermida, Spanish Trans.). Rockville, MD: Center for Substance Abuse Treatment, Substance Abuse and Mental Health Services Administration. Retrieved from http://ebtx.chestnut.org/Portals/0/Documents/Manual_del_ACRA_rev_FINALAgo12.pdf

Godley, S. H., Smith, J. E., Passetti, L. L., & Subramaniam, G. (2014). The Adolescent Community Reinforcement Approach (A-CRA) as a model paradigm for the management of adolescents with substance use disorders and co-occurring psychiatric disorders. *Substance Abuse, 35*(4), 352–363. doi:10.1080/08897077.2014.936993

Godley, S. H., White, W. L., Diamond, G. S., Passetti, L. L., & Titus, J. C. (2001). Therapists' reactions to manual-guided therapies for the treatment of adolescent marijuana users. *Clinical Psychology: Science and Practice, 8*, 405–417. doi:10.1093/clipsy.8.4.405

Godley, S. H., White, M. K., & Passetti, L. L. (2006). Employment and adolescent alcohol and drug treatment and recovery: An exploratory study. *American Journal on Addictions, 15*, 137–143. doi: 10.1080/10550490601006295

Gonzalez, R., & Swanson, J. M. (2012). Long-term effects of adolescent-onset and persistent use of cannabis. *Proceedings of the National Academy of Sciences of the United States of America, 109*(40), 15970-15971. doi:10.1073/pnas.1214124109

Gruber, S. A., Sagar, K. A., Dahlgren, M. K., Racine, M., & Lukas, S. E. (2012). Age of onset of marijuana use and executive function. *Psychology of Addictive Behaviors, 26*(3), 496–506. doi:10.1037/a0026269

Guo, J., Chung, I. J., Hill, K. G., Hawkins, J. D., Catalano, R. F., & Abbott, R. D. (2002). Developmental relationships between adolescent substance use and risky sexual behavior in young adulthood. *Journal of Adolescent Health, 31*, 354–362. doi:10.1016/S1054-139X(02)00402-0

Hanson, K. L., Medina, K. L., Padula, C. B., Tapert, S. F., & Brown, S. A. (2011). Impact of adolescent alcohol and drug use on neuropsychological functioning in young adulthood: 10-year outcomes. *Journal of Child and Adolescent Substance Abuse, 20*, 135–154. doi:10.1080/1067828X.2011.555272

Henderson, C. E., Wevodau, A. L., Henderson, S. E., Colbourn, S. L., Gharagozloo, L., North, L. W., & Lotts, V. A. (2016). An independent replication of the Adolescent Community Reinforcement Approach with justice-involved youth. *American Journal on Addictions, 25*(3), 233–240. doi:10.1111/ajad.12366

Higgins, S. T., & Abbott, P. J. (2001). CRA and treatment of cocaine and opioid dependence. In R. J. Meyers & W. R. Miller (eds.), *A Community Reinforcement Approach to Addiction Treatment* (pp. 123–146). New York: Cambridge University Press.

Higgins, S. T., Budney, A. J., Bickel, W. K., & Badger, G. J. (1994). Participation of significant others in outpatient behavioral treatment predicts greater cocaine abstinence. *American Journal of Drug and Alcohol Abuse, 20*, 47–56.

Higgins, S. T., Budney, A. J., Bickel, W. K., Badger, G. J., Foerg, F. E., & Ogden, D. (1995). Outpatient behavioral treatment for cocaine dependence: One-year outcome. *Experimental Clinical Psychopharmacology, 3*(2), 205–212. doi:10.1037/1064-1297.3.2.205

Higgins, S. T., Budney, A. J., Bickel, W. K., Hughes, J. R., Foerg, F. E., & Badger, G. J. (1993). Achieving cocaine abstinence with a behavioral approach. *American Journal of Psychiatry, 150*, 763–769. doi:10.1176/ajp.150.5.763

Higgins, S. T., Delaney, D. D., Budney, A. J., Bickel, W. K., Hughes, J. R., Foerg, F., & Fenwick, J. W. (1991). A behavioral approach to achieving initial cocaine abstinence. *American Journal of Psychiatry, 148*, 1218–1224. doi:10.1176/ajp.148.9.1218

Higgins, S. T., Sigmon, S. C., Wong, C. J., Heil, S. H., Badger, G. J., Donham, R., Dantona, R. L., & Anthony, S. (2003). Community Reinforcement Therapy for cocaine-dependent outpatients. *Archives of General Psychiatry, 60*, 1043–1052. doi:10.1001/archpsyc.60.9.1043

Holder, H., Longabaugh, R., Miller, W. R., & Rubonis, A. V. (1991). The cost-effectiveness of treatment for alcoholism: A first approximation. *Journal of Studies on Alcohol, 52*, 517–540. doi:10.15288/jsa.1991.52.517

Hopfer, C. (2014). Implications of marijuana legalization for adolescent substance use. *Substance Abuse, 35*(4), 331–335. doi:10.1080/08897077.2014.943386

Hopfer, C. J., Khuri, E., Crowley, T. J., & Hooks, S. (2002). Adolescent heroin use: A review of the descriptive and treatment literature. *Journal of Substance Abuse Treatment, 23*, 231–237. doi:10.1016/S0740-5472(02)00250-7

Hopfer, C. J., Mikulich, S. K., & Crowley, T. J. (2000). Heroin use among adolescents in treatment for substance use disorders. *Journal of the American Academy of Child and Adolescent Psychiatry, 39*(10), 1316–1323. doi:10.1097/00004583-200010000-00021

Hops, H. (1998, January). From adolescence to adulthood: A 10-year family perspective on substance use and abuse. Keynote address presented at the Eighth International Conference on Treatment of Addictive Behaviors, Santa Fe, NM.

Hunt, G. M., & Azrin, N. H. (1973). A community reinforcement approach to alcoholism. *Behavior Research and Therapy, 11*, 91–104. doi:10.1016/0005-7967(73)90072-7

Hunter, B. D., Godley, M. D., & Godley, S. H. (2014). Feasibility of implementing the Adolescent Community Reinforcement Approach in school settings for adolescents with substance use disorders. *Advances in School Mental Health Promotion, 7*(2), 105–122. doi:10.1080/1754730X.201.888224

Hunter, B. D., Godley, S. H., Hesson-McInnis, M., & Roozen, H. G. (2014). Longitudinal change mechanisms for substance use and illegal activity for adolescents in treatment. *Psychology of Addictive Behaviors, 28*, 507–515. doi:10.1037/a0034199

Hupp, C. L., Mertig, K., Krall (Malek), K. L., Godley, M. D., & Godley, S. H. (2009). *Adolescent Community Reinforcement Approach (A-CRA) and Assertive Continuing Care (ACC) supervisor rating manual.* Normal, IL: Chestnut Health Systems.

Hwang, W.-C., Wood, J. J., Lin, K. -M., & Cheung, F. (2006). Cognitive-Behavioral Therapy with Chinese Americans: Research, theory, and clinical practice. *Cognitive and Behavioral Practice, 13*, 293–303. doi:10.1016/j.cbpra.2006.04.010

Institute for Social Research. (1997). Monitoring the Future Study, Data Tables and Figures. Ann Arbor, MI: University of Michigan. Retrieved from http://www.isr.umich.edu/src/mtf

Laska, K. M., Gurman, A. S., & Wampold, B. E. (2014). Expanding the lens of evidence-based practice in psychotherapy: A common factors perspective. *Psychotherapy, 51*(4), 467–481. doi:10.1037/a0034332

Levy, S. (2013). Effects of marijuana policy on children and adolescents. *JAMA Pediatrics, 167*(7), 600–602. doi:10.1001/jamapediatrics.2013.2270

Lynne-Landsman, S. D., Livingston, M. D., & Wagenaar, A. C. (2013). Effects of state medical marijuana laws on adolescent marijuana use. *American Journal of Public Health, 103*, 1500–1506. doi:10.2105/AJPH.2012.301117

Lynskey, M. T., Coffey, C., Degenhardt, L., Carlin, J. B., & Patton, G. (2003). A longitudinal study of the effects of adolescent cannabis use on high school completion. *Addiction, 98*, 685–692. doi:10.1046/j.1360-0443.2003.00356.x

Lynskey, M., & Hall, W. (2000). The effects of adolescent cannabis use on educational attainment: A review. *Addiction, 95*(11), 1621–1630. doi:10.1046/j.1360-0443.2000.951116213.x

Lyoo, I. K., Yoon, S., Kim, T. S., Lim, S. M., Choi, Y., Kim, J. E., . . . Renshaw, P. F. (2015). Predisposition to and effects of methamphetamine use on the adolescent brain. *Molecular Psychiatry. Advance online publication.* doi:10.1038/mp.2014.191

McGarvey, E. L., Leon-Verdin, M., Bloomfield, K., Wood, S., Winters, E., & Smith, J. (2014). Effectiveness of A-CRA/ACC in treating adolescents with cannabis-use disorders. *Community Mental Health Journal, 50*(2), 150–157. doi:10.1007/s10597-012-9566-2

McKay, M., Rogers, P. D., & McKay, J. (Eds.) (1989). *When anger hurts: Quieting the storm within.* Oakland, CA: New Harbinger Publications.

Medina, K. L., Hanson, K. L., Schweinsburg, A. D., Cohen-Zion, M., Nagel, B. J., & Tapert, S. F. (2007). Neuropsychological functioning in adolescent marijuana users: Subtle deficits detectable after a month of abstinence. *Journal of the International Neuropsychological Society, 13*(5), 807–820. doi:10.1017/S1355617707071032

Medina, K. L., McQueeny, T., Nagel, B. J., Hanson, K. L., Schweinsburg, A. D., & Tapert, S. F. (2008). Prefrontal cortex volumes in adolescents with alcohol use disorders: Unique gender effects.

Alcoholism: Clinical and Experimental Research, 32, 386–394. doi:10.1111/j.1530-0277.2007.00602.x

Medina, K. L., Schweinsburg, A. D., Cohen-Zion, M., Nagel, B. J., & Tapert, S. F. (2007). Effects of alcohol and combined marijuana and alcohol use during adolescence on hippocampal volume and asymmetry. *Neurotoxicology and Teratology, 29*, 141–152. doi:10.1016/j.ntt.2006.10.010

Meier, M. H., Caspi, A., Ambler, A., Harrington, H., Houts, R., Keefe, R. S. E., . . .Moffitt, T. E. (2012). Persistent cannabis users show neuropsychological decline from childhood to midlife. *Proceedings of the National Academy of Sciences of the United States of America, 109*, E2657–2664. doi:10.1073/pnas.1206820109

Meier, P. S., Barrowclough, C., & Donmall, M. C. (2005). The role of the therapeutic alliance in the treatment of substance misuse: A critical review of the literature. *Addiction, 100*(3), 304–316. doi:10.1111/j.1360-0443.2004.00935.x

Melidonis, G. G., & Bry, B. H. (1995). Effects of therapist exceptions questions on blaming and positive statements in families with adolescent behavior problems. *Journal of Family Psychology, 9*, 451–457. doi:10.1037/0893-3200.9.4.451

Meyers, R. J., Dominguez, T. P., & Smith, J. E. (1996). Community reinforcement training with concerned others. In V. B. Van Hasselt & M. Hersen (Eds.), *Sourcebook of psychological treatment manuals for adult disorders* (pp. 257–294). New York, NY: Plenum Press.

Meyers, R. J., & Godley, M. D. (2001). The community reinforcement approach. In R. J. Meyers & W. R. Miller (eds.), *A community reinforcement approach to addiction treatment* (pp. 1–7). Cambridge, United Kingdom: Cambridge University Press.

Meyers, R. J., & Smith, J. E. (1995). *Clinical guide to alcohol treatment: The community reinforcement approach*. New York, NY: Guilford.

Meyers, R. J., & Smith, J. E. (1997). Getting off the fence: Procedures to engage treatment-resistant drinkers. *Journal of Substance Abuse Treatment, 14*(5), 467–472. doi:10.1016/S0740-5472(97)00122-0

Miller, S. D., Hubble, M. A., Duncan, B. L., & Wampold, B. E. (2010). Delivering what works. In B. L. Duncan, S. D. Miller, B. E. Wampold, & M. A. Hubble (eds.), *The heart and soul of change: Delivering what works in therapy* (2nd ed., pp. 421–429). Washington, DC: American Psychological Association.

Miller, W. R., & Baca, L. M. (1983). Two-year follow-up of bibliotherapy and therapist-directed controlled drinking training for problem drinkers. *Behavior Therapy, 14*(3), 441–448. doi:10.1016/S0005-7894(83)80107-5

Miller, W. R., Brown, J. M., Simpson, T. L., Handmaker, N. S., Bien, T. H., Luckie, L. F., . . . Tonigan, J. S. (1995). What works? A methodological analysis of the alcohol treatment outcome literature. In R. K. Hester & W. R. Miller (Eds.), *Handbook of alcoholism treatment approaches: Effective alternatives* (pp. 12–44). Boston: Allyn & Bacon.

Miller, W. R., & Moyers, T. B. (2014). The forest and the trees: Relational and specific factors in addiction treatment. *Addiction, 110*(3), 401–413. doi:10.1111/add.12693

Miller, W. R., Wilbourne, P. L., & Hettema, J. E. (2003). What works? A summary of alcohol treatment outcome research. In R. K. Hester & W. R. Miller (eds.), *Handbook of alcoholism treatment approaches: Effective alternatives* (3rd ed., pp. 13–63). Boston: Allyn & Bacon.

Miller, W. R., Zweben, A., DiClemente, C. C., & Rychtarik, R. G. (1995). *Motivational enhancement therapy (MET) manual, Project MATCH.* Rockville, MD: National Institute on Alcohol Abuse and Alcoholism.

Miller, W. R., Zweben, J., & Johnson, W. R. (2005). Evidence-based treatment: Why, what, where, when, and how? *Journal of Substance Abuse Treatment, 29*(4), 267–276. doi:10.1016/j.jsat.2005.08.003

Moyers, T. B., & Miller, W. R. (2013). Is low therapist empathy toxic? *Psychology of Addictive Behavior, 27*, 878–884. doi:10.1037/a0030274

Nagel, B. J., Schweinsburg, A. D., Phan, V., & Tapert, S. F. (2005). Reduced hippocampal volume among adolescents with alcohol use disorders without psychiatric comorbidity. *Psychiatry Research, 139*(3), 181–190. doi:10.1016/j.pscychresns.2005.05.008

Norcross, J. C., & Wampold, B. E. (2011). Evidence-based therapy relationships: Research conclusions and clinical practices. In J. C. Norcross (ed.), *Psychotherapy relationships that work: Evidence-based responsiveness* (2nd ed., pp. 423–430). New York: Oxford University Press.

Office of Applied Studies (OAS). (1995). *Services research outreach survey.* Rockville, MD: Substance Abuse and Mental Health Services Administration, OAS.

Office of Applied Studies (OAS). (1997). Preliminary results from the 1996 *National Household Survey on Drug Abuse (NHSDA).* Rockville, MD: Substance Abuse and Mental Health Services Administration, OAS.

Palamar, J. J. (2014). An examination of opinions toward marijuana policies among high school seniors in the United States. *Journal of Psychoactive Drugs, 46*, 351–361. doi:10.1080/02791072.2014.962716

Patton, G. C., Coffey, C., Carlin, J. B., Degenhardt, L., Lynskey, M., & Hall, W. (2002). Cannabis use and mental health in young people: Cohort study. *British Medical Journal, 325*, 1195–1198.

The President's New Freedom Commission on Mental Health. (2003). *Achieving the promise: Transforming mental health care in America.* Rockville, MD: Author.

Resko, S. M. (2015). Shifts in marijuana policies and the impact on adolescents. *Journal of Social Work Practice in the Addictions, 15*(2), 227–231. doi:10.1080/1533256X.2015.1029417

Rey, J. M., Martin, A., & Krabman, P. (2004). Is the party over? Cannabis and juvenile psychiatric disorder: The past 10 years. *Journal of the American Academy of Child and Adolescent Psychiatry, 43*, 1194–1205. doi:10.1097/01.chi.0000135623.12843.60

Roozen, H. G., Kerkhof, A. J., & Van Den Brink, W. (2003). Experiences with an outpatient relapse program (Community Reinforcement Approach) combined with naltrexone in the treatment of opioid dependence: Effect on addictive behaviors and the predictive value of psychiatric comorbidity." *European Addiction Research, 9*, 53–58. doi:10.1159/000068808

Roozen, H. G., Van Beers, S. E. C., Weevers, H. J. A., Breteler, M. H. M., Willemsen, M. C., Postmus, P. E., & Kerhof, J. F. M. (2006). Effects on smoking cessation: Naltrexone combined with a cognitive behavioral treatment based on the Community Reinforcement Approach. *Substance Use and Misuse*, *41*, 45–60. doi:10.1080/10826080500318665

Ruiz, B. S., Korchmaros, J. D., Greene, A., & Hedges, K. (2011). Evidence-based substance abuse treatment for adolescents: Engagement and outcomes. *Practice*, *23*(4), 215–233. doi:10.1080/09503153.2011.597207

Schottenfeld, R. S., Pantalon, M. V., Chaarski, M. C., & Pakes, J. (2000). Community reinforcement approach for combined opioid and cocaine dependence: Patterns of engagement in alternate activities. *Journal of Substance Abuse Treatment*, *18*, 225–261. doi:10.1016/S0740-5472(99)00062-8

Schweinsburg, A., Brown, S., & Tapert, S. (2008). The influence of marijuana use on neurocognitive functioning in adolescents. *Current Drug Abuse Reviews*, *1*, 99–111.

Secades-Villa, R., Garcia-Rodriguez, O., Higgins, S. T., Fernandez-Hermida, J. R., & Carballo, J. L. (2008). Community reinforcement approach plus vouchers for cocaine dependence in a community setting in Spain: Six-month outcomes. *Journal of Substance Abuse Treatment*, *34*, 202–207. doi:10.1016/j.jsat.2007.03.006

Shaner, A., Roberts, L. J., Eckman, T. A., Tucker, D. E., Tsuang, J. W., Wilkins, J. N., & Mintz, J. (1997). Monetary reinforcement of abstinence from cocaine among mentally ill patients with cocaine dependence. *Psychiatric Services*, *48*, 807–810.

Slesnick, N., Prestopnik, J. L., Meyers, R. J., & Glassman, M. (2007). Treatment outcome for street-living, homeless youth. *Addictive Behaviors*, *32*, 1237–1251. doi:10.1016/j.addbeh.2006.08.010

Smith, D. C., Godley, S. H., Godley, M. D., & Dennis, M. L. (2011). Adolescent community reinforcement approach outcomes differ among emerging adults and adolescents. *Journal of Substance Abuse Treatment*, *41*, 422–430. doi:10.1016/j.jsat.2011.06.003

Smith, J. E., Gianini, L. M., Garner, B. R., Krall (Malek), K. L., & Godley, S. H. (2014). A behaviorally-anchored rating system to monitor treatment integrity for community clinicians using the Adolescent Community Reinforcement Approach. *Journal of Child and Adolescent Substance Abuse*, *23*, 185–199. doi:10.1080/1067828X.2012.729258

Smith, J. E., Lundy, S. L., & Gianini, L. (2007). *Community Reinforcement Approach (CRA) and Adolescent Community Reinforcement Approach (A-CRA) therapist coding manual*. Normal, IL: Chestnut Health Systems.

Smith, J. E., Meyers, R. J., & Delaney, H. D. (1998). The community reinforcement approach with homeless alcohol-dependent individuals. *Journal of Consulting and Clinical Psychology*, *66*, 541–548. doi:10.1037//0022-006X.66.3.541

Strunz, E., Jungerman, J., Kinyua, J., & Frew, P. M., (2015). Evaluation of an assertive continuing care program for Hispanic adolescents. *Global Journal of Health Science*, *7*(5), 2015. doi:10.5539/gjhs.v7n5p106

Subramaniam, G. A., Stitzer, M. L., Woody, G., Fishman, M. J., & Kolodner, K. (2009). Clinical characteristics of treatment-seeking adolescents with opioid versus cannabis/alcohol use disorders. *Drug and Alcohol Dependence, 99*, 141–149. doi:10.1016/j.drugalcdep.2008.07.016

Subramaniam, G. A., Warden, D. Minhajuddin, A., Fishman, M. J., Stitzer, M. L., Adinoff, B, Trivedi, M, Weiss, R., Potter, J., Poole, S. A., & Woody, G. E. (2011). Predictors of abstinence: National Institute of Drug Abuse multisite buprenorphine/naloxone treatment trial in opioid-dependent youth. *Journal of the American Academy of Child & Adolescent Psychiatry, 50*(11), 1120–1128. doi:10.1016/j.jaac.2011.07.010

Substance Abuse and Mental Health Services Administration (SAMHSA). (2007). Treatment episode data set (TEDS): 1992–2005: Concatenated data [computer file]. Retrieved from http://www.icpsr.umich.edu/icpsrweb/SAMHDA/series/00056

Substance Abuse and Mental Health Services Administration (SAMHSA). (2012). *Results from the 2011 National Survey on Drug Use and Health: Summary of national findings.* NSDUH Series H-44, HHS Publication No. (SMA) 12-713. Rockville, MD: Author.

Substance Abuse and Mental Health Services Administration (SAMHSA), & Office of Applied Studies (OAS). (2008). *Treatment Episode Data Set (TEDS): 1996–2006.* National Admissions to Substance Abuse Treatment Services, DASIS Series: S-43, DHHS Publication No. (SMA) 08-4347. Rockville, MD: Author.

Sue, D. W., Bernier, J. E., Durran, A., Feinberg, L., Pedersen, P., Smith, E. J., & Vasquez-Nuttall, E. (1982). Position paper: Cross-cultural counseling competencies. *Counseling Psychologist, 10*, 45–52. doi:10.1177/0011000082102008

Sue, S. (2006). Cultural competency: From philosophy to research and practice. *Journal of Community Psychology, 34*(2), 237–245. doi:10.1002/jcop.20095

Sundram, S. (2006). Cannabis and neurodevelopment: Implications for psychiatric disorders. *Human Psychopharmacology*, 21, 245–54. doi:10.1002/hup.762

Tapert, S. F., & Brown, S. A. (2000). Substance dependence, family history of alcohol dependence and neuropsychological functioning in adolescence. *Addiction, 95*(7), 1043–1053. doi:10.1046/j.1360-0443.2000.95710436.x

Tapert, S. F., Granholm, E., Leedy, N. G., & Brown, S. A. (2002). Substance use and withdrawal: Neuropsychological functioning over eight years in youth. *Journal of the International Neuropsychological Society, 8*, 873–883. doi:10.1017/S1355617702870011

Tapert, S. F., Schweinsburg, A. D., Barlett, V. C., Brown, S. A., Frank, L. R., Brown, G. G., & Meloy, M. J. (2004). Blood oxygen level dependent response and spatial working memory in adolescents with alcohol use disorders. *Alcoholism: Clinical and Experimental Research, 28*(10), 1577–1586. doi:10.1097/01.ALC.0000141812.81234.A6

Tobin, T., Huntington, N., Lang, D., Carpenter, J., Centerbar, D., & Fulmore, D. (2012). *Program Evaluation for Assertive Adolescent and Family Treatment (AAFT): Final Report.* Sudbury, MA: Advocates for Human Potential, Inc.

United States Department of Health and Human Services (DHHS). (2001). *Report of a Surgeon General's working meeting on the integration of mental health services and primary health care.* Rockville, MD: Author.

United States Department of Health and Human Services (DHHS), Substance Abuse and Mental Health Services Administration (SAMHSA), & Office of Applied Studies (OAS). (2008). Treatment Episode Data Set-Admissions (TEDS-A), 2008 [Computer file]. ICPSR27241-v2. Ann Arbor, MI: Inter university Consortium for Political and Social Research [distributor], 2010-03-31. doi:10.3886/ICPSR27241

Volkow, N. D., Baler, R. D., Compton, W. M., & Weiss, S. R. B. (2014). Adverse health effects of marijuana use. *New England Journal of Medicine, 370,* 2219–2227.

Waldron, H. B., & Slesnick, N. (1998). Treating the family. In W. R. Miller & N. E. Heather (eds.), *Treating addictive behaviors: Processes of change* (pp. 271–285). New York: Plenum.

Wall, M. M., Poh, E., Cerda, M., Keyes, K. M., Galea, S., & Hasin, D. S. (2011). Adolescent marijuana use from 2002 to 2008: Higher in states with medical marijuana laws, cause still unclear. *Annals of Epidemiology, 21,* 714–716. doi:10.1016/j.annepidem.2011.06.001

Wampold, B. E. (2010). The research evidence for the common factors models: A historically situated perspective. In B. L. Duncan, S. D. Miller, B. E. Wampold, & M. A. Hubble (eds.), *The heart and soul of change: Delivering what works in therapy* (2nd ed., pp. 49–81). Washington, DC: American Psychological Association.

Whelan, R., Conrod, P. J., Poline, J. B., Lourdusamy, A., Banaschewski, T., Barker, G. J., . . . IMAGEN Consortium. (2012). Adolescent impulsivity phenotypes characterized by distinct brain networks. *Nature Neuroscience, 15,* 920–925. doi:10.1038/nn.3092

Winward, J. L., Hanson, K. L., Tapert, S. F., & Brown, S. A. (2014). Heavy alcohol use, marijuana use, and concomitant use by adolescents are associated with unique and shared cognitive decrements. *Journal of the International Neuropsychological Society, 20*(8), 784–795. doi:10.1017/S1355617714000666

Wolfe, B. L., & Meyers, R. J. (1999). Cost-effective alcohol treatment: The Community Reinforcement Approach. *Cognitive and Behavioral Practice, 6,* 105–109. doi:10.1016/S1077-7229(99)80018-2

Wolitzky-Taylor, K., Bobova, L., Zinbarg, R. E., Mineka, S., & Craske, M. G. (2012). Longitudinal investigation of the impact of anxiety and mood disorders in adolescence on subsequent substance use disorder onset and vice versa. *Addictive Behaviors, 37,* 982–985. doi:10.1016/j.addbeh.2012.03.026

Appendix

Appendix 1: Sample Script for Permission to Record

We find it helpful to record our meetings with our clients. The purpose of the recordings is so my supervisors can give me advice on how to better help youth who need our services. They may also check some of the recordings to see how much time I spend with you on different counseling techniques.

I'm asking for your permission to audio record our meetings for these purposes and to then send the recording to my supervisor and our quality assurance reviewer at Chestnut Health Systems, both of whom will maintain your confidentiality in accordance with federal regulations. Although I may use your first name during our meetings, I will not mention your last name, nor will we put your name or other identifying information in the label for this recording—only an identification number and the date of our meeting, which will mean nothing to the people who listen to the recording. Any recording we make will be kept in a secure, password-protected file and destroyed 5 years from this date.

Again, the purpose of these recordings is ultimately to help me help people like you, so I hope you will sign this agreement to allow me to record our meetings. If you do sign today, it is always your choice to turn the recorder off for a brief period of time or to discontinue recording altogether.

Do you have any questions?

Appendix 2: Certificate of Completion

CERTIFICATE OF COMPLETION

This is to certify that on _____
                              Date

_____
Participant Name

Completed the requirements for participation in the Adolescent Community Reinforcement Approach (A-CRA).

_____   _____
Clinician   Clinical Supervisor

Appendix 3: Online Resources

A-CRA website (www.ebtx.chestnut.org): This website features detailed information about the Adolescent Community Reinforcement Approach (A-CRA), the Community Reinforcement Approach (CRA) for adults, and Assertive Continuing Care (ACC) pertaining to research, cultural and gender relevance, young adults, juvenile justice, co-occurring disorders, dissemination and implementation, and training and certification. The website also includes comprehensive lists of literature references for A-CRA, CRA, and ACC, as well as multicultural issues in adolescent treatment.

A-CRA online learning (www.training.a-cra-acc.org): Used by clinicians and supervisors, this website supplements in-person A-CRA training with online courses such as an A-CRA training preparation quiz, research and background, clinical supervisor training, co-occurring disorders and A-CRA, and ACC training.

A-CRA certification website (www.ebtx.org; www.ebtx.org/regional): This secure website is used by clinicians and clinical supervisors to upload recordings of clinical sessions and enter session data. Clinical sessions are reviewed by an expert rater, who provides numeric ratings and narrative feedback. Session data (procedures completed during the session, urinalysis results, etc.) is used for the creation of management reports (used by clinicians, supervisors, and administrators) and the case review report (used by clinicians and clinical supervisors). The website also features sample sessions with actual clinicians and their clients using the A-CRA procedures.

California Evidence-Based Clearinghouse for Child Welfare (CEBC; http://www.cebc4cw.org/program/adolescent-community-reinforcement-approach): The CEBC reviews and rates evidence-based practices and provides a database of programs that can be utilized by professionals that serve children and families involved with the child welfare system. A-CRA has a scientific rating of 2 and a Child Welfare System Relevance Level of medium.

National Institutes of Justice Office of Justice Programs (http://www.crimesolutions.gov/ProgramDetails.aspx?ID=137): The National Institute of Justice reviews and scores evidence-based practices and aims to help practitioners and policymakers understand what works in justice-related programs and practices. A-CRA is rated as "Effective—More than one study."

SAMHSA's National Registry of Evidence-Based Programs and Practices (NREPP; http://nrepp.samhsa.gov/ProgramProfile.aspx?id=116): NREPP is an evidence-based repository and review system designed to provide reliable information on mental health and substance abuse interventions. All interventions in the registry, including A-CRA, have met the requirements for review. The programs' effects on individual outcomes have been independently assessed and rated by certified NREPP reviewers.

Washington State Institute for Public Policy's Inventory of Evidence-Based, Research-Based, and Promising Practices (WSIPP; http://www.wsipp.wa.gov/ReportFile/1373/Wsipp_Updated-Inventory-of-Evidence-Based-Research-Based-and-Promising-Practices_Full-Report.pdf): WSIPP reviews evidence-based, research-based, and promising practices and services. A-CRA meets the criteria for a research-based practice.

Robert J. Meyers & Associates (www.robertjmeyersphd.com): This website by one of the developers of A-CRA and CRA features background information and publications about A-CRA and CRA.

About the Authors

Susan Harrington Godley, RhD, is an Emeritus Senior Research Scientist at the Lighthouse Institute of Chestnut Health Systems in Normal, IL. Since receiving her doctorate in 1982 from Southern Illinois University at Carbondale, she has been the principal investigator, co-investigator, evaluator, or project director on over 10 federally funded studies and projects spanning 25 years, including serving as one of the site principal investigators for the Cannabis Youth Treatment (CYT) study. In that role she was responsible for overseeing the development and fidelity monitoring of the Adolescent Community Reinforcement Approach (A-CRA). She has also served as a co-principal investigator of Assertive Continuing Care (ACC) studies that incorporated A-CRA in continuing care after residential treatment and principal investigator of the Adolescent Outpatient and Continuing Care Study (AOCCS) that evaluated two different types of outpatient treatment with and without continuing care. Dr. Godley has authored over 100 peer reviewed articles, chapters, monographs, and treatment manuals. From 2006 to 2014, Dr. Godley led the development of the national infrastructure to disseminate A-CRA and ACC, which has been used to train and certify over 1,000 certified clinicians in more than 270 provider organizations throughout the Unites States and abroad.

Jane Ellen Smith, PhD, is the Chair of the Psychology Department and Professor at the University of New Mexico in Albuquerque, NM. She received her PhD in clinical psychology from the State University of New York at Binghamton. Specializing in both alcoholism and eating disorders, Dr. Smith has written over 100 books, articles, and chapters on these topics. She is the first author of a 2004 book with Dr. Meyers about the Community Reinforcement and Family Training (CRAFT) program, *Motivating Substance Abusers to Enter Treatment: Working with Family Members*. Additionally, Dr. Smith is the co-author of a 1995 book on the Community Reinforcement Approach (CRA) for adults, *Clinical Guide to Alcohol Treatment: The Community Reinforcement Approach*. Along with Dr. Meyers, she assisted in the adaptation of CRA to the adolescent version, the Adolescent Community Reinforcement Approach (A-CRA). Dr. Smith is the first author of the therapist coding manual for A-CRA.

Robert J. Meyers, PhD, is the Director of Robert J. Meyers, PhD & Associates and an Emeritus Associate Research Professor at the University of New Mexico's Center on Alcoholism, Substance Abuse and Addiction. He began his work with the Community Reinforcement Approach (CRA) in 1976, when he helped develop CRA outpatient procedures. In the late 1990s, he helped establish the adolescent version of CRA, the Adolescent Community Reinforcement Approach (A-CRA). Dr. Meyers also developed the science-based intervention for engaging resistant substance abusers into treatment: Community Reinforcement and Family Training (CRAFT). His CRAFT work led him to be featured in an *Oprah* magazine article (2006) and in a segment of the Emmy Award–winning HBO *Addiction* series. Dr. Meyers is the winner of the 2002 Dan Anderson Research Award from Hazelden, the 2003 Young Investigator Award from the Research Society on Alcoholism, and the 2005 Alumni Achievement Award from the School of Social Work at Southern Illinois University. He has trained therapists throughout the US and in 11 countries on four continents. Dr. Meyers has published over 70 scientific articles and chapters and co-authored five books on addiction treatment, including *Get Your Loved One Sober: Alternatives to Nagging, Pleading and Threatening* and *Motivating Substance Abusers to Enter Treatment: Working with Family Members*.

Mark D. Godley, PhD, is a Senior Scientist and Director of the Evidence-Based Treatment Center at Chestnut Health Systems. Prior to joining Chestnut, Dr. Godley served as a clinician and treatment program director and worked on the early development of the Community Reinforcement Approach (CRA) with Drs. Nathan Azrin and Robert Meyers. He is also one of the original developers of the Adolescent Community Reinforcement Approach (A-CRA) as well as the Assertive Continuing Care (ACC) model. Dr. Godley has published numerous scientific papers and has served as an advisor on

265

expert panels to the Office of National Drug Control Policy (ONDCP), the Substance Abuse and Mental Health Services Administration (SAMHSA), and the Centers for Medicaid and Medicare Services (CMS) on the effectiveness of treatment and continuing care for youth and young adults with substance use disorders. Since 2006, he has co-led the development of a national infrastructure to disseminate A-CRA and ACC resulting in over 1,000 certified clinicians in more than 270 provider organizations throughout the Unites States and abroad.

Subject Index

Printed in the USA
CPSIA information can be obtained
at www.ICGtesting.com
LVHW080019131123
763720LV00009B/790